THERMAL PHYSICS

THERMAL PHYSICS

Edward A. Desloge

Florida State University

Holt, Rinehart and Winston, Inc.

*New York Chicago San Francisco Atlanta
Dallas Montreal Toronto London*

PREFACE

Thermal physics is the study of physical phenomena that depend on temperature. The present book is designed as a text for a one-quarter, one-semester, or two-quarter course in thermal physics at the junior or senior level.

The title *Thermal Physics*, rather than the more customary title *Thermodynamics*, has been chosen for two reasons: first to emphasize the fact that the book has been written from the point of view of a physicist rather than that of a chemist or an engineer, and second because much of thermal physics is concerned with static rather than dynamic states of matter. In conformity with common usage, however, I will use the term *thermodynamics* rather than *thermal physics* throughout the body of the text.

In studying the thermal behavior of a system, for example a piece of iron or a glass of water, it is possible to take a macroscopic or a microscopic approach. In the macroscopic approach, we accept the system at its face value as an apparently continuous medium, whose properties depend on a few simple parameters. From this point of view, the temperature of a system is simply a macroscopic property, which is defined in terms of the operations we use to measure it, and the object of thermal physics consists of finding and exploiting relationships between the temperature and the other macroscopic properties of the system. In the microscopic approach, drawing on our knowledge of atomic physics, we envision a system as composed of a very large number of very small particles, which are in rapid motion and which are interacting with one another. From this point of view, the macroscopic behavior of a system is a result of the collective action of these particles, and the temperature is simply a convenient parameter, which arises when we average over the individual behavior of the particles to obtain their statistical behavior.

There is a division of opinion among authors of textbooks whether it is pedagogically preferable to present thermal physics as a strictly macroscopic and autonomous discipline, or to integrate thermal physics with a microscopic or atomic picture of matter. There are strong arguments for both sides. On the one hand, if thermal physics is treated as a discipline distinct from atomic physics, the student quickly comes to the important realization that thermal physics provides him with a group of powerful ideas and methods, which permit him to describe and derive relations between macroscopic observations without recourse to a particular physical model of matter. Furthermore, he is able to concentrate on learning to use the tools of thermal physics without the burden and confusion of simultaneously attempting to master the statistical techniques necessary to bridge the gap between the microscopic picture and the macroscopic results. If, on the other hand, the microscopic and the macroscopic are freely mixed, the student avoids compartmentalizing his knowledge. He learns to move freely from microscopic model to macroscopic measurement and is led to realize that the results of thermal physics have played and are playing an important part in the development of atomic theory, and conversely that atomic theory has led to the discovery of macroscopic facts in the domain of thermal physics that would otherwise have probably long remained unobserved.

In the present book, I have directed my attention primarily to the macroscopic aspects of thermal physics, but, in an attempt to avoid isolating the subject from the rest of physics, I have formulated the basic principles in terms of a set of postulates that are closely related to the microscopic approach, rather than in terms of the more immediately experimental laws of thermodynamics. Furthermore, no attempt has been made to hide the microscopic picture from the student, since it is frequently possible from the microscopic point of view to make some of the difficult concepts, which one encounters, a little more intelligible. I have, however, hopefully avoided pursuing the microscopic approach beyond the point where it ceases to be an economical source of illumination for the macroscopic aspects of thermal physics.

In addition to making it easier to harness the microscopic and macroscopic approaches together, the postulates chosen have another equally important property: They emphasize the analytical structure of thermal physics rather than its historical or philosophical foundations. They, thus, provide an excellent starting point for actually solving problems in thermal physics.

Although I have approached thermal physics from a microscopically oriented set of postulates, I have shown in detail the equivalence of these postulates and the usual three laws. My purpose in this was to bring the student in closer contact with the experimental evidence on which the postulates are based, and to strengthen his grasp of these postulates. Since the three laws are more immediately connected with the experimental facts than the postulates, it might appear to be more logical to start with the three laws and then derive the postulates. This is in effect what is done, though not explicitly, in most textbooks. Though appealing in principle, this approach suffers from some pedagogical disadvantages. The student who is following this approach is typically led from the laws to a pair of mysterious functions called the internal energy and the entropy. Until he has used these functions, he finds it difficult to grasp their significance; even after he has used them, he finds them elusive. Since it is a relatively arduous task for the student to pass from the raw laws to a feeling for the significance of the internal energy and the entropy, it usually takes him a long time to develop any real facility for working problems. Furthermore, if he has been taught to think of these functions exclusively in terms of their macroscopic operational definitions, he ordinarily encounters a great deal of difficulty in reconciling the microscopic and the macroscopic approaches. The postulational approach that I have chosen hopefully avoids these difficulties.

The basic approach and the choice of material in the present book have been strongly influenced and directed by the thermodynamics text of H. B. Callen, who in turn was influenced by L. Tisza, who again in turn was influenced by the work of J. W. Gibbs. It is a pleasure to acknowledge my indebtedness to these men.

I would also like to thank H. Price Kagey and Bruno Linder who reviewed the final manuscript and provided many helpful suggestions, and Rod Jory whose detailed suggestions and criticisms and whose generous assistance at all stages in the preparation of this text have contributed significantly to its final form.

Edward A. Desloge

Tallahassee, Florida
August 1968

CONTENTS

THERMAL PHYSICS

PART ONE

The Basic Principles of Thermodynamics for Simple One-Component Systems

Both equilibrium and nonequilibrium phenomena fall within the scope of thermal physics. It has been suggested that equilibrium thermal physics be given the name thermostatics and nonequilibrium thermal physics the name thermodynamics. Although this choice of names is probably the most logical, it is customary to find equilibrium thermal physics called equilibrium thermodynamics or simply thermodynamics, and to find nonequilibrium thermal physics called nonequilibrium thermodynamics, irreversible thermodynamics, or the thermodynamics of the steady state. In the present part we are interested in equilibrium thermal physics, which in conformity with the most common usage, we call thermodynamics.

CHAPTER 1

The Scope
of Thermodynamics

DEFINITION OF THERMODYNAMICS

Thermodynamics may be defined as a study of the macroscopic equilibrium properties of systems for which temperature is an important variable.

In the following sections we shall attempt to gain some idea of the meaning of the various terms in the above definition.

SYSTEM

We shall use the term *system* to mean a portion of the universe as defined by a closed mathematical surface. The rest of the universe will be referred to as the *surroundings*. The boundary between a system and its surroundings could be the actual physical surface of a container, as would be the case if we were investigating a gas or liquid contained within a cylinder. On the other hand, the boundary could be a purely mental one, as would be the case if we were investigating a gas contained within an imaginary volume element in the atmosphere. For the sake of concreteness, we shall always speak of the systems we are studying as if they were actually enclosed within a physical container or enclosure. Since we shall encounter various types of systems, as well as walls or boundaries, it will be helpful at this point to define some of the more important types.

A *rigid wall* is a wall whose shape and position are fixed.

An *impermeable wall* is a wall that prevents the passage of matter.

A *permeable wall* is a wall that allows the passage of matter and, consequently, also of energy.

An *adiabatic wall* is a wall which, when held rigid, will, in the absence of any external force fields such as electric, magnetic, or gravitational fields, prevent the passage of matter or energy. If a system is contained within a rigid adiabatic container, and no external force field is present, it is impossible to change the state of the system from without. On the other hand, if it is possible to change the state of a system from without, even though the system is contained in a rigid container and no external force field is present, the walls are *not* adiabatic. A thermos bottle is an example of a container whose walls are approximately adiabatic. As we shall see later, an adiabatic wall is a wall that prevents the flow of heat, but at this point in our study of thermodynamics, we have not yet defined the term "heat."

A *diathermic* or *diathermal wall* is a wall which, when held rigid, will, in the absence of any external force field, prevent the passage of matter but allow the passage of energy. Alternatively, it is a wall that is impermeable but not adiabatic. A plain metal container, such as an aluminum can, is an example of a container whose walls are diathermal.

A *closed system* is a system enclosed by impermeable walls.

An *open system* is a system enclosed by permeable walls.

An *isolated system* is a system enclosed by rigid, adiabatic walls and not acted upon by any external force field.

A *one-component system* is a system composed of a single chemical species. A piece of copper, the water in a glass, the helium in a balloon are examples of one-component systems. A multicomponent system, such as a sample of air, can be treated as a one-component system when the components do not interact chemically and the composition does not vary.

A *simple system* is a system (1) that is macroscopically homogeneous and isotropic, (2) that is not acted upon by any external force other than the uniform surface force of the container, and (3) whose local properties are unaffected by a change in the shape of the system or by a partition dividing the system into independent subsystems.

An *elementary system* is a simple one-component system that cannot be decomposed into a set of more fundamental systems. If we interpret this definition in its strictest sense, the only elementary systems would be those composed of the fundamental particles of nature. However, for most thermodynamic enterprises, there is a set of systems which, though not absolutely elementary, is nevertheless relatively elementary. For example, in those problems in chemistry and physics which do not involve nuclear reactions, a system composed of one of the chemical elements can usually be considered as an elementary system. And if chemical reactions do not occur, any simple system composed of a single chemical species, that is, any simple one-component system, would constitute an elementary system. Finally, when we are dealing with mixtures in which the chemical composition is held fixed, any simple system will be an elementary system.

A *composite system* is a system made up of two or more spatially distinct, simple systems. It should be noted that, according to the above definition, two systems between which there is an appreciable electric, magnetic, or gravitational force do not constitute a composite system, since the sub-systems cannot be treated as simple systems. This does not mean that there can be no interaction between the subsystems, since it is possible for forces to be exerted and for energy or matter to be exchanged at the boundaries separating adjacent subsystems.

MICROSCOPIC AND MACROSCOPIC

Given a system which we wish to study, for example a gas contained in a cylinder, we may proceed in any of a number of directions. We could attempt to find the stuff of which the gas is made by breaking it down into smaller and smaller parts. Proceeding in this fashion, we would find the gas was composed of molecules, the molecules of atoms, the atoms of protons, neutrons, electrons, and so forth. We do not directly observe these building blocks of matter, but through the media of various instruments, one such particle can be made to set up a chain of reactions that ultimately ends in a directly observable effect.

On the other hand, we could attempt to study the properties of the gas directly. We might push it, squeeze it, heat it, or stir it. In doing so, we would discover many properties of the gas such as pressure, mass, and volume, as well as relationships between these quantities, which can be studied with little or no reference to the atomic structure of the gas. These properties are called *macroscopic properties*. In contrast to the macroscopic properties of matter, properties that explicitly depend upon the particle nature of matter are termed *microscopic properties*.

The microscopic and macroscopic properties of matter are not indepen-dent. The atomic properties of a piece of matter must be consistent with its more directly observable large-scale properties. The large-scale properties thus act as a constant guide and check for the physicist's excursions into the atomic and subatomic worlds. Conversely, an atomic "picture" of matter, because of its greater logical simplicity, is able to lead physicists to discover large-scale properties of matter that might otherwise long remain unobserved. By exploiting both approaches and the interrelationships between them, physics progressively increases man's knowledge of the nature and properties of matter. Since thermodynamics is a study of the macroscopic properties of matter, it is possible to develop the subject of thermodynamics without reference to the particle structure of matter. From this point of view, a set of laws is developed by studying the macroscopic behavior of thermodynamical systems in general. The consequences of these laws are then exploited and applied to particular systems. Alternatively, starting entirely from a microscopic point of view, and using a number of statistical postulates, one can arrive at the laws of thermodynamics. The strictly macroscopic point of view is much more directly connected with tangible, experimental results than is the microscopic point of view, and therefore it is easier, by starting from this approach, to justify the basic laws of thermodynamics. On the other hand, by means of the microscopic point of view, some of the difficult analytical concepts that one encounters in thermodynamics become a little more intelligible. In the present text we have attempted to unite the good features of both approaches but to avoid the accompanying dangers.

EQUILIBRIUM STATES

When a system is isolated by enclosure within a rigid adiabatic container and elimination of all external force fields, the system will ultimately arrive at a state in which the macroscopic properties remain constant in time. If this state is such that it is impossible in practice to change the system to another state in which the macroscopic properties remain constant, without at the same time producing some net change in the surroundings, the state is called an *equilibrium state*. The exact interpretation of the above definition depends upon the means available for stimulating or catalyzing a change in an isolated system. Suppose, for example, a quiescent mixture of two different chemical species capable of reacting chemically when properly catalyzed is considered. Suppose further that it is impossible, except by stimulating the chemical reaction, to change the state of the system without producing a net change in the surroundings. The mixture would then be in equilibrium as long as the possibility of chemical reactions was excluded, but it would not be in equilibrium if chemical reactions were allowed.

It is, of course, possible for a system to be in an equilibrium state even when it is not isolated, provided that it is in equilibrium with its surroundings. In this case, however, it would in principle be possible to insert walls between the system and its surroundings without changing the surroundings or any of the properties of the system, and we can therefore treat the system as an isolated system.

In the present text we shall be interested in studying primarily the equilibrium states of matter.

TEMPERATURE

Thermodynamics is a study of the macroscopic equilibrium properties of systems for which *temperature* is an important variable. Although the concept of temperature is more naturally and logically introduced at a later stage in the development of thermodynamics, a preliminary discussion of temperature at this point is helpful in order to understand the scope of thermodynamics. In a later chapter we shall reconsider the subject in greater detail.

If two systems, otherwise isolated, are brought into contact with one another by means of a rigid diathermal wall, and no change occurs in the macroscopic properties of either system, we say the systems are in thermal equilibrium, that is, they have the same temperature.

Experiment shows that when each of two systems is in thermal equilibrium with a third system, then they are in thermal equilibrium with each other. This experimental fact is frequently elevated to the status of a law and is called the *zeroth law* of thermodynamics. By virtue of the zeroth law it is possible to separate all possible states of all systems in the universe into sets of the same temperature. The different sets can be identified by assigning a number to each. This number is called the *temperature* of the set. As we shall see later, there is a very natural method of assigning numbers to each set, leading to a type of temperature scale called the *absolute temperature scale*. Later references to temperature usually refer to this scale. For the present, however, a qualitative concept of the meaning of temperature is sufficient.

A *thermometer* is a device used to measure temperature. Any system whose properties have been calibrated in terms of the temperature can be used as a thermometer, since the temperature of an unknown system can be measured by simply bringing the above system into thermal equilibrium with it. In measuring the temperature of an unknown system, care must of course be taken to choose a thermometer that will not, by the act of measurement, significantly alter the properties of the system being measured.

CONCLUSION

The techniques of thermodynamics are applicable to a wide variety of systems. The properties of dielectrics, paramagnetic solids, surface films, stretched wires, and so forth all depend upon temperature and, as such, are subject matter for thermodynamic analysis. Although it is possible to develop the laws of thermodynamics quite generally, with no reference to a particular type of thermodynamic system, it is much more convenient to develop the laws of thermodynamics in terms of a particular type of system. The generalization of the results to more complex systems is then straight-forward. We shall therefore restrict initial discussion to simple one-component systems.

PROBLEMS

1.1   A cylindrical container of cross-sectional area A, closed at one end by a frictionless piston of mass M and at the other by a rigid wall, contains a large number N of randomly distributed point particles of mass $m \ll M$. On the average, half of the particles are moving with a velocity $+v$ and half with a velocity $-v$ along the axial direction of the cylinder. The collisions of the particles with the piston and the end wall are perfectly elastic. The piston is held in position by a force F, and no gravitational forces are present. Show that $pV = 2E$, where p is the average force per unit area exerted on the piston, V the average volume enclosed in the cylinder, and E the total kinetic energy of the particles.

1.2   Show that when the volume discussed in the preceding problem is slowly increased or decreased by a gradual decrease or increase in the force exerted on the piston, the quantity pV^3 will remain constant.

1.3   If the density of a gas is sufficiently small, it is found that if and only if the temperature is held constant, the pressure will be directly proportional to the density. How could you use this fact to construct a thermometer?

1.4   A mixture of deuterium and oxygen is enclosed in a rigid, impermeable, and well-insulated container; it is allowed to reach a state of constant and uniform temperature and pressure. The mixture is exploded by a spark of neglible energy, and again allowed to come to a state of constant and uniform temperature and pressure.
(a) Is the initial state an equilibrium state?
(b) Is the final state an equilibrium state?

CHAPTER 2

Internal Energy

INTRODUCTION

A large number of macroscopic parameters can be used to describe a simple one-component system. We shall initially be interested in three, the energy, the volume, and the amount of matter.

The meaning of the volume of a system, which we shall designate by the letter V, is apparent.

The meaning of the amount of matter in a system, though not quite so obvious as the meaning of volume, nevertheless becomes apparent when we indicate the units in which it is measured. In thermodynamics the amount of matter in a one-component system is most commonly designated by the number of molecules or the number of moles. A *mole* is equal to the amount of matter contained in one gram molecular weight and corresponds to approximately 6.023×10^{23} molecules. Since a mole is more obviously a macroscopic quantity than is a molecule, we shall indicate the amount of matter in a one-component system by the number of moles or the mole number, which we designate by the letter N.

Since the exact meaning of the energy of a system is a little more subtle, we shall spend the remainder of this chapter considering it.

THE INTERNAL ENERGY

From a microscopic point of view, a thermodynamic system is composed of a large number of particles that are in motion and interacting with one another; consequently, the particles possess kinetic energy and potential energy. The total energy, kinetic plus potential, of a simple system is called its internal energy and will be designated by the letter E. For each state of a system, there is one and only one value of internal energy.

In a study of the thermodynamic properties of a system that is not simple, for example, a system undergoing some macroscopic motion or being acted upon by an external field, there is, in addition to the kinetic energy due to the random motion of the particles, also kinetic energy due to the macroscopic motion of the system, and in addition to the potential energy due to mutual interaction of the particles, there is potential energy due to interaction of the system and the external field. In such cases we must distinguish between internal energy and external energy. It is for this reason that E is called the internal energy and not simply the energy.

A number of properties of the internal energy of a system, though quite apparent from a microscopic point of view, must be simply accepted from a macroscopic point of view. We note first that once a reference state has been chosen for the potential energy of a collection of molecules, the value of the internal energy in a particular state is unique, that is, the internal energy is a single-valued property of the state. We next note that it is possible in principle to increase the energy of a collection of molecules indefinitely, but not to decrease the energy without limit. Thus the internal energy of a closed system has a lower bound but no upper bound.

MEASUREMENT OF THE INTERNAL ENERGY

Thermodynamics is a macroscopic subject; thus if we wish to define the internal energy E as a macroscopic property, we must provide a means of defining, or what is equivalent, devise a scheme to measure, the internal energy on a strictly macroscopic level.

In principle, we could determine the internal energy of a simple system by using the relativistic formula $E = Mc^2$. Thus, when we know the mass of a system exactly, we can calculate its internal energy. However, this method is not very practical for a number of reasons. In the first place, thermodynamics deals with energy changes that are of the order of joules, and the corresponding mass change ($\sim 10^{-17}$ kg) is beyond the accuracy of instruments available for measuring macroscopic masses. In the second place, we never need to know the absolute value of the internal energy of a given state of a system. What we do need to know is the difference between the internal energy of the given state and that of any other state of the same system or of any system that can be obtained by decomposition of the given system. Since, by definition, an elementary system cannot be decomposed, an arbitrary value can be assigned to the internal energy of one state of each elementary system. All other internal energies can then be measured with respect to this set of reference states.

The simplest way to determine the difference in internal energy between two states of the same system is to calculate the amount of energy that must be put into the system or taken out of the system in order to bring it from the first state to the second, or vice versa. As long as we can measure the input or output of energy, and as long as energy is conserved, the difference in internal energy between the two states can be measured. Energy can be put into or taken out of the system in any number of ways. The system can be heated, squeezed, or have a current passed through it. However, if we wish to measure the energy change, only those means for which the input or output can be measured should be used. At the present stage in our discussion no way is known of measuring energy transferred between a system and it surroundings by virtue of a temperature difference. Such energy is called heat and will be designated by the letter Q. All other forms of energy transfer will be called *work* and will be designated by the letter W. Both Q and W will be taken to be positive when energy is transferred to the system from the surroundings, and negative when energy is transferred from the system to the surroundings. To prevent heat flow a system can be enclosed within adiabatic walls. A system enclosed by adiabatic walls can still be brought from one arbitrary state to another in many ways. For example, work can be done on the system by compressing it by means of a piston, or a resistor of negligible mass can be inserted into the system, and a current allowed to flow through the resistor. If we know the force on the piston and the displacement of the piston, we can calculate the work done by the piston on the system. If we know the current, the resistance, and the length of time the current is flowing, we can calculate the amount of energy dissipated by the resistor.

The techniques discussed above can be used to measure the energy difference between states of a one-component system containing the same number of moles. Suppose, however, we wish to measure the energy difference between a particular state 1 in which there are N_1 moles and a second state 2 in which there are N_2 moles, where for convenience we assume $N_2 > N_1$. Since we can measure the energy difference between any two states containing the same number of moles, it follows that as long as we can measure the energy difference between some state with N_1 moles and some state with N_2 moles, we can measure the energy difference between states 1 and 2. To connect a state having N_1 moles with a state having N_2 moles, we could start with a state in which the system was homogeneous and isotropic and in which there were N_2 moles. We could then simply divide the system into two systems, one containing N_1 moles and the other containing $N_2 - N_1$ moles. If the energy of the original system containing N_2 moles is E, the energy of the system containing N_1 moles would simply be $(N_1/N_2)E$.

Because of the nature of elementary systems, the energy difference between states of two different elementary systems cannot be measured. We are, therefore, free to assign an arbitrary value of the internal energy to one state of each elementary system. Suppose, however, we wish to measure the energy difference between one state of each of two nonelementary systems. To measure this difference, it is necessary only to measure the energy of the state of each of the two nonelementary systems with respect to the energy of the respective elementary systems into which each system can be decomposed. This measurement can be accomplished by first bringing the component elementary systems together in the proper proportions and at appropriate temperatures within a rigid adiabatic container, and then allowing them to interact to form the nonelementary system. The internal energy of the resultant system, after the reaction, will then be equal to the sum of the internal energies of the component elementary systems before the reaction.

HEAT

For a process in which energy is transferred not only in the form of work W but also in the form of heat Q, the change in the internal energy will be equal to the sum of the two energies. Thus

$$E_f - E_i = Q + W \tag{2.1}$$

where E_i and E_f are the initial and final internal energies, respectively.

Since W and $E_f - E_i$ can in principle be measured, we can use Equation (2.1) to calculate Q. From a strictly macroscopic point of view, this relation is the definition of Q. The values of Q and W depend on the process by which the system passes from the initial to the final state. The quantities Q and W are therefore not properties of the system.

For a process in which the system changes by an infinitesimal amount, Equation (2.1) is sometimes written

$$dE = đQ + đW \tag{2.2}$$

The bars on $đQ$ and $đW$ indicate that $đQ$ and $đW$ are not exact differentials, that is, there are no functions of which dQ and dW are differentials. Before we can integrate, therefore, we must know the type of process involved. (See Appendix 7.)

THE INTERNAL ENERGY OF AN ISOLATED SYSTEM

If a system is isolated, we cannot transfer energy to the system either in the form of work or heat. The internal energy of an isolated system therefore remains constant.

Actually, the internal energy in an isolated system is constant only on a macroscopic level. On a microscopic level, the energy of a simple system, enclosed within a container that has been made as rigid and adiabatic as possible, is not, as one might expect, constant. Since the container's walls are themselves composed of atoms in motion, it is impossible to eliminate completely all interaction between the system and its surroundings. Furthermore, no practical wall is really capable of eliminating all influences of the outside world on the confined system. Stray particles and fields will penetrate the container and disturb the system. As a result of these interactions of the system both with the container and the outside world, the energy of the system will not be constant but will fluctuate about an average value.

Although less obvious, the volume and number of moles of a system are also not fixed quantities. Consider, for example, a gas contained in a box. Since the atoms in the walls of the container are in motion, the exact boundaries of the system are indeterminate. Furthermore, the molecules in the gas will occasionally adhere to the walls of the container, thus being removed from the system; or in the case of a polyatomic gas, the molecules, though relatively stable, may undergo some dissociation, and as a result the composition of the system will be changed.

From a macroscopic view, we are not interested in these minute fluctuations in energy, volume, or mole number, but simply in the respective average values about which the fluctuations take place.

When we speak of the internal energy E, volume V, and number of moles N of a macroscopic system, we do not mean that the energy, volume, and number of moles assume the exact values E, V, and N, but rather that they fluctuate about these values. As a matter of fact, the instruments used to measure E, V, and N, even though capable of making fairly delicate measurements, are usually completely insensitive to these relatively slight fluctuations and record average values only.

THE INTERNAL ENERGY OF A COMPOSITE SYSTEM

Let us consider two systems A and B that form a composite system AB. If the adiabatic work required to change system A from state a' to state a'' is $W(a' \rightarrow a'')$, and the adiabatic work required to change system B from state b' to state b'' is $W(b' \rightarrow b'')$, the adiabatic work required to change the composite system AB from the state $a'b'$ to the state $a''b''$ will then simply be $W(a' \rightarrow a'') + W(b' \rightarrow b'')$. This relation is a consequence of the nature of a composite system. It therefore follows that the internal energy of a composite system is simply the sum of the internal energies of the component systems.

CONCLUSION

We can summarize the results of the present chapter in the form of a postulate, a corollary, and a definition.

Postulate I.   For every system there exists a quantity E, called the internal energy, that has the following properties:

(a) A unique value of the internal energy is associated with each state of the system.

(b) The internal energy of a closed system has a lower bound but no upper bound.

(c) The difference between the internal energy in one state and the internal energy in another state of a closed system is equal to the work required to bring the system, while adiabatically enclosed, from the one state to the other.

Corollary I.

(a) The internal energy is constant in an isolated system.

(b) The internal energy of a composite system is equal to the sum of the internal energies of its component systems.

(c) An arbitrary value of the internal energy can be assigned to one state of each elementary system.

Definition I.   The heat transferred to a closed system during an infinitesimal process is defined by the relation

$$dE = dQ + dW \tag{2.3}$$

where dE is the change in internal energy, dQ is the heat transferred to the system, and dW is the work done on the system.

EXAMPLE

Problem.   A system consists of a fixed number of moles of a certain hypothetical substance contained in a well-insulated container. If the volume of the system is changed slowly, the pressure is found to change in accordance with the equation $p = \text{const } V^{-2}$. If a resistor of resistance R is inserted into the system and a current I is passed through the resistor while the volume is held fixed, the pressure is found to increase slowly at a rate $dp/dt = I^2R/V$. Obtain an expression for the difference in the internal energy between two arbitrary states (p_0,V_0) and (p_1,V_1).

Solution. The work done during an infinitesimal stage of the first process can be shown to be given by $dW = -pdV$. The work done during an infinitesimal stage of the second process can be shown to be given by $dW = I^2Rdt$. Since the container is well insulated, both of the above processes are adiabatic. The adiabatic work $W_a(0 \to x)$, required to take the system from the state (p_0,V_0) to the state $(p_x,V_1) \equiv [(p_0V_0^2)V_1^{-2},V_1]$, can therefore be obtained by employing the first process and is given by

$$W_a(0 \to x) = -(p_0V_0^2) \int_{V_0}^{V_1} V^{-2} \, dV = p_0V_0^2\left(\frac{1}{V_1} - \frac{1}{V_0}\right)$$

and the adiabatic work $W_a(x \to 1)$, required to take the system from the state (p_x,V_1) to the state (p_1,V_1), is given by

$$W_a(x \to 1) = \int_t^{t+\Delta t} I^2R \, dt = \int_t^{t+\Delta t} V_1 \frac{dp}{dt} \, dt$$

$$= \int_{p_x}^{p_1} V_1 \, dp = V_1(p_1 - p_x)$$

$$= V_1[p_1 - (p_0V_0^2)V_1^{-2}]$$

where Δt is the period during which the current must be flowing in order to produce the desired change of state. Combining the two above processes and noting that the adiabatic work required to take the system from the state (p_0,V_0) to the state (p_1,V_1) is equal to the change in internal energy, we obtain

$$E(p_1,V_1) - E(p_0,V_0) = W_a(0 \to 1)$$
$$= W_a(0 \to x) + W_a(x \to 1)$$
$$= p_1V_1 - p_0V_0$$

PROBLEMS

2.1   Show that the work required to slowly change the volume V of a simple system from a volume V_1 to a volume V_2 is given by $W_{12} = -\int_1^2 pdV$, where p is the pressure. What is meant by "slowly"?

2.2   A mixture of fuel and oxygen is burned inside a container whose walls are rigid, impermeable, and diathermic, while the container is immersed in a water bath. As the fuel burns, the temperature of the water is observed to rise. Regard the mixture of fuel and oxygen as the system.

(a) Has heat been transferred?

(b) Has work been done?

(c) Has the internal energy changed?

2.3   A rigid, impermeable, and well-insulated vessel is divided into two parts by a partition. One part contains a gas, and the other has been evacuated. If the partition is suddenly broken, what change occurs in the internal energy of the gas?

2.4   When a system is taken from state *a* to state *b*, as shown in Figure 2.1, along the path *acb*, 80 J of heat flow into the system, and the system does 30 J of work.

(a) How much heat flows into the system along path *adb* when the work done by the system is 10 J?

(b) When the system is returned from *b* to *a* along the curved path,

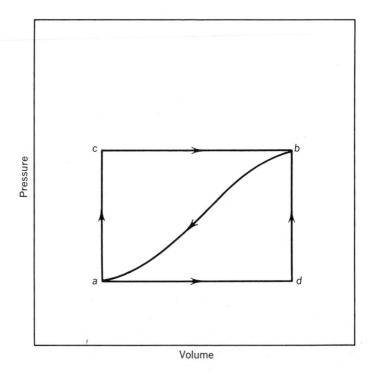

FIGURE 2.1

the work done on the system is 20 J. Does the system absorb or liberate heat during the return? How much?

(c) If $E_a = 0$ and $E_d = 40$ J, and the only work done on the system is accomplished by slowly changing the volume, find the heat absorbed in the processes ad and db.

2.5 A given system of fixed mass is such that when the volume is changed slowly and adiabatically, the pressure is found to change in accordance with the equation $p = \text{const } V^{-5/3}$. Four processes: acb, adb, aeb, and afb, indicated in Figure 2.2, are initiated in the state a with a pressure of 32 atm and volume of 1 liter, and each process terminates in the state b with a pressure of 1 atm and a volume of 8 liters. The process aeb is an adiabatic process. Work is done on the system in each case by slowly changing the volume. Using the results of Problem 2.1, find the work done on the system and the heat transferred to the system in each process: (a) acb, (b) adb, (c) aeb, and (d) afb.

2.6 A small paddle wheel is installed in the system described in Problem

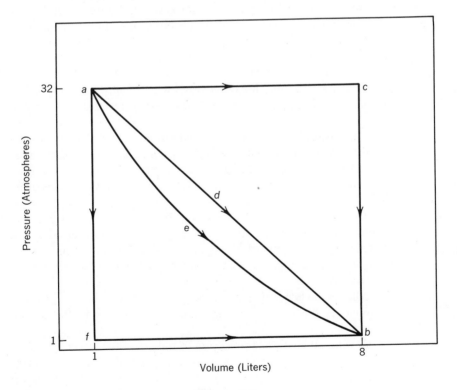

FIGURE 2.2

2.5. The shaft of the paddle wheel extends through the walls of the system and can be driven at 240 rps by an external motor. The viscous torque on the paddle wheel is then 10^4 cm-dyn. When the motor is thus permitted to do work on the system while the volume is kept constant and the system is adiabatically enclosed, the pressure is found to increase at a rate $dp/dt = 2\,\omega\tau/3V$, where τ is the viscous torque and ω the angular velocity of the paddle wheel. Using the information just given and also the conditions for the process of adiabatic expansion described in Problem 2.5, find the internal energy of an equilibrium state with arbitrary pressure p and arbitrary volume V. Choose state a as the reference state.

2.7 Using the results of Problems 2.5 and 2.6, calculate the heat transferred to the system in processes ac, cb, af, and fb.

2.8 An ideal gas is a gas having the two following properties: (1) the pressure p, volume V, temperature T, and number of moles N are related by the equation $pV = NRT$, where R is a universal constant having a value 8.314 J$(°K)^{-1}(mole)^{-1}$ and (2) the internal energy E can be expressed as a function of T and N. How many joules of heat are absorbed by one mole of an ideal gas which expands isothermally at a temperature $T = 300°K$ from an initial pressure of 3 atm to a final pressure of 1 atm?

2.9 A mass of 10 kg moves through a height of 3 m, causing a paddle wheel to stir 500 g of water.

(a) If the water is contained in a vessel whose walls are rigid, impermeable, and well insulated, what is the change in internal energy of the water?

(b) If the walls of the vessel are diathermal rather than adiabatic, and the vessel is immersed in a constant temperature heat bath, what is the change in internal energy of the water?

(c) Calculate the work done on the water and the heat transferred to the water in 2.9 (a) and (b).

2.10 A gas expands from a pressure p_1 and temperature T_1 to a pressure p_2 and a temperature T_2. In the process the heat transferred to the system is Q, and the work done on the system is W. An amount of work W' is then used to restore the gas to the pressure p_1 and the temperature T_1.

(a) What is the internal energy change of the gas in the first process?

(b) What is the internal energy change of the gas in the second process?

(c) How much heat was transferred to the gas in the second process?

2.11 The internal energy of two moles of a particular one-component system is found to be given by $E = pV^2$. Determine the complete dependence of E upon p, V, and N for an arbitrary number of moles.

2.12   The energy of a fixed mass of a certain gas is given by the relation $E = A + BpV$, where A and B are constants and p and V the pressure and volume, respectively. Calculate the change in energy, the work done on the gas, and the heat transferred to the gas in each of the following processes, assuming that the only means of work consists in slowly compressing the gas or allowing it to expand slowly:
(a) Constant volume process from p_1, V_1, to p_2, V_1.
(b) Constant pressure process from p_1, V_1 to p_1, V_2.
(c) Constant energy process from p_1, V_1 to p_2, V_2.

2.13   Water at 32°F weighs 62.4 lb/ft^3, and ice at the same temperature weighs 57.2 lb/ft^3. How much work does a 1-in. ice cube do on the atmosphere when it melts?

2.14   A 200-kg chunk of lead falls from a height of 30 m and smashes into a rigid concrete floor. Calculate the increase in the internal energy of the lead, assuming that no energy is transferred as heat from the lead.

2.15   A meteorological balloon rises from 0 to 15,000 ft. In this ascent the pressure inside the balloon drops from 1 bar to $\frac{1}{2}$ bar, and the volume of the balloon increases from 1 m^3 to 1.8 m^3. Assume that the gas in the balloon obeys the ideal gas law $pV = NRT$, that the volume changes are directly proportional to the pressure changes, and that the internal energy of the gas in the balloon is $E = 800T$ J.
(a) If the initial temperature in the balloon was 300°K, what is the final temperature?
(b) How much work is done by the gas in the balloon?
(c) How much heat does it absorb?

CHAPTER 3

Equilibrium States

If a certain amount of matter is contained in a rigid, adiabatic container, its energy, volume, and mole number will be fixed. Even with these constraints, however, an immense number of macroscopically different arrangements or states could in principle be assumed by the system. In thermodynamics we are interested only in equilibrium states. In the present chapter we shall consider the nature of such states.

MACROSTATES

States of a system that are macroscopically distinguishable from one another are called macrostates. States for which E, V, and N differ by a macroscopically measurable amount are obviously different macrostates. But even for given values of E, V, and N, respectively, the number of macroscopically distinguishable states is immense. Consider, for example, a one-component solid, liquid, or gas enclosed in a rigid, adiabatic container and not acted upon by any external fields, that is, an isolated one-component system. Let $n(x,y,z)$ be the number of moles per unit volume and $\epsilon(x,y,z)$

the energy per unit volume at a point (x,y,z) in the container. Since the system is isolated, the total number of moles and the total energy will remain fixed, and, therefore, $\iiint_V n(x,y,z)dxdydz = N = $ const, and $\iiint_V \epsilon(x,y,z)dxdydz = E = $ const. An immense number of macroscopically distinguishable pairs of functions $n(x,y,z)$ and $\epsilon(x,y,z)$ satisfy these two conditions. Therefore, an immense number of macroscopically distinguishable states of a one-component system have the same values of E, V, and N.

THE EQUILIBRIUM STATE

Although many macrostates of a simple system are consistent with given values of E, V, and N, an isolated system will usually select only one. To illustrate this fact, suppose we have prepared a set of isolated systems, each of which contains the same kind of matter and has the same respective values of E, V, and N. Although the initial macrostates of the systems at the moment of preparation may be quite different, we shall usually find if we wait long enough that all the systems will tend toward the same final macrostate. If this state is such that it is impossible, with the means at our disposal, to change the system to another state in which the macroscopic properties remain constant in time without at the same time producing some net change in the surroundings, the state is called an equilibrium state.

If, depending on its past history, there is more than one quiescent state to which a given isolated system can evolve, only one of these states will satisfy the above criteria. We shall restrict the term equilibrium state to this one state. With each set of values of E, V, and N, we thus have a unique equilibrium state. Many sets of variables other than E, V, and N uniquely determine the state of a system, but this set is the most convenient for our purposes.

Since thermodynamics is primarily concerned with equilibrium states, we shall generally use the term state to mean equilibrium state. Context will make clear our references to states other than the equilibrium state.

STATE FUNCTION

If a simple one-component system is in an equilibrium state, there are quantities that are fully determined by its state at that instant and that are independent of the previous history of the system. Such quantities are called state functions. The internal energy E, volume V, and mole number N are examples of state functions. Any quantity that is a function of E, V, and N or of any set of variables that uniquely determines the state of a system is also a state function. Conversely a state function can be expressed as a function of E, V, and N.

INTENSIVE AND EXTENSIVE PARAMETERS

The various parameters used in our discussions of the equilibrium states of systems will generally fall into two types: extensive parameters and intensive parameters. Suppose we have M identical systems A, in the same identical state and separated by walls of negligible thickness. If the walls are removed, we have a single system R. A parameter X, such that $X_R = MX_A$, is called an extensive parameter. A parameter I, such that $I_R = I_A$, is called an intensive parameter. Pressure and density are examples of intensive parameters. The volume V and mole number N are examples of extensive parameters. Since the internal energy of a composite system is the sum of the internal energies of the component systems, the internal energy is an extensive variable.

If we are given a set of intensive variables u, v, w, $\cdots$, and a set of extensive variables X, Y, Z, $\cdots$, then from the definition of intensive and extensive variables and the results of Appendix 6 the following theorems can be readily proved.

Theorem I (a).   The function $F(u,v, \cdots ,X,Y, \cdots)$ is an extensive variable if and only if $F(u,v, \cdots ,\lambda X,\lambda Y, \cdots) = \lambda F(u,v, \cdots ,X,Y, \cdots)$ for arbitrary positive λ.

Theorem I (b).   The function $f(u,v, \cdots ,X,Y, \cdots)$ is an intensive variable if and only if $f(u,v, \cdots ,\lambda X,\lambda Y, \cdots) = f(u,v, \cdots ,X,Y, \ldots)$ for arbitrary positive λ.

Theorem II (a).   If f and g are arbitrary intensive variables, then fg, f/g, $\partial f/\partial g$, and $f + g$ are intensive variables.

Theorem II (b).   If F and G are arbitrary extensive variables, then $F + G$ is an extensive variable, and F/G and $\partial F/\partial G$ are intensive variables.

Theorem II (c).   If f is an arbitrary intensive variable and F an arbitrary extensive variable, then fF, F/f, and $\partial F/\partial f$ are extensive variables.

It is possible for a parameter to be neither intensive nor extensive. Such parameters, however, are inconvenient to use and can usually be reduced to either extensive or intensive parameters. As an example, the volume squared is neither an extensive nor intensive parameter.

SUMMARY

We can summarize the results of the present chapter in the form of a postulate.

Postulate II.   There exists a state of an isolated, simple one-component system, called the equilibrium state that is uniquely determined by the internal energy E, volume V, and number of moles N.

PROBLEMS

3.1   Indicate whether each of the quantities listed below is a state function or not. If the quantity in question is a state function, indicate whether it is an intensive variable, an extensive variable, or neither. Assume that the quantity S is an extensive state function.

(a) $p \equiv - (\partial E/\partial V)_{S,N}$ (e) $E + pV$ (i) $(\partial T/\partial V)_{p,N}$

(b) $T \equiv (\partial E/\partial S)_{V,N}$ (f) $E + p^2V$ (j) $(1/V)(\partial V/\partial T)_{p,N}$

(c) Q (g) $E + pV^2$ (k) $V(\partial p/\partial V)_{T,N}$

(d) W (h) $(\partial E/\partial T)_{V,N}$

3.2   The following information about a certain function $f(x,y,z)$ is known: (1), $f(2,y,z) = \sin[4(1 + y)/z^2]$ and (2), $f(x,y,z)$ is homogeneous of degree zero in the variables x, y, and z, that is, $f(\lambda x, \lambda y, \lambda z) = f(x,y,z)$. Find the function.

3.3   The following information about a certain function $f(x,y,z)$ is known: (1), $f(x,y,3) = 3 \exp (xy/9)$ and (2), $f(x,y,z)$ is homogeneous of degree one in the variables x, y, and z. Find the function.

CHAPTER 4

Entropy

We have seen in the last chapter that although a large number of macrostates are associated with a given set of values of E, V, and N, an isolated system will usually "select" only one set of these. In the present chapter we wish to investigate the cause.

MICROSTATES

On a microscopic level, a simple system is composed of millions of particles in motion. Classically, the state of such a system can be determined if the positions and velocities of each of the particles are known. Since the position and velocity of a particle are independently and continuously variable, the number of different distributions in the positions and velocities of these particles that are sufficiently alike as to be macroscopically indistinguishable is infinite.

It can be shown however, in the light of the discoveries of the present century, that this classical view is not a true picture of the microscopic behavior of matter. The properties of matter are not continuous in the classical sense. The number of distinct and completely independent micro-scopic states associated with a particular macrostate is finite. We call one of these states a microstate.

ENTROPY

With each macrostate of a simple system, a large but finite number of microstates is associated. On a microscopic level, it is assumed that every microstate accessible to a system at a given instant of time is equally likely to occur. It follows that the probability of a particular macrostate will be proportional to the number of microstates that are associated with it. We call this number the *thermodynamic probability* and designate it by the letter W. The larger W is for a particular macrostate, the more probable will that macrostate be. It can be shown on a microscopic level and verified experimentally on the macroscopic level that the equilibrium macrostate is so overwhelmingly probable that we can neglect the probability of any other macrostate, and simply assume an isolated system will always be in this state. We shall designate the thermodynamic probability of this state by W^*. For each combination of values of E, V, and N, there is a single equilibrium state; hence for each distinct combination of values of E, V, and N, there is a unique value of W^*. Therefore, W^* is a single-valued function of E, V, and N.

For a composite system consisting of two simple systems 1 and 2 in the states (E_1,V_1,N_1) and (E_2,V_2,N_2), respectively, the number of microstates W^*_{12} associated with the macrostate $(E_1,V_1,N_1,E_2,V_2,N_2)$ is simply the product of the number of microstates associated with the system 1 and the number of microstates associated with the system 2, that is

$$W^*_{12}(E_1,V_1,N_1,E_2,V_2,N_2) = W^*_1(E_1,V_1,N_1)W^*_2(E_2,V_2,N_2) \qquad (4.1)$$

It follows that the function $W^*(E,V,N)$ is neither an extensive nor an intensive variable. Since we prefer to work with extensive or intensive variables, we introduce a new function

$$S = k \ln W^* \qquad (4.2)$$

where k is simply a proportionality constant. It can be shown that the exact value of k will depend on the choice of a temperature scale. For our present purposes, however, we do not need to know the value of k. For the composite system discussed above,

$$
\begin{aligned}
S_{12}(E_1,&V_1,N_1,E_2,V_2,N_2) \\
&= k \ln W^*_{12} = k \ln W^*_1 W^*_2 = k \ln W^*_1 + k \ln W^*_2 \\
&= S_1(E_1,V_1,N_1) + S_2(E_2,V_2,N_2) \qquad (4.3)
\end{aligned}
$$

The function $S(E,V,N)$ is an extensive variable and is called the entropy.

Since $W^*(E,V,N)$ is a single-valued function of E, V, and N, it follows that $S(E,V,N)$ is a single-valued function of E, V, and N.

THE BASIC PROBLEM OF THERMODYNAMICS

Suppose we have two simple systems 1 and 2 that are separated and surrounded by rigid, impermeable, and well-insulated walls, that is, rigid adiabatic walls, as shown in Figure 4.1. The pair constitutes a composite system. The state of system 1 is determined by the parameters E_1, V_1, and N_1; the state of system 2 is determined by the parameters E_2, V_2, and N_2; and the state of the composite system is determined by the parameters E_1, E_2, V_1, V_2, N_1, and N_2.

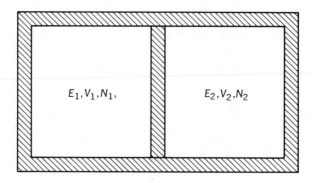

FIGURE 4.1

Within such external walls, the energy, volume, and number of moles in the composite system are fixed, that is,

$$E_1 + E_2 = E_T = \text{const} \tag{4.4}$$

$$V_1 + V_2 = V_T = \text{const} \tag{4.5}$$

$$N_1 + N_2 = N_T = \text{const} \tag{4.6}$$

The insulation, rigidity, and impermeability of the outside walls maintain the above conditions and are called external constraints. The insulation, rigidity, and impermeability of the wall separating the two systems are called internal constraints. These constraints, together with the external constraints, maintain E_1, E_2, V_1, V_2, N_1, and N_2 fixed.

Removal of one or more of the internal constraints causes the equilibrium states of the individual systems and, consequently, the equilibrium state of the composite system to change. Many possible final states are still consistent with conditions (4.4), (4.5), (4.6), and the remaining internal constraints. The basic problem of thermodynamics is to determine which of these final states will occur. We have, in principle, already solved this problem in the preceding section, as we shall now see.

If W_1 and W_2 are the thermodynamic probabilities associated with particular macrostates of the two component systems when they are completely isolated, then $W_{12} = W_1 W_2$ will be the thermodynamic probability associated with the corresponding macrostate for the composite system. The value of the thermodynamic probability for the composite system in equilibrium will be

$$W_{12}^*(E_1,V_1,N_1,E_2,V_2,N_2) = W_1^*(E_1,V_1,N_1)W_2^*(E_2,V_2,N_2) \qquad (4.7)$$

In terms of the entropy

$$S_{12}(E_1,V_1,N_1,E_2,V_2,N_2) = S_1(E_1,V_1,N_1) + S_2(E_2,V_2,N_2) \qquad (4.8)$$

When one or more of the internal constraints is removed, a large number of new macrostates becomes accessible to the composite system, and the composite system will proceed to the macrostate for which W_{12} is a maximum. In this state the component systems, in addition to being in internal equilibrium, will be in mutual equilibrium with one another. To find the conditions of mutual equilibrium, we therefore simply determine the maximum value which $W_{12}^*(E_1,V_1,N_1,E_2,V_2,N_2)$ or $S_{12}(E_1,V_1,N_1,E_2,V_2,N_2)$ can assume subject to the remaining constraints. It follows that if we know the functions $S_1(E_1,V_1,N_1)$ and $S_2(E_2,V_2,N_2)$ for two simple one-component systems, and if we allow these two systems to interact thermodynamically then, knowing the initial states of the two systems, we can predict their final states.

IRREVERSIBLE EFFECTS

If an internal constraint is removed from an isolated composite system whose subsystems are not in equilibrium, the system will proceed toward a new equilibrium state of higher entropy. Once the spontaneous change has taken place, the composite system cannot be restored to its original state by the manipulation of internal constraints, since any further change would require an additional increase in the entropy, or at least would require the entropy to remain constant.

It is, of course, possible to restore the system to its original state by some mechanism outside the system. Suppose, for example, the insulation were removed from the interior wall in a composite system, for which the temperatures of the subsystems were T_1 and T_2, respectively. Heat would then flow from one subsystem to the other until thermal equilibrium has been established. If the interior wall is reinsulated, the only way in which the two subsystems can return to their original states is by means of some outside mechanism. For instance, we could bring each of the subsystems, respectively, in thermal contact with heat baths at temperatures T_1 and T_2, and thus restore them to their respective original states at the expense of changes in the heat baths.

Our analysis is not restricted to a composite system containing only two subsystems. If an internal constraint is removed from an isolated composite system having any number of subsystems and if a spontaneous process takes place, the entropy will increase. Since the universe can be considered as one large composite system, it follows that, if the internal constraints between any two subsystems in the universe that are not in equilibrium are removed, the entropy of the universe will increase, and therefore, except for the possibility of some extra-universal influence, the universe will be irremediably altered. We call any effect in which the entropy of the *universe* increases an *irreversible effect*.

It does not follow from the above that, in principle, nothing can happen in the universe without producing an irreversible effect. When a mass on an ideal spring, for which there is no damping, is set in motion, it will periodically return to its initial configuration. The movement of the mass is therefore not irreversible. In practice, of course, there is always some damping effect, and the oscillation of the mass does produce an irreversible effect.

If an effect takes place in such a way that the universe is not irremediably altered, the entropy of the universe does not increase, and the effect is called reversible. Since the entropy of the universe cannot decrease, a reversible effect is one for which the entropy of the universe remains constant.

QUASISTATIC PROCESSES

Suppose we wish to change a system, for example, a gas in equilibrium in the state (E_1, V_1, N_1), which we call state 1, to the state (E_2, V_2, N_2), which we call state 2. For convenience we assume $N_1 > N_2$. We could, if desired, rapidly change the volume from V_1 to V_2, let some gas escape until the number of moles is N_2, and then immerse the system in a heat bath until the gas arrives at E_2. During this process the equilibrium of the gas would be destroyed, and the intermediate states could not be described simply by the parameters E, V, and N. The gas would pass from state 1 to state 2 through a series of nonequilibrium states.

If, on the other hand, we change the volume slowly, allow the gas to effuse slowly from the container, and bring the gas in contact with the heat bath by means of a very poor heat-conductor, the intermediate states of the gas would closely approximate equilibrium states. If the system passes from state 1 to state 2 through a succession of equilibrium states, we call the process *quasistatic*.

Many authors call a process in which the system passes from one state to another through a succession of equilibrium states a reversible process, rather than a quasistatic process. We shall, however, reserve the term *reversible process* to indicate a process that takes place in such a way that the entropy of the universe remains constant, or, alternatively, in such a way that the universe is not irremediably altered. A reversible process is always quasistatic, but a quasistatic process is not always reversible. As an example of a quasistatic process that is not reversible, suppose two objects at different temperatures are periodically brought into contact and allowed to exchange a small amount of heat. As long as the intervals between contacts are not too short, the systems will approach thermal equilibrium with one another through a succession of equilibrium states, but the process is not reversible. It should also be noted that if an observer is restricted to making local measurements within a system, he has no way of distinguishing between a quasistatic process and a reversible process; therefore, the question of reversibility or irreversibility of a process must be decided by an observer who can watch both the change in the system and the means by which the change is being produced.

QUASISTATIC ADIABATIC PROCESSES

Let us consider a simple system that is in equilibrium and that is contained in an insulated cylinder by an insulated, frictionless piston.

If the system is quasistatically compressed by a slow increase of the force on the piston and then is allowed to quasistatically expand by a slow decrease of the force on the piston, it will be found that, during the expansion, the system retraces the path which it took during its compression. The system acts like an ideal spring. The work done on the system during the compression is returned in the expansion. Since the only entropy change that can occur in this process is in the entropy of the system, it follows that the entropy of an insulated system remains constant during a quasistatic change in volume.

A THERMODYNAMIC DESCRIPTION OF A SYSTEM

In thermodynamics we are interested in the macroscopic properties of systems that are in equilibrium. To measure the macroscopic properties of a thermodynamic system, the system must be brought into contact with some other system whose properties are known. To measure the temperature of a system, for example, the system is brought into contact with a thermometer. Or to measure the pressure of a system, the system is brought into contact with a manometer. However, a thermometer or a manometer is simply a constrained thermodynamic system whose allowed states have been calibrated in terms of temperature and pressure, respectively. If we investigate all the means by which the thermodynamic properties of a system are studied, we shall find that measurement consists essentially in bringing two thermodynamic systems into contact and allowing them to come to equilibrium. It should be noted that the boundary between the system whose properties are being measured and the known system being used to measure those properties could be diathermal, moveable, or even permeable, depending on the nature of the instrument.

If the entropy of a simple one-component system is known as a function of its internal energy, volume, and mole number, then we can predict the result of any measurement that involves bringing this system into contact with a second system of known properties. It follows that entropy, when expressed as a function of internal energy, volume, and mole number, contains a complete thermodynamic description of a system.

It is important to note that the preceding statement is true if we know the entropy as a function of internal energy, volume, and mole number. It does not follow, however, that when we know the entropy as a function of some other set of variables, for example pressure, volume and mole number, we have a complete thermodynamic description of the system.

THE ENTROPY POSTULATE

We can summarize the results of the preceding sections in the form of a postulate and a corollary.

Postulate III. For every system there exists a state function S, called the entropy, that has the following properties:

(a) For a simple one-component system, S is a single-valued function of E, V, and N.

(b) The entropy of a composite system is equal to the sum of the entropies of its component systems.

(c) If an internal constraint is removed from an isolated composite system, consisting of n simple one-component systems 1, 2, $\cdots$, n, and the system is allowed to come to an equilibrium state, then the values assumed by the extensive variables, E_1, V_1, N_1, E_2, V_2, N_2, $\cdots$, E_n, V_n, N_n, will be those values, consistent with the remaining internal and external constraints, that maximize the entropy of the composite system.

(d) During a quasistatic adiabatic change in volume of a simple system, the entropy of the system remains constant.

Corollary II. The entropy of a simple one-component system, when expressed as a function of its internal energy, volume, and mole number, contains a complete thermodynamic description of the system.

In the present chapter we have discussed the existence of a function called the entropy. For entropy to have a macroscopic meaning, however, it must be able to be measured macroscopically. This problem will be considered in the following chapter.

PROBLEMS

4.1 (a) If two dice are cast, there are eleven possible total numbers which can show up, that is, 2, 3, . . . , 12. If we call each of these numbers a macrostate and call a particular ordered combination of numbers on the two dice a microstate, how many microstates are there associated with each of the macrostates?

(b) Repeat the above problem using three dice.

4.2 A set of N coins is cast on a table. We designate a microstate by specifying the state, heads or tails, of each coin in the set. We designate a macrostate by specifying how many heads and how many tails there are. For example, if $N = 2$, there are four possible microstates: HH, HT, TH, and TT, but only three possible macrostates: two heads (2H), two tails (2T), and one head and one tail (1H, 1T). Each microstate has a probability of $\frac{1}{4}$. The macrostates have probabilities of $\frac{1}{4}$, $\frac{1}{4}$, and $\frac{1}{2}$, respectively, and thermodynamic probabilities of 1, 1, and 2, respectively. Answer the following questions for $N = 4$ and $N = 50$:

(a) How many microstates are there?

(b) How many macrostates are there?

(c) What is the probability of each microstate?

(d) What is the thermodynamic probability of the macrostate NH?

(e) What is the thermodynamic probability of the macrostate $NH/2$, $NT/2$?

(f) What is the probability of the macrostate NH?

(g) What is the probability of the macrostate $NH/2$, $NT/2$?

4.3   What is the number of microstates for three indistinguishable particles whose positions are quantized to a 3×3 grid. Assume that multiple occupancy of a grid point is not allowed. Group the microstates into macrostates having the same number of particles on the perimeter; determine the probability and the thermodynamic probability of each macrostate. Repeat the above problem assuming that multiple occupancy is allowed.

4.4   Show that if $W_{12}^* = W_1^* W_2^*$ and we wish to define a function $S = f(W^*)$, such that $S_{12} = S_1 + S_2$, then the function f will be of the form $f(W^*) = k \ln W^* + C$, where k and C are constants.

4.5   The functions $S(E,V,N)$ occurring in the expressions below are supposed to be entropy functions for various systems. Which of them is inconsistent with Postulate III? Why? In each case A and B are constants. In all cases in which fractional exponents appear, only the real positive root is to be taken.

(a) $S = A(EVN)^{1/3}$ (c) $S = AV^3/EN$

(b) $S = A(EN/V)^{2/3}$ (d) $E = AS \exp(-BS/N)$

4.6   A rigid, impermeable, and well-insulated container is divided into two sections by a rigid, impermeable, and diathermic wall. One section has a volume of 9 cm³ and contains 3 moles of a certain substance whose entropy is given by $S = C(EVN)^{1/3}$, where C is a constant. The second section has a volume of 1 cm³ and contains 1 mole of the same substance. The total energy of the composite system is 20 J. When the composite system is in equilibrium, what are the internal energies of the individual subsystems?

4.7   An isolated composite system consists of 4 moles of a substance whose entropy in MKS units is given by $S = 2A(EVN)^{1/3}$ and 2 moles of a substance whose entropy in MKS units is given by $S = A(E^2V^2N^{-1})^{1/3}$, occupying volumes of 4 m³ and 2 m³, respectively. The two subsystems are separated by a rigid, impermeable, and diathermic wall. If the total energy of the composite system is 6 J, what are the internal energies of the individual subsystems when the composite system is in equilibrium?

4.8   If the internal wall described in the preceding problem is replaced by a diathermic piston, what will be the equilibrium energy and volume of each subsystem?

4.9   Starting with the fact that the entropy of one mole of an ideal monatomic gas is given by $S = R \ln(E^{3/2}V) + C$, where R and C are constants, show that for N moles $S = NR \ln(E^{3/2}VN^{-5/2}) + CN$.

CHAPTER 5

Measurement
of the Entropy

INTRODUCTION

In the preceding chapter we postulated the existence of an entropy function on the basis of microscopic arguments. In order for the entropy to have a macroscopic meaning, we must provide a means of defining, or, what is equivalent, devise a scheme to measure the entropy on a strictly macroscopic level. In the present chapter we shall consider this problem.

TEMPERATURE

Let us suppose we have an isolated composite system, consisting of two subsystems 1 and 2 that are separated by a rigid adiabatic wall, as shown in Figure 4.1. Let $S_1(E_1, V_1, N_1)$ be the entropy of system 1 and $S_2(E_2, V_2, N_2)$ be the entropy of system 2. The entropy of the composite system is

$$S_{12}(E_1, V_1, N_1, E_2, V_2, N_2) = S_1(E_1, V_1, N_1) + S_2(E_2, V_2, N_2) \qquad (5.1)$$

If the insulation is removed from the internal wall, we can determine the

33

final equilibrium state by maximizing S_{12}, while holding V_1, V_2, N_1, N_2 and $E_1 + E_2 = E_{12}$ constant. This is mathematically equivalent (Appendix 4) to maximizing the function

$$\psi(E_1) = S_1(E_1, V_1, N_1) + S_2[E_2(E_1), V_2, N_2] \qquad (5.2)$$

where $E_2(E_1) \equiv E_{12} - E_1$ and also V_1, N_1, V_2, N_2, and E_{12} are constants. To determine the value of E_1, which maximizes $\psi(E_1)$, we set the derivative of $\psi(E_1)$ equal to zero and obtain

$$\left(\frac{\partial S_1}{\partial E_1}\right)_{V_1, N_1} + \left(\frac{\partial S_2}{\partial E_2}\right) \frac{dE_2(E_1)}{dE_1} = 0 \qquad (5.3)$$

Noting that $dE_2(E_1)/dE_1 = -1$ we get

$$\left(\frac{\partial S_1}{\partial E_1}\right)_{V_1, N_1} = \left(\frac{\partial S_2}{\partial E_2}\right)_{V_2, N_2} \qquad (5.4)$$

Noting (Appendix 1) that $(\partial S/\partial E)_{V,N} = [(\partial E/\partial S)]^{-1}_{V,N}$, we can rewrite Equation (5.4) as

$$\left(\frac{\partial E_1}{\partial S_1}\right)_{V_1, N_1} = \left(\frac{\partial E_2}{\partial S_2}\right)_{V_2, N_2} \qquad (5.5)$$

If two systems that are otherwise isolated are brought into contact by means of a rigid diathermic wall and if there is no change in the macroscopic properties of either system, then the systems are defined as having the same temperature. According to the above argument, if two systems that are otherwise isolated are brought into contact by means of a rigid diathermic wall and if there is no change in the state of either system, then the systems are in equilibrium, and the values of $(\partial E/\partial S)_{V,N}$ are the same for each system. The quantity $(\partial E/\partial S)_{V,N}$ can therefore be used to define temperature, which we designate by the letter T. Thus

$$T \equiv \left(\frac{\partial E}{\partial S}\right)_{V,N} \qquad (5.6)$$

Since the temperature is the derivative of an extensive variable, it is, according to the results of Chapter 3, an intensive variable. In terms of the temperature T, the condition of equilibrium (5.5) becomes

$$T_1 = T_2 \tag{5.7}$$

In a later section we shall see how the temperature T, as defined by Equation (5.6), can be measured.

PRESSURE

Let us now suppose that instead of simply removing the insulation from the internal wall of the composite system, the internal wall is replaced by a moveable diathermic piston. We can determine the final equilibrium state of the composite system under these conditions by maximizing S_{12}, while holding $N_1, N_2, E_1 + E_2 = E_{12}$ and $V_1 + V_2 = V_{12}$ constant. This operation is equivalent (see Appendix 4) to maximizing the function

$$\psi(E_1,V_1) = S_1(E_1,V_1,N_1) + S_2[E_2(E_1),V_2(V_1),N_2] \tag{5.8}$$

where $E_2(E_1) = E_{12} - E_1$, $V_2(V_1) = V_{12} - V_1$, and N_1, N_2, V_{12}, and E_{12} are constants. To determine the values of E_1 and V_1, which maximize $\psi(E_1,V_1)$, we set the first derivatives of $\psi(E_1,V_1)$ with respect to E_1 and V_1 equal to zero, and we obtain

$$\left(\frac{\partial S_1}{\partial E_1}\right)_{V_1,N_1} = \left(\frac{\partial S_2}{\partial E_2}\right)_{V_2,N_2} \tag{5.9}$$

$$\left(\frac{\partial S_1}{\partial V_1}\right)_{E_1,N_1} = \left(\frac{\partial S_2}{\partial V_2}\right)_{E_2,N_2} \tag{5.10}$$

Noting (Appendix 1) that $(\partial S/\partial E)_{V,N} = [(\partial E/\partial S)_{V,N}]^{-1}$ and $(\partial S/\partial V)_{E,N} = -(\partial S/\partial E)_{V,N}(\partial E/\partial V)_{S,N}$, the two conditions above can be replaced by the two equivalent conditions:

$$\left(\frac{\partial E_1}{\partial S_1}\right)_{V_1,N_1} = \left(\frac{\partial E_2}{\partial S_2}\right)_{V_2,N_2} \tag{5.11}$$

$$-\left(\frac{\partial E_1}{\partial V_1}\right)_{S_1,N_1} = -\left(\frac{\partial E_2}{\partial V_2}\right)_{S_2,N_2} \tag{5.12}$$

The quantity $(\partial E/\partial S)_{V,N}$ has already been defined as the temperature T. We now define the quantity $-(\partial E/\partial V)_{S,N}$ as the pressure p. Thus

$$p \equiv -\left(\frac{\partial E}{\partial V}\right)_{S,N} \tag{5.13}$$

Since the pressure is the derivative of an extensive variable with respect to an extensive variable, it is, according to the results of Chapter 3, an intensive variable. In terms of the temperature T and pressure p, the conditions of equilibrium (5.11) and (5.12) become

$$T_1 = T_2 \tag{5.14}$$

$$p_1 = p_2 \tag{5.15}$$

In the following section we shall see how p can be measured.

MEASUREMENT OF THE PRESSURE

Let us consider a simple one-component system that is contained in a cylinder. Let us assume that the cylinder has a cross-sectional area A and is closed at the top by a weightless, frictionless piston that is held in position by a force of magnitude F, as shown in Figure 5.1. Since the piston is

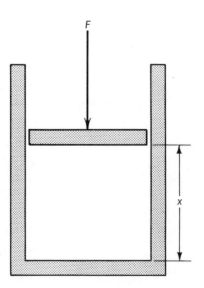

FIGURE 5.1

weightless, frictionless, and at rest, the magnitude F is also equal to the magnitude of the force exerted by the system on the piston. If the force on the piston is slowly increased by an infinitesimal amount dF, the volume will change by an amount $dV = A dx$, and work dW will be done on the system where

$$dW = -F dx = -\frac{F}{A} dV \tag{5.16}$$

The minus sign is necessary since dx will be negative when the work dW is positive. Although we have derived this result for a particular geometry, that is, a piston in a cylinder, it can be shown that if P is the magnitude of the force per unit area exerted by a system of arbitrary shape on its surroundings, then for any quasistatic change in the volume of a system, the work done on the system due to this change is given by

$$dW = -P dV \tag{5.17}$$

We shall now show that P, the force per unit area exerted by the system on its surroundings, is equal to pressure p as defined by Equation (5.13). To prove this, let us suppose the cylinder shown in Figure 5.1 is replaced by an insulated cylinder. If the system within the cylinder is then compressed quasistatically, the work done during an infinitesimal portion of the process is still given by Equation (5.17). Since the cylinder is insulated, however, there will be no heat transfer to the system during the process and therefore

$$dQ = 0 \tag{5.18}$$

Substituting (5.17) and (5.18) in Equation (2.2), we obtain

$$dE = -P dV \tag{5.19}$$

Alternatively, if we knew E as a function of S, V, N, we could calculate the change in energy from the relation

$$dE = \left(\frac{\partial E}{\partial S}\right)_{V,N} dS + \left(\frac{\partial E}{\partial V}\right)_{S,N} dV + \left(\frac{\partial E}{\partial N}\right)_{S,V} dN \tag{5.20}$$

In the process described above, N is constant, and by virtue of postulate III(d), S is also constant; therefore,

$$dE = \left(\frac{\partial E}{\partial V}\right)_{S,N} dV \equiv -p dV \tag{5.21}$$

Comparing (5.19) and (5.21), we obtain

$$p = P \tag{5.22}$$

It follows that the pressure, as defined by Equation (5.13), is equal to the magnitude of the force per unit area exerted by the system on its surroundings. To determine the pressure of a system, we therefore simply measure this force.

WORK AND HEAT

If a closed system undergoes some arbitrary process in which its volume is changed and heat flows between the system and its surroundings, then at any stage in this process the change in energy of the system satisfies the relation

$$dE = dQ + dW \tag{5.23}$$

If the process is quasistatic, then from Equations (5.17) and (5.22)

$$dW = -p \, dV \tag{5.24}$$

To determine dQ, we note that in a quasistatic process, in which N is held constant, the change in the energy is given by

$$dE = \left(\frac{\partial E}{\partial S}\right)_{V,N} dS + \left(\frac{\partial E}{\partial V}\right)_{S,N} dV \tag{5.25}$$
$$\equiv T dS - p \, dV$$

Combining Equations (5.23), (5.24), and (5.25), we obtain

$$dQ = T dS \tag{5.26}$$

It should be noted that Equations (5.24) and (5.26) are true only when the process satisfies the following conditions: (1) it is quasistatic and (2) the only work done is the mechanical work due to a change in volume.

If a closed, one-component system undergoes a quasistatic process from a state 1 to a state 2 and if the only work done is mechanical work, due to a change in volume, then Equations (5.24) and (5.26) can be used to calculate Q, the heat flow to the system, and W, the work done on the system. Thus

$$Q = \int_1^2 T dS \tag{5.27}$$

$$W = -\int_1^2 p \, dV \tag{5.28}$$

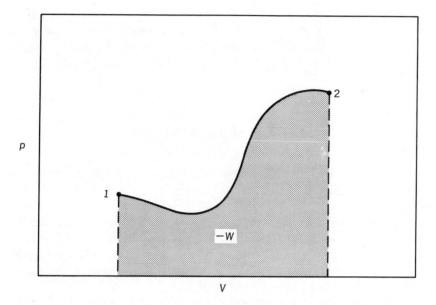

FIGURE 5.2

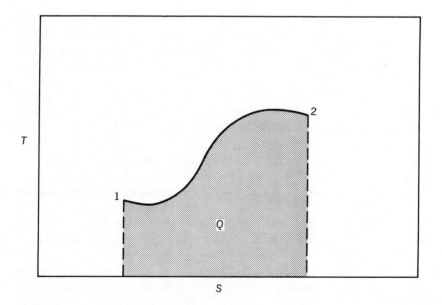

FIGURE 5.3

It is of interest to note that when the process is plotted on a p-V diagram, as shown by the solid line in Figure 5.2, then the shaded area under the curve is equal to $-W$, and when the process is plotted on a T-S diagram, as shown by the solid line in Figure 5.3, then the shaded area under the curve is equal to Q.

HEAT AND WORK RESERVOIRS

In discussing the thermodynamic properties of a system, it is frequently convenient to introduce the notion of a heat, or a work, reservoir.

A *heat reservoir* is a system that is: (1) enclosed by a rigid, impermeable, and diathermal wall; (2) capable of establishing internal equilibrium so rapidly that all processes of interest within it are essentially quasistatic; and (3) sufficiently large to allow its temperature to remain essentially unaltered as heat flows into, or out of, it.

The only possible flow of energy into, or out of, a heat reservoir is in the form of heat, so that $dE = dQ = TdS$.

Any large, constant-temperature heat-bath, such as the atmosphere, will approximate the properties of a heat reservoir.

A *work reservoir* is a system which is: (1) enclosed by an adiabatic but moveable wall; (2) capable of establishing internal equilibrium so rapidly that all processes of interest within it are essentially quasistatic; and (3) sufficiently large to allow its pressure to remain essentially unaltered as work flows into, or out of, it.

The only possible flow of energy into, or out of, a work reservoir is in the form of mechanical work due to a change in volume, so that $dE = dW = -pdV$. Since all changes in the volume are adiabatic and quasistatic, any energy which goes into the system due to the work of compression can be fully recovered by simply allowing the system to expand. A work reservoir is, therefore, capable of storing energy in a form that can be completely converted into mechanical work. A variety of mechanical systems approximate the energy storage properties of a work reservoir. For example, energy stored in a compressed spring or in an elevated weight can be completely regained in the form of mechanical work. Since the entropy of a work reservoir does not change when energy is put in or taken out, it is always possible, by employing suitable intermediate devices, to transfer energy between one work reservoir and another. It is, therefore, possible and convenient to think of a work reservoir as simply a storehouse of energy in such form that it is capable of being converted entirely into whatever type of mechanical work needed. By employing suitable intermediate devices, the energy stored in an arbitrary work reservoir can be used, for instance, to turn a paddle wheel or compress a gas.

MEASUREMENT OF THE TEMPERATURE

For the sake of convenience, let us assume we have a complete collection of heat reservoirs covering every possible temperature. If we knew the temperature of each of these reservoirs, it would be possible in principle to determine the temperature of an arbitrary object, simply by finding the reservoir that, when brought into thermal contact with the object, would not cause a change in the state of the object. The problem of how to measure temperature can thus be reduced to the problem of determining the temperature of an arbitrary heat reservoir.

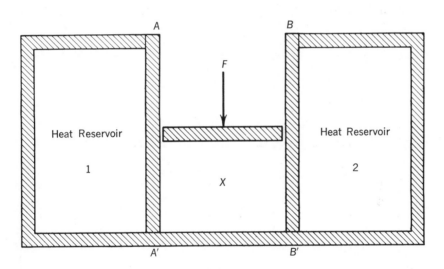

FIGURE 5.4

Let us consider the system schematically illustrated in Figure 5.4. The region X represents some system whose properties we know, and the regions 1 and 2 are two heat reservoirs whose temperatures T_1 and T_2 we wish to measure. The walls are adiabatic. For convenience, we assume T_2 to be greater than T_1. We first remove the insulation from the wall AA' and allow the system X to come to equilibrium with reservoir 1. We shall designate the resultant state of the system by the letter a. The temperature of the system in state a is T_1. We now replace the insulation and compress the system X quasistatically until it arrives at temperature T_2 of reservoir 2. We shall designate this state as state b. Since no heat is transferred to the system X during this process, the entropy of system X, by virtue of Equation (5.26), remains constant. The process ab is thus a constant entropy process. We next remove the insulation from the wall BB' and allow the system to expand quasistatically to some state c. Since the system remains in thermal contact with reservoir 2 during this process, the process bc is a constant temperature process at temperature T_2. We now replace the insulation on BB' and allow the system X to expand further until it arrives at temperature T_1. We designate the resultant state, state d. Since no heat is transferred to the system X during the process, the entropy of system X remains constant. The process cd is thus a constant entropy process. Finally, we remove the insulation from the wall AA' and compress the system quasistatically until it arrives at the initial state a. The process da is a constant temperature process at temperature T_1.

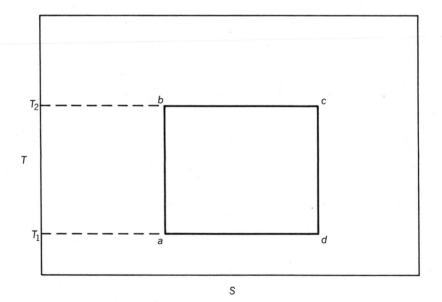

FIGURE 5.5

When the process $abcda$ is represented on a T-S diagram, it appears as shown in Figure 5.5. From the figure it is evident that the ratio of the temperature T_2 to the temperature T_1 is equal to the ratio of the area under the curve bc to the area under the curve ad, that is,

$$\frac{T_2}{T_1} = \frac{\int_b^c TdS}{\int_a^d TdS} = -\frac{\int_b^c TdS}{\int_d^a TdS} \tag{5.29}$$

But $\int_b^c TdS$ is simply the heat transferred from reservoir 2 to the system X during the isothermal process bc, which we shall designate Q_{2X}; and $\int_d^a TdS$ is simply the heat transferred from reservoir 1 to the system X during the isothermal process da, which we shall designate Q_{1X}. We can therefore write Equation (5.29) as

$$\frac{T_2}{T_1} = -\frac{Q_{2X}}{Q_{1X}} \tag{5.30}$$

The cycle $abcda$ through which system X proceeded, that is, (ab) constant entropy compression, (bc) constant temperature expansion, (cd) constant entropy expansion, and (da) constant temperature compression, is known as a Carnot cycle.

Since we can in principle measure Q_{1X} and Q_{2X}, it is possible to determine the ratio of the temperatures of any two reservoirs. This is as far as we can go theoretically. In order to specify the temperature numerically, we must assign a particular value to the temperature of one of the reservoirs. The choice is not dictated by any a priori arguments. As we shall see later, at only one temperature can water simultaneously exist as vapor, liquid, and solid. It follows that we can assign a value to this temperature and thus uniquely fix the temperature scale. The most common choice for this value is 273.16; the resultant temperature scale is called the Kelvin scale, and its units are called degrees Kelvin (°K). Another common choice is to assign this temperature the value 491.688. The resultant temperature scale is called the Rankine scale and the units are called degrees Rankine (°R). Two other temperature scales in common use are the Celsius (C) and the Fahrenheit (F) scales, defined as follows:

$$T_C = T_K - 273.15$$

$$T_F = T_R - 459.67$$

where T_C, T_K, T_F, and T_R are the values of the temperature on the Celsius, Kelvin, Fahrenheit, and Rankine scales, respectively. The Celsius and

Fahrenheit scales are not true thermodynamic scales as defined by Equation (5.30). In working problems, unless one is dealing strictly with the differences between temperatures, it is therefore usually necessary to convert degrees Celsius and degrees Fahrenheit to degrees Kelvin and degrees Rankine.

Although we can, in principle, measure the temperature of an arbitrary system by the methods discussed above, once we have successfully calibrated the properties of some system, for example, a mercury thermometer, in terms of the temperature, this system can be used to measure the temperature of other systems.

ENTROPY

If a closed system undergoes a quasistatic change from an arbitrary state 1 to an arbitrary state 2 and the only work done is mechanical work, due to a change in volume, then the entropy change at any stage in the process is, from Equation (5.26), given by

$$dS = \frac{dQ}{T} \tag{5.31}$$

and the total entropy change of the system, in going from state 1 to state 2, is

$$S_2 - S_1 = \int_1^2 \frac{dQ}{T} \tag{5.32}$$

Since we can, in principle, measure dQ and T, we can calculate the entropy difference between the two states. It should be carefully noted that Equation (5.32) can be used to calculate the entropy difference only if the process is quasistatic and the work done is due to a change in the volume. If we wish to calculate the entropy change in a process in which the above conditions are not satisfied, then we simply replace the given process by a process that takes the system between the same initial and final states, respectively, and also satisfies the above conditions. Since the entropy is a state function, the entropy difference will depend only on the initial and final states and, therefore, must be the same for both processes. Equation (5.32) allows us to calculate the entropy difference between any two states of a closed system. Before we can assign a numerical value to the entropy for a particular system, we must know the value of the entropy for at least one state. In the case of internal energy, we were free to assign an arbitrary value to the internal energy of one state of each of the elementary systems. As we shall see in the following chapter, we are not free to follow a similar procedure with the entropy.

SUMMARY

The results of the present chapter follow from Postulate III and can be summarized in the following corollary.

Corollary III.

(a)   If we define the pressure p as

$$p \equiv -\left(\frac{\partial E}{\partial V}\right)_{S,N} \tag{5.33}$$

then the pressure is equal to the magnitude of the force per unit area exerted by the system on its surroundings.

(b)   If we define the temperature T as

$$T \equiv \left(\frac{\partial E}{\partial S}\right)_{V,N} \tag{5.34}$$

then for a system which undergoes a Carnot cycle between two reservoirs at temperatures T_1 and T_2

$$\frac{T_1}{T_2} = \frac{\text{heat transferred } to \text{ the reservoir at } T_1}{\text{heat transferred } from \text{ the reservoir at } T_2} \tag{5.35}$$

(c)   If a closed simple system undergoes an infinitesimal quasistatic change, in which the only work done on the system is the mechanical work due to a change in the volume, then

$$dW = -pdV \tag{5.36}$$

$$dQ = TdS \tag{5.37}$$

The latter equation can be used to calculate the entropy difference between any two states of a closed simple system.

EXAMPLE

Problem.   A system consists of a fixed number of moles of a certain hypothetical substance, contained in a well-insulated container. If the volume of the system is changed slowly, the temperature is found to change in accordance with the equation $T = $ const V^{-1}. If a resistance R is inserted into the system and a current I is passed through the resistor, while the volume is held fixed, the temperature is found to increase slowly at a rate $dT/dt = CI^2RT^{-1/2}V^{-1/2}$, where C is a constant. Obtain an expression for the difference in the entropy between two arbitrary states (T_0,V_0) and (T_1,V_1).

Solution.   The first process is one of constant entropy, and therefore $dS = 0$ during this process. The second process is equivalent to a quasistatic process, in which $dW = -pdV = 0$ and $dQ = I^2Rdt$; therefore, the entropy change during this process is given by $dS = I^2Rdt/T = C^{-1}T^{-1/2}V^{1/2}dT$. Using the first process to take the system from the state (T_0,V_0) to the state $[(T_0V_0)V_1^{-1},V_1]$, and the second process to take the system from the state $[(T_0V_0)V_1^{-1},V_1]$ to the state (T_1,V_1), we obtain

$$\int_{T_0,V_0}^{T_1,V_1} dS = 0 + \int_{(T_0V_0)V_1^{-1}}^{T_1} C^{-1}T^{-1/2}V_1^{1/2}\, dT$$

and therefore

$$S(T_1,V_1) - S(T_0,V_0) = 2C^{-1}[(T_1V_1)^{1/2} - (T_0V_0)^{1/2}]$$

PROBLEMS

5.1   The entropy of a certain substance is given by $S = C(EVN)^{1/3}$, where C is a constant. Obtain expressions for the pressure and temperature as functions of E, V, and N.

5.2   An isolated composite system consists of system 1, whose energy is given by $E_1 = 3N_1RT_1$, and system 2, whose energy is given by $E_2 = 5N_2RT_2$. The two systems are separated by a diathermal piston. If the composite system has a total energy of 10^4 J and if there are two moles in system 1 and two moles in system 2, what is the internal energy of each subsystem in equilibrium?

5.3   An ideal monatomic gas satisfies the following equations: $E = 3NRT/2$ and $pV = NRT$. Show that the entropy is given by $S = NR$ ln $(E^{3/2}VN^{-5/2}) + CN$, where C and R are constants.

5.4   Using the results of Problem 5.3, show that when a fixed number of moles of an ideal monatomic gas undergoes a quasistatic, adiabatic expansion, the quantity $pV^{5/3}$ remains constant.

5.5   Show that the following processes are irreversible.
(a) A mass of water at a temperature T_1 is placed in contact with an equal mass of water at a temperature $T_2 \neq T_1$. The two masses of water are kept in contact until their temperatures are equalized.

(b) An isolated container is divided into two equal parts. One part is evacuated, and the other part contains a monatomic ideal gas (see Problem 5.3). The partition is broken, and the gas expands freely, filling the entire volume of the container.

5.6   The entropy of many ideal gases can be written in the form $S = NR \ln (E^a V N^{-a-1}) + NC$, where R is a universal constant and a and C are constants which depend upon the type of gas. The entropy and energy of a mixture of two such ideal and different gases contained in the same volume V, are given by: $S = N_1 R \ln (E_1{}^{a_1} V N_1{}^{-a_1-1}) + N_1 C_1 + N_2 R \ln (E_2{}^{a_2} V N_2{}^{-a_2-1}) + N_2 C_2$ and $E = E_1 + E_2$.

(a) Show that the above statement implies that two such gases can be mixed reversibly.

(b) Devise a method for mixing the gases reversibly.

(c) Show that the above statement is not true if the gases are identical.

(d) How would the above statement be modified for identical gases?

5.7   (a) One kg of water at 273°K is placed in contact with a heat reservoir at 373°K. When the water has reached 373°K, what has been the entropy change of the water? Of the heat reservoir? Of the universe? Assume that the heat required to raise the temperature of 1 g of water 1°K is a constant 1 cal.

(b) If the water had been heated from 273°K to 373°K, by bringing it first in contact with a reservoir at 323°K and second with a reservoir at 373°K, what would have been the entropy change of the universe?

(c) Explain how the water might be heated from 273°K to 373°K with almost no change of entropy of the universe.

5.8   An electric current of 10 A is maintained for 1 sec in a resistor of 30 Ω. The resistor is maintained at a constant temperature by immersing the resistor in a heat bath of temperature $T = 27°C$.

(a) What is the entropy change of the resistor?

(b) What is the entropy change of the universe?

The same current is maintained for the same length of time in the same resistor, but the resistor is now thermally insulated. The mass of the resistor is 10 g, and the specific heat is 0.50 J(g)$^{-1}$(°K)$^{-1}$. The initial temperature of the resistor is 27°C.

(c) What is the entropy change of the resistor?

(d) What is the entropy change of the universe?

5.9   Sketch a Carnot cycle on a p–V plane for an ideal monatomic gas (see Problem 5.3). Write the equation of each curve on the diagram.

5.10   A Carnot cycle operates between 300°K and 100°K. The heat supplied during the 300°K isothermal process is 100 J. Determine the heat rejected during the 100°K isothermal process. How much work was done by the system during the cycle?

5.11   During a reversible process, the temperature and entropy are related by the equation $T = A(S/N) + B(S/N)^2$, where A and B are positive constants. Calculate the heat added between the temperatures T_1 and T_2,

5.12 A substance changes state at 77°C by the addition of 350 cal. What is the gain in entropy?

5.13 Two identical masses of liquid for which $E = NCT$, where C is a constant, are initially at temperatures T_1 and T_2, respectively. Show that when they are mixed, the entropy change of the universe is $2\,NC\ln\left[(T_1 + T_2)/2(T_1T_2)^{1/2}\right]$, and show that this change is positive. Assume that the volume change of the liquid is negligible.

5.14 During the heating of a certain substance at 57°C, it expands, doing 25 J of work, and gains 8 J of internal energy. What is the gain of entropy?

CHAPTER 6

Absolute Entropy

In Chapter 4 we postulated the existence of an entropy function. In Chapter 5 we determined how to measure the entropy difference between two states. In the present chapter we shall investigate some additional properties of the entropy function.

From a microscopic point of view, the entropy of an isolated system in equilibrium is given by

$$S(E,V,N) = k \ln W^*(E,V,N) \qquad (6.1)$$

where $W^*(E,V,N)$ is the number of microstates associated with the equilibrium state, and k is a constant that is determined by the choice of temperature scale.

If we examine microscopically the specific values of $W^*(E,V,N)$ for quite general types of systems, we find that certain properties of $W^*(E,V,N)$ seem to be true for any type of system.

In the first place, if V and N are held fixed, the number of microstates W^* associated with the equilibrium state is found to increase with increase of energy. The greater the energy is for a given value of V and N, the more numerous are the ways in which the equilibrium state can be achieved.

This relationship is intuitively intelligible, since it stands to reason that the more energy available for distribution among the molecules of the system, the more ways can that energy be distributed. We can state this result mathematically as $(\partial W^*/\partial E)_{V,N} \geq 0$, or in terms of the entropy, as $(\partial S/\partial E)_{V,N} \geq 0$. Since $S(E,V,N)$ is a single-valued function of E, it follows that

$$\left(\frac{\partial E}{\partial S}\right)_{V,N} \equiv T \geq 0 \tag{6.2}$$

If V and N are held fixed and E decreased, it is further found that W^* will decrease in such a way that, at the minimum of energy,

$$\left(\frac{\partial E}{\partial S}\right)_{V,N} \equiv T = 0 \tag{6.3}$$

Finally, it will be found to be quite generally true that if V and N are held fixed and E is decreased, then as E approaches $E_0(V,N)$, its minimum value, the number of microstates associated with the equilibrium state becomes negligibly small, compared to its value for higher E, and we can assume that it approaches the value 1, that is, $W^*(E_0,V,N) = 1$. It follows that

$$S(E_0,V,N) = k \ln W^*(E_0,V,N) = 0 \tag{6.4}$$

It should be noted that we are not merely assigning a specific value of the entropy to a single state. The generality of this result rests with the facts: (1) The entropy is zero for an entire set of states, namely, all those states for which $T = 0$, irrespective of the values of any other parameters of which S may be a function; (2) It refers to any system. It should also be noted that the macroscopic content of this fact would not be changed if the entropy approached some universal molar constant other than zero.

In Figure 6.1 we have plotted a form of S as a function of E for a fixed value of V and N that will satisfy the above conditions. We note in Figure 6.1 that the slope of the curve is always positive, that it approaches zero at $E = E_0$, and that at $E = E_0$, $S = 0$.

SUMMARY

The results of this chapter can be summarized in a new postulate.

Postulate IV.   The temperature and entropy of a closed system of fixed volume vanish in the state of minimum energy and are greater than zero in all other states.

The above postulate does not enjoy the same universal acceptance as do the preceding postulates. Many authorities define an equilibrium state of an isolated system as simply a state of quiescence, that is, a state in which none of the thermodynamic properties is changing appreciably with time. In our definition, we require the additional condition that it is impossible to change the system to a new quiescent state without producing some net change in the surroundings. If the former definition is used, then the entropy is no longer necessarily a single-valued function of the energy, volume, and mole number; it is also possible to have states in which the temperature is zero, but in which the energy is not at its minimum value and in which the entropy is not zero.

A further difficulty with the above postulate is the inability to check it experimentally to the same degree of certitude as can be achieved in checks of the other postulates. We can approach the state of minimum energy only experimentally; we cannot actually reach it. Furthermore, there are apparent exceptions to the above postulate. These exceptions can be explained by assuming that the system is not in true equilibrium as we have defined equilibrium; but in many cases the experiments necessary to verify this assumption cannot be carried out.

Nevertheless, since there are no absolute and unquestionable exceptions to the above postulate, and since it is completely consistent with micro-

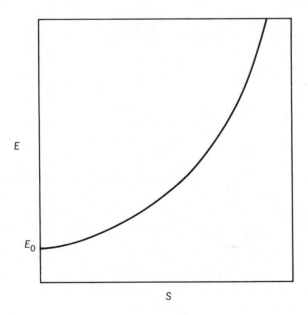

FIGURE 6.1

scopic theory, we shall assume it to be true. (The reader who wishes to pursue the question further can begin by referring to the *third law of thermodynamics*, or *Nernst's postulate*, in the books listed in the Bibliography.)

PROBLEMS

6.1 The following functions are supposed to be entropy functions for various systems. Which of them is inconsistent with Postulate IV? Why? In each case C is a positive constant, and in all cases in which fractional exponents appear, only the real positive root is to be taken.

(a) $S = C(EVN)^{1/3}$ (c) $S = CN \ln (E^{3/2} V N^{-5/2})$

(b) $S = CV^3/NE$ (d) $S = C(EN)^{1/2} \exp(-V^2/N^2)$

6.2 Determine $S(T,V)$ for the system described in the example toward the end of Chapter 5. The only constant which should appear in your answer is the constant C.

CHAPTER 7

The Three Laws of Thermodynamics

INTRODUCTION

In the preceding chapters, starting from an intuitive microscopic analysis, we have arrived at a set of postulates that form the foundation of thermodynamics. All the results of classical thermodynamics, as applied to simple one-component systems, can be derived from these postulates. Although we have attempted to make the postulates meaningful from a microscopic point of view, they do not depend for their macroscopic validity on a microscopic picture. Macroscopically they are valid, because they predict results that are in agreement with experiment. The same basic postulates could have been expressed in many different forms and with a considerably greater economy of words and ideas. The formulation we have chosen, however, provides a particularly convenient and easy starting point, from which concrete analytical results can be derived with a minimum of mathematical complexity.

Historically, the pioneers of thermodynamics knew little or nothing about the atomic structure of matter. For them, matter was continuous and, in principle, infinitely divisible into parts having the same general properties as the whole. It is not immediately apparent from the analysis of the

53

preceding chapters exactly how they would have arrived at the same basic postulates that we have.

In the present chapter, we wish to recast the basic postulates in a form that will make them more immediately apparent on a macroscopic level. Our purpose is twofold. In the first place, the resultant reformulation will emphasize the fact that thermodynamics is a macroscopic science and that the basic laws of thermodynamics are simple generalizations of a series of macroscopic facts, easily grasped and verifiable by direct experiments. In the second place, it will make the actual historical development of thermodynamics from a macroscopic point of view more understandable.

THE THREE LAWS OF THERMODYNAMICS

Starting from the postulates of thermodynamics, it is possible to derive a number of simple theorems. We shall derive three theorems; they will be in such form that they can be treated as direct generalizations from a series of macroscopic experiments, rather than as consequences of a set of a priori postulates. It is customary to call such generalizations laws of physics; consequently, we shall apply the word "law" rather than "theorem" to these results.

Law I.   The amount of work required to change an adiabatically enclosed system from one state to another depends only on the initial and final states of the system, and is independent both of the way in which the work is performed and the path through which the system passes from the initial to the final state.

This theorem follows directly from Postulate I, and no proof is necessary.

Law II.   It is impossible for the universe to undergo a change, the only effect of which is the transfer of a positive amount of energy from a single heat reservoir to a work reservoir.

To prove Law II, let us suppose that we were able to construct a device capable of receiving heat Q from a single heat reservoir and of using the energy to do an amount of work $W = Q$, but which itself was unchanged during the process. Let us further assume that the work W was stored in a work reservoir. As a result of such a transformation, the only changes that would occur in the universe would be: (1) a change in the state of the heat reservoir and (2) a change in the state of the work reservoir. Since heat would supposedly be flowing out of the heat reservoir, and since temperature is always positive (by Postulate IV), the entropy of the heat reservoir would decrease. The entropy of the work reservoir would not be changed, since there can be no flow of heat to a work reservoir. The entropy change of the universe would therefore be equal to the entropy change of the heat reservoir, and thus the entropy of the universe would decrease. But this process would be a violation of Postulate III. Therefore, heat Q cannot be converted from a single heat reservoir entirely into work W without at the same time producing some other change in the universe.

The second law of thermodynamics is often stated in the following equivalent form: It is impossible for the universe to undergo a change, the only effect of which is the transfer of a positive amount of energy from one heat reservoir to another heat reservoir at a higher temperature.

To prove the second law in this form, we note that if the above statement were not true, then it would be possible to take an amount of heat Q out of a reservoir at temperature T_1 and put the same amount of heat Q into a second reservoir at temperature T_2, where T_2 is greater than T_1, without producing any other change in the universe. As a result, the entropy of the reservoir at temperature T_1 would change by an amount $-Q/T_1$, and the entropy of the reservoir at temperature T_2 would change by an amount Q/T_2. These changes are assumed to be the only ones taking place in the universe, and hence the entropy of the universe would change by an amount $(Q/T_2) - (Q/T_1)$. For T_2 greater than T_1, the entropy of the universe would therefore decrease, but such a decrease would be a violation of Postulate III. It is, therefore, impossible to produce a flow of heat from a low-temperature heat reservoir to a high-temperature heat reservoir without at the same time producing some other change in the universe.

From the second law, it follows that energy stored in a work reservoir is more useful than energy stored in a heat reservoir; moreover, energy stored in a high-temperature heat reservoir is more useful than energy stored in a low-temperature heat reservoir.

Law III.   The entropy of any system vanishes in those equilibrium states for which the temperature is zero.

This theorem follows directly from Postulate IV, and no proof is necessary. Although it would be convenient to express Law III without any reference to temperature or entropy, it is extremely difficult to do so without losing some of its informational content. Since we shall, in what follows, show how the concepts of temperature and entropy are developed from the second law, and since, historically, these concepts were actually developed before the third law was proposed, the third law can, even in the above form, be considered as a direct generalization from a series of macroscopic measurements, and not simply as a postulate arrived at on the basis of a microscopic analysis.

Laws I, II, and III can be used in place of Postulates I, II, III, and IV as the starting point of thermodynamics. The laws of thermodynamics are more immediately connected with macroscopic facts than are the postulates, and for this reason it is easier for someone being introduced to thermodynamics to accept them than the postulates. However, as we have mentioned earlier, it is far easier to arrive at quantitative results starting from the postulates than from the laws. Ideally, the best approach would seem to be to start from the three laws and derive Postulates I, II, III, and IV, as most textbooks do. Although such an approach is logically appealing, it suffers from certain pedagogical disadvantages that are discussed in the Preface. We have, in the present text, attempted to arrive as quickly and as meaningfully as possible at the basic postulates of thermodynamics by exploiting their microscopic significance. To further increase our grasp of these postulates, we shall in the following chapter derive them, starting from the three laws.

CONCLUSION

In the present chapter we have shown that the following three laws are consequences of the four basic postulates, introduced earlier.

Law I. The amount of work required to change an adiabatically enclosed system from one state to another depends only on the initial and final states of the system, and is independent both of the way in which the work is performed and the path through which the system passes from the initial to the final state.

Law II. It is impossible for the universe to undergo a change, the only effect of which is the transfer of a positive amount of energy from a single heat reservoir to a work reservoir.

Law III. The entropy of any system vanishes in those equilibrium states for which the temperature is zero.

PROBLEMS

7.1 The energy of a fixed number of moles of an ideal gas is a function of temperature only. It follows that if an ideal gas that is in contact with a heat reservoir at a temperature T undergoes an isothermal expansion, an amount of heat Q will flow out of the reservoir, and the gas will perform an equivalent amount of work W. Is this a violation of the second law of thermodynamics? Explain your answer.

7.2 Show that the following two statements of the second law of thermodynamics are equivalent:

(a) It is impossible for the universe to undergo a change, the only effect of which is the transfer of a positive amount of energy from a single heat reservoir to a work reservoir.

(b) It is impossible for the universe to undergo a change, the only effect of which is the transfer of a positive amount of energy from one heat reservoir to another heat reservoir at a higher temperature.

CHAPTER 8

Equivalence
of the Postulates
and the Laws

In the preceding chapter we derived the three laws of thermodynamics from the four fundamental postulates of thermodynamics. In the present chapter we shall derive the fundamental postulates from the three laws, thereby demonstrating the equivalence of the laws and the postulates. It should be remembered in the following sections that we cannot, without justification, draw on any results that were postulated or proved in the preceding chapters other than the three laws stated at the end of the last chapter. At times it will appear that we are simply repeating material that we have previously proved. If the reader is careful to remember the point of view of the present chapter, he will realize that we are not.

PRESUPPOSITIONS

Our objective is to derive the fundamental postulates from the three laws. It quickly becomes apparent, when we try to do this, that some of the information contained in the basic postulates cannot be derived directly from the three laws, not because the basic postulates contain more information than the three laws, but because some of the information contained in the basic postulates is simply presupposed as self-evident when one is working with the three laws. In the present section we shall consider these presuppositions.

We shall first presuppose that there exist equilibrium states for an isolated simple system that are uniquely determined by a small number of macroscopic parameters. In particular, for a one-component system three independent parameters are sufficient. An equilibrium state, as defined in Chapters 1 and 3, is a state from which no change is possible without some net change in the surroundings.

We next presuppose that it is possible in principle to separate all the systems in the universe into sets of systems having the same temperature. Let us briefly recall from Chapter 1 what is meant by the same temperature. If two otherwise isolated systems are brought into contact by means of a rigid, diathermal wall and if there is no change in the macroscopic properties of either system, then we say that the systems are in thermal equilibrium. If we assume that two systems which are each in thermal equilibrium with a third system are in thermal equilibrium with each other, an assumption called the *zeroth law* of thermodynamics, then it is possible to separate all systems in the universe into sets of systems, such that all the systems within a set are in thermal equilibrium with one another. We can then identify each set by assigning a number to the set. We call this number the temperature of the set. As we shall see in the following sections, there is a very natural way to assign a temperature to each set. At this stage it is sufficient to know what is meant by two systems being at the same temperature.

Finally, we shall presuppose the existence of reversible processes. A reversible process is one that is performed in such a way that, at the conclusion of the process, both the system and its surroundings, that is, the rest of the universe, may be restored to their respective initial states. Since the system together with its surroundings constitute the entire universe, a reversible process is one that is performed in such a way that the universe is not irremediably altered. It should be noted that although every reversible process is quasistatic, every quasistatic process is not reversible. For example, if we bring two bodies, initially at different temperatures, into contact by means of a rigid wall that is a poor conductor of heat, the two systems will slowly establish thermal equilibrium. Since the intermediate states of the systems are essentially equilibrium states, the process is quasistatic. However, the process is not reversible, since once the systems have established thermal equilibrium, it is impossible to restore them to their respective initial states without producing some net change in the rest of the universe.

We shall be particularly interested in two types of reversible processes: the reversible isothermal process and the reversible adiabatic process. A reversible isothermal process is a reversible process in which the temperature of the system of interest remains constant. If, for example, a system is quasistatically compressed while remaining in contact with a heat reservoir, the process is a reversible isothermal process. By simply allowing the system to quasistatically expand while remaining in contact with the heat reservoir, the system will retrace, in the reverse direction, the path it followed during the compression; the heat reservoir will be restored to its original state; and the work of compression will be regained. A reversible adiabatic process is a reversible process during which the system of interest remains thermally insulated from its surroundings. If an insulated system is quasistatically compressed, the process is a reversible adiabatic process, since the system can be made to retrace its steps in reverse direction and the work of compression regained by simply allowing the system to quasistatically expand.

With the above presuppositions, we are now in a position to derive the basic postulates of thermodynamics from the three laws.

THE INTERNAL ENERGY

Let us assume that we have a closed system X that by some process passes from a state x_1 to a state x_2. The work done on the system, which we designate by $W(x_1 \to x_2)$, will in general depend on the process. However, if the process is adiabatic then, according to the first law, the work done will depend only on the initial and final states, that is,

$$W_a(x_1 \to x_2) = \text{fcn}(x_1, x_2) \tag{8.1}$$

where the subscript a is used to indicate that the process is adiabatic. From Equation (8.1) it follows that it is possible to define a function $E(x)$ by the relation

$$E(x) = W_a(x_0 \to x) + E_0 \tag{8.2}$$

where the state x_0 is some arbitrary reference state, and E_0 is an arbitrary constant. The quantity $E(x)$ is called the internal energy of the system.

Having defined the internal energy, we can define the heat transferred to a system during an arbitrary process from the state x_1 to the state x_2 by the relation

$$Q(x_1 \to x_2) = [E(x_2) - E(x_1)] - W(x_1 \to x_2) \tag{8.3}$$

TEMPERATURE

If we had a complete collection of heat reservoirs covering every possible temperature, it would be possible to assign a distinct number to each reservoir and in this way determine a temperature scale. However, as we shall see in the present section, there is a particularly convenient way to establish a scale.

Let us consider two arbitrary heat reservoirs 1 and 2, whose temperatures we designate as T_1 and T_2, respectively. Making use of the two heat reservoirs, a work reservoir R, and whatever auxiliary mechanical devices are needed, we can take some arbitrary system X through a cyclic process consisting of the following stages: (1) a reversible adiabatic compression from state x_1 at temperature T_1 to state x_2 at temperature T_2, (2) a reversible isothermal expansion at temperature T_2 from state x_2 to a state x_3, (3) a reversible adiabatic expansion from state x_3 at temperature T_2 to state x_4 at temperature T_1, and (4) a reversible isothermal compression at temperature T_1 from state x_4 to state x_1. The above reversible cycle is called a *Carnot cycle*. The net effect of the cycle is: (1) an amount of heat Q_{X1} has flowed from system X to the heat reservoir 1, (2) an amount of heat Q_{2X} has flowed from the heat reservoir 2 to system X, and (3) an amount of work W_{XR} has flowed from system X to the work reservoir. This process is schematically illustrated on the left-hand side of Figure 8.1. In a similar fashion we can take some arbitrary system Y through a similar cycle with similar results, as shown on the right-hand side of Figure 8.1. The net effect of the two cycles treated as a unit is: (1) an amount of heat $Q_{X1} + Q_{Y1}$

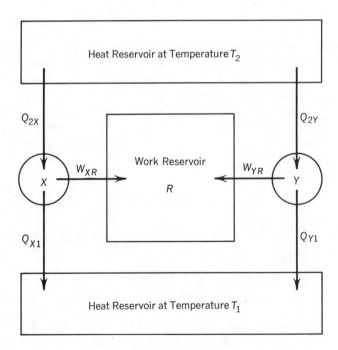

FIGURE 8.1

has flowed into heat reservoir 1, (2) an amount of heat $Q_{2X} + Q_{2Y}$ has flowed out of heat reservoir 2, and (3) an amount of work $W_{XR} + W_{YR}$ has flowed into the work reservoir. By adjusting the amount of material in the system X, or the extent of the isothermal process at temperature T_1, or by replacing the single cycle with more than one cycle, we can adjust the magnitude of Q_{X1} arbitrarily. Since all the processes are reversible, we can also change the sign of Q_{X1} by simply reversing the direction of the cycle. We can similarly adjust the value of Q_{2X}, but as we shall now show, we cannot arbitrarily adjust both Q_{X1} and Q_{2X} at the same time. In the same way we can arbitrarily adjust the value of either Q'_{Y1} or the value of Q_{2Y}, but we cannot arbitrarily adjust the value of both at the same time. To prove the above statements, let us adjust the values of Q_{X1} and Q_{Y1} such that

$$Q_{X1} + Q_{Y1} = 0 \qquad (8.4)$$

If condition (8.4) is satisfied, then the combined effect of the cyclic process executed by the systems X and Y is: (1) an amount of heat $Q_{2X} + Q_{2Y}$ is surrendered by the heat reservoir 2 and (2) an amount of work $W_{XR} + W_{YR}$ is received by the work reservoir. By virtue of the first law

$$Q_{2X} + Q_{2Y} = W_{XR} + W_{YR} \qquad (8.5)$$

If we reverse the direction of the cycles performed by systems X and Y, then, since the cycles are reversible, the effect will be a simple change in the sign of each quantity appearing in Equations (8.4) and (8.5). We can, therefore, simultaneously change the direction of both processes without affecting the validity of (8.4) and (8.5). Let us choose the direction such that $Q_{2X} + Q_{2Y} \geq 0$. But if $Q_{2X} + Q_{2Y} > 0$, then a positive amount of heat is surrendered by heat reservoir 2, and an equivalent amount of work is delivered to the work reservoir. This result is a violation of the second law and therefore

$$Q_{2X} + Q_{2Y} = 0 \qquad (8.6)$$

Combining Equations (8.4) and (8.6) and noting that $Q_{X1} = -Q_{1X}$, and so on, we obtain

$$\frac{Q_{1X}}{Q_{X2}} = \frac{Q_{1Y}}{Q_{Y2}} \qquad (8.7)$$

Since X and Y are entirely arbitrary systems, it follows that the ratio Q_{1X}/Q_{X2} is the same for all Carnot cycles that operate between the same two reservoirs. The ratio Q_{1X}/Q_{X2} thus depends only on the temperatures T_1 and T_2, that is,

$$\frac{Q_{1X}}{Q_{X2}} = f(T_1,T_2) \tag{8.8}$$

where $f(T_1,T_2)$ is some function of T_1 and T_2. The function $f(T_1,T_2)$ is not entirely arbitrary, as we shall see, but is restricted to functions of the form $g(T_1)/g(T_2)$, where $g(T)$ is some arbitrary function of T. To prove this, let us consider three reservoirs 1, 2, and 3 and three systems X, Y, and Z, executing Carnot cycles between 1 and 2, 2 and 3, and 3 and 1, respectively, as shown in Figure 8.2. If we adjust Q_{Y2} such that

$$Q_{X2} + Q_{Y2} = 0 \tag{8.9}$$

and Q_{Z1} such that

$$Q_{X1} + Q_{Z1} = 0 \tag{8.10}$$

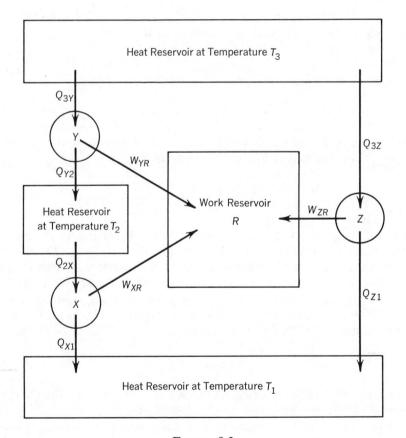

FIGURE 8.2

then there is no net heat transfer to reservoirs 1 and 2. By the same argument as previously advanced, there can be no net heat transfer to reservoir 3, that is,

$$Q_{3Y} + Q_{3Z} = 0 \tag{8.11}$$

Combining Equations (8.9), (8.10), and (8.11) and noting that $Q_{1X} = -Q_{X1}$, and so on, it follows that

$$\frac{Q_{1X}}{Q_{X2}} \frac{Q_{2Y}}{Q_{Y3}} = \frac{Q_{1Z}}{Q_{Z3}} \tag{8.12}$$

Making use of (8.8) in (8.12), we obtain

$$f(T_1, T_2) f(T_2, T_3) = f(T_1, T_3) \tag{8.13}$$

Equation (8.13) must be true for arbitrary values of T_1, T_2, and T_3. In particular, if we set T_3 equal to a constant C, we obtain

$$f(T_1, T_2) = \frac{g(T_1)}{g(T_2)} \tag{8.14}$$

where $g(T) = f(T, C)$. It follows that if $f(T_1, T_2)$ satisfies condition (8.13), then it must satisfy condition (8.14). Conversely, if $f(T_1, T_2)$ satisfies condition (8.14), condition (8.13) is satisfied. The two conditions are therefore equivalent. Combining (8.8) and (8.14) we obtain

$$\frac{Q_{1X}}{Q_{X2}} = \frac{g(T_1)}{g(T_2)} \tag{8.15}$$

Since we do not as yet have a temperature scale, we are free to choose the function $g(T)$ arbitrarily. If we choose a particular function $g(T)$ and also assign a numerical value to the temperature of one reservoir, then we can determine the temperature of any other reservoir by simply: (1) operating an arbitrary Carnot cycle between this reservoir and the reference reservoir, (2) measuring the heat transferred to each reservoir, and (3) making use of Equation (8.15). The temperature scales that result if we choose

$$g(T) = T \tag{8.16}$$

are called absolute temperature scales. When we refer to temperature in the present text, we shall always mean absolute temperatures. If we assign the value 273.16 to the temperature at which water can simultaneously exist as liquid, solid and vapor, the resulting absolute temperature scale is called the Kelvin scale. If, however, we assign the value 491.688 to that temperature, the resulting absolute temperature scale is called the Rankine scale. These two are the most commonly used absolute scales. Combining Equations (8.15) and (8.16), we obtain the relation

$$\frac{Q_{1X}}{Q_{X2}} = \frac{T_1}{T_2} \tag{8.17}$$

Thus the ratio of the absolute temperatures of two reservoirs 1 and 2 is equal to the ratio of the heat transferred from reservoir 1 to the heat transferred to reservoir 2 when an arbitrary Carnot cycle is operated between the two reservoirs.

If a positive number is chosen for the temperature of the reference reservoir, then all absolute temperatures will be positive. If this were not so, there would exist at least two reservoirs such that $(-T_1/T_2) \equiv (Q_{1X}/Q_{2X}) > 0$. A Carnot engine operating between these two reservoirs could extract heat from both reservoirs and perform an amount of work $Q_{1X} + Q_{2X}$. If part of this work were used to return the reservoir T_2 to its original state, the net result would be that an amount of heat Q_{1X} had been extracted from reservoir T_1 and an equivalent amount of work performed. But this would be a violation of the second law.

ENTROPY

Let us consider a system X that undergoes a cyclic process. We suppose that during the cycle the system receives heat from, or surrenders heat to, a set of heat reservoirs $1, 2, \cdots, n$, having the temperatures $T_1, T_2, \cdots, T_n$, respectively. The amount of heat transferred from reservoir i to system X will be designated by Q_{iX}. We shall now show that, in general

$$\sum_{i=1}^{n} \frac{Q_{iX}}{T_i} \leq 0 \tag{8.18}$$

and if the process is reversible,

$$\sum_{i=1}^{n} \frac{Q_{iX}}{T_i} = 0 \tag{8.19}$$

In order to prove (8.18) and (8.19), let us suppose that in addition to system X, we introduce a set of systems $1', 2', \cdots, n'$, that execute Carnot cycles between reservoirs $1, 2, \cdots, n$, respectively, and another heat reservoir 0 at temperature T_0. The heat transferred from reservoir i' to the system

i will be designated $Q_{i'i}$, and the heat transferred from the system i' to the reservoir 0 will be designated $Q_{i'0}$. We shall adjust each such Carnot cycle so that

$$Q_{i'i} = Q_{iX} \tag{8.20}$$

that is, in such a way that the system i' in executing a Carnot cycle between reservoirs 0 and i supplies exactly the amount of heat to reservoir i that was removed by system X. As a result of the combined effect of the cyclic process executed by system X and the set of systems $1', 2', \cdots, n'$, an amount of heat

$$Q \equiv \sum_i Q_{i'0} = \sum_i \frac{T_0}{T_i} Q_{ii'} = -\sum_i \frac{T_0}{T_i} Q_{i'i}$$
$$= -\sum_i \frac{T_0}{T_i} Q_{iX} = -T_0 \sum_i \frac{Q_{iX}}{T_i} \tag{8.21}$$

is transferred to the heat reservoir 0, but reservoirs $1, 2, \cdots, n$ remain unchanged. If we assume that the work done on system X and on systems $1', 2', \cdots, n'$ was supplied by a single work reservoir R, and if we designate the work done on system X during the cycles as W_{RX} and the work done on system i' as $W_{Ri'}$, then the total amount of work surrendered by the work reservoir will be

$$W = W_{RX} + \sum_i W_{Ri'} \tag{8.22}$$

Since system X and systems $1', 2', \cdots, n'$ are restored to their original states at the end of the cycle, and since no change has taken place in reservoirs $1, 2, \cdots, n$, the net effects of the total cycle are that: (1) an amount of energy W has been lost by the work reservoir and (2) an amount of energy Q has been gained by heat reservoir 0. By virtue of the first law

$$Q = W \tag{8.23}$$

and by virtue of the second law

$$Q \geq 0 \tag{8.24}$$

Substituting Equation (8.21) in (8.24) we obtain

$$\sum_{i=1}^{n} \frac{Q_{iX}}{T_i} \leq 0 \tag{8.25}$$

If the cycle performed by system X is reversible, then by reversing this cycle and all Carnot cycles executed by systems $1', 2', \cdots, n'$, we can reverse the signs of Q and W. Since (8.24) is always true, the only way the sign of Q can be changed without violating the second law is for Q to be equal to zero. It follows that if the cycle performed by system X is reversible, then

$$\sum_{i=1}^{n} \frac{Q_{iX}}{T_i} = 0 \quad \text{(reversible)} \quad (8.26)$$

If an infinite number of reservoirs is involved in taking the system through the cyclic process, then the summation in (8.25) becomes an integral, and we have

$$\oint \frac{dQ}{T'} \leq 0 \quad (8.27)$$

where dQ is the amount of heat transferred to the system during an infinitesimal stage in the process, and the temperature T' is the temperature of the reservoir with which the system is in contact at this stage but not necessarily the temperature of the system. Since Equation (8.27) is true for an arbitrary cyclic process, the intermediate states need not be equilibrium states; hence, we may not even be able to speak of a temperature of the system during the process. Equation (8.27) is called the *Clausius inequality*. If the process is reversible then

$$\oint \frac{dQ^*}{T} = 0 \quad (8.28)$$

where the asterisk is used to indicate that the process is reversible. Note that since the temperature of the system, that is, T, and the temperature of the reservoir with which the system is in contact at any stage in the process, that is, T', are equal in a reversible process, we were able to replace the temperature T' in Equation (8.28) by the temperature T.

From Equation (8.28) and the results of Appendix 7, it follows that the integral of dQ/T along any reversible path joining the two states x_1 and x_2 of a closed system X will be independent of the path; hence, it is possible to define a function $S(x)$ by the relation

$$S(x) = \int_{x_0}^{x} \frac{dQ^*}{T} + S_0 \quad (8.29)$$

where the state x_0 is some arbitrary reference state, S_0 is a constant, and the integration is carried out along some reversible path joining the state x_0 with the state x. The quantity $S(x)$ is called the entropy of the system.

The numerical value of the constant S_0 in Equation (8.29) can, in principle, be determined by the third law, which states that the entropy approaches zero as the temperature approaches zero. In differential form, Equation (8.29) becomes

$$dQ^* = TdS \qquad (8.30)$$

It should be noted that if a simple one-component system undergoes a quasistatic change in which the only work done on the system is the mechanical work due to a change in the volume, then the values of dQ and T at any stage in the process will be identical with those at the respective stages for the same process carried out reversibly. It is, therefore, possible to extend the validity of Equations (8.29) and (8.30) to processes that are not necessarily reversible. However, Equations (8.29) and (8.30) are certainly true for reversible processes, and this information is sufficient to define the entropy function.

From the definition of the entropy function as given by Equation (8.29), it is apparent that the entropy of a composite system is equal to the sum of the entropies of the component systems.

ENTROPY MAXIMIZATION

In the previous section we have proved the existence of an entropy function. In the present section we wish to show that if a process takes place in an isolated system, the entropy must increase or remain constant.

Let us consider a transformation which occurs in an isolated composite system in which the system goes from a state a to a state b. Let us represent

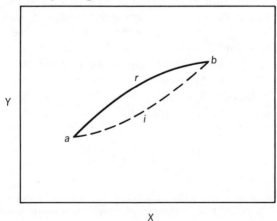

FIGURE 8.3

this change by the dotted line *aib* shown in Figure 8.3. The process need not be reversible. Now suppose that we return the system from state *b* to state *a* by a reversible process *bra*. The process *aibra* is a cyclic process, and hence from relation (8.27),

$$\int_{aibra} \frac{dQ}{T'} \leq 0 \tag{8.31}$$

The integral in (8.31) can be rewritten

$$\int_{aibra} \frac{dQ}{T'} = \int_{aib} \frac{dQ}{T'} + \int_{bra} \frac{dQ}{T'} = \int_{aib} \frac{dQ}{T'} - \int_{arb} \frac{dQ}{T'} \tag{8.32}$$

Since the system is isolated during the process *aib*, no heat is transferred during the process, and hence

$$\int_{aib} \frac{dQ}{T'} = 0 \tag{8.33}$$

Since the process *arb* is reversible,

$$\int_{arb} \frac{dQ}{T'} = S(b) - S(a) \tag{8.34}$$

Substituting Equations (8.32), (8.33), and (8.34) in (8.31), we obtain

$$S(b) \geq S(a) \tag{8.35}$$

Thus for any transformation occurring in an isolated system, the entropy of the final state can never be less than that of the initial state.

It follows that if an internal constraint is removed from an isolated composite system, the system can spontaneously move only to a state of higher entropy. If there is nothing to prevent the change, the system will arrive at equilibrium only when it has arrived at the state of maximum entropy consistent with the remaining constraints.

SOME PROPERTIES OF ENERGY, ENTROPY, AND TEMPERATURE

We have shown earlier in our discussion of temperature that the second law of thermodynamics requires that the temperature be positive if our reference temperature is chosen as positive.

It can further be shown that if two systems are brought into thermal contact, heat will flow from the system at the higher temperature to the system at lower temperature. Consider an isolated composite system consisting of two systems 1 and 2 in thermal contact. If a positive amount of heat dQ_{12} flows from system 1 to system 2, then the entropy change in the composite system will be

$$dS = \frac{dQ_{12}}{T_2} + \frac{dQ_{21}}{T_1} = dQ_{12}\left(\frac{1}{T_2} - \frac{1}{T_1}\right) \tag{8.36}$$

Since dS must be greater than zero, it follows that $T_1 > T_2$. It follows that if the volume V and mole number N of a system are held fixed, energy can always be extracted from the system, unless it is at zero temperature, by putting the system in contact with a reservoir at a lower temperature. We conclude that the zero temperature state corresponds to the state of minimum energy for the given values of V and N. By virtue of the third law, this state is also a state of zero entropy.

If V and N are held fixed and if the energy is increased from its minimum value by bringing the system in contact with a heat reservoir at a nonzero temperature, the temperature will increase. Since $dS = dQ/T$ and both dQ and T are positive, the entropy will also increase. It follows that for given V and N, the temperature and entropy are greater than zero in all states except in the states of minimum energy. Furthermore, since we can add energy indefinitely to a system, there is no upper bound on temperature, energy, or entropy.

CONCLUSION

When we review the results of the present chapter, we find that every statement in the fundamental postulates has been encountered, either as a presupposition or as a consequence of the three laws. We conclude that the three laws, considered to include the presuppositions, contain essentially the same information as that contained in the fundamental postulates.

PROBLEMS

8.1   One cubic meter of a gas that is otherwise adiabatically enclosed contains a resistor of resistance 10 Ω through which a current of 10 amp is passed for 100 min while the volume is held constant. At the end of that period, the pressure is observed to have increased from 1 bar to 32 bars. The substance is subsequently allowed to expand adiabatically, finally returning to atmospheric pressure, at which time the volume is found to be 8 m³. It is observed that during this process the quantity p^3V^5 remains constant. Calculate the time for which the current would need to flow in the resistor if the substance were taken from the initial to the final state by passing the current through the resistor and allowing the substance to expand at constant pressure.

8.2 A Carnot cycle receives 20 J of heat at a constant temperature of 400°K and rejects 15 J at a lower constant temperature. Determine the lower sink temperature.

8.3 Prove that it is impossible for two quasistatic adiabatic curves to intersect. (*Hint:* Assume that they do intersect, and complete the cycle with an isothermal curve. Show that the performance of this cycle violates the second law.)

CHAPTER 9

A Summary
of the Basic Principles
of Thermodynamics

In the preceding chapters we have established the basic principles that constitute the foundation of thermodynamics. For convenience, we have gathered them together in the present chapter.

THE BASIC POSTULATES OF THERMODYNAMICS

Starting from a microscopic analysis of simple systems, one obtains the following postulates:

Postulate I. For every system there exists a quantity E, called the internal energy, that has the following properties:

(a) A unique value of the internal energy is associated with each state of the system.

(b) The internal energy of a closed system has a lower bound but no upper bound.

(c) The difference between the internal energy in one state and the internal energy in another state of a closed system is equal to the work required to bring the system, while adiabatically enclosed, from the one state to the other.

Corollary I.

(a) The internal energy is constant in an isolated system.
(b) The internal energy of a composite system is equal to the sum of the internal energies of its component systems.
(c) An arbitrary value of the internal energy can be assigned to one state of each elementary system.

Definition I. The heat transferred to a closed system during an infinitesimal process is defined by the relation

$$dE = dQ + dW \qquad (9.1)$$

where dE is the change in internal energy, dQ is the heat transferred to the system, and dW is the work done on the system.

Postulate II. There exists a state of an isolated, simple one-component system, called the equilibrium state, that is uniquely determined by the internal energy E, volume V, and number of moles N.

Postulate III. For every system there exists a state function S, called the entropy, that has the following properties:

(a) For a simple one-component system, S is a single-valued function of E, V, and N.
(b) The entropy of a composite system is equal to the sum of the entropies of its component systems.
(c) If an internal constraint is removed from an isolated composite system, consisting of n simple one-component systems $1, 2, \cdots, n$, and the system is allowed to come to an equilibrium state, then the values assumed by the extensive variables, $E_1, V_1, N_1, E_2, V_2, N_2, \cdots, E_n, V_n, N_n$, will be those values, consistent with the remaining internal and external constraints, that maximize the entropy of the composite system.
(d) During a quasistatic, adiabatic change in volume of a simple system, the entropy of the system remains constant.

Corollary II. The entropy of a simple one-component system, when expressed as a function of its internal energy, volume, and mole number, contains a complete thermodynamic description of the system.

Corollary III.

(a) If we define the pressure p as

$$p \equiv -\left(\frac{\partial E}{\partial V}\right)_{S,N} \qquad (9.2)$$

then the pressure is equal to the magnitude of the force per unit area exerted by the system on its surroundings.

(b) If we define the temperature T as

$$T \equiv \left(\frac{\partial E}{\partial S}\right)_{V,N} \tag{9.3}$$

then for a system which undergoes a Carnot cycle between two reservoirs at temperatures T_1 and T_2

$$\frac{T_1}{T_2} = \frac{\text{heat transferred } to \text{ the reservoir at } T_1}{\text{heat transferred } from \text{ the reservoir at } T_2} \tag{9.4}$$

(c) If a closed system undergoes an infinitesimal quasistatic change, in which the only work done on the system is the mechanical work due to a change in the volume, then

$$dW = -p\,dV \tag{9.5}$$

$$dQ = T\,dS \tag{9.6}$$

The latter equation can be used to calculate the entropy difference between any two states of a closed system.

Postulate IV. The temperature and entropy of a closed system of fixed volume vanish in the state of minimum energy and are greater than zero in all other states.

THE THREE LAWS OF THERMODYNAMICS

The following laws or theorems can be shown to be essentially equivalent to the preceding postulates.

Law I. The amount of work required to change an adiabatically enclosed system from one state to another depends only on the initial and final states of the system, and is independent both of the way in which the work is performed and the path through which the system passes from the initial to the final state.

Law II. It is impossible for the universe to undergo a change, the only effect of which is the transfer of a positive amount of energy from a single heat reservoir to a work reservoir.

Law III. The entropy of any system vanishes in those equilibrium states for which the temperature is zero.

PART TWO

Methods
of Thermodynamics

In Part I we established the
basic principles of thermodynamics. Our ultimate objective is to apply these
principles to particular thermodynamic systems. Before
discussing particular systems, however, we shall, in
the present part, develop
some general methods that
will be helpful in attaining
this objective.

CHAPTER 10

Thermodynamic Potentials

INTRODUCTION

The entropy of a simple one-component system, when expressed as a function of its internal energy, volume, and mole number, contains a complete thermodynamic description of the system. We refer to a function that, when expressed in terms of a particular set of variables, contains a complete thermodynamic description of a system as a *thermodynamic potential* or as a *characteristic function*. The variables in the set are called the *characteristic variables* for the potential. An equation in which a particular potential is expressed as a function of its characteristic variables is called a *fundamental equation*. The entropy S of a simple system is a thermodynamic potential, and its characteristic variables are E, V, and N. The equation $S = S(E,V,N)$ is a fundamental equation. Since S is a monotonically increasing function of E, we can invert the function $S(E,V,N)$ to obtain $E(S,V,N)$, a single-valued function of S, V, and N, containing the same information as $S(E,V,N)$. Thus the internal energy E is also a thermodynamic potential, and its characteristic variables are S, V, and N. In the present chapter we are interested in deriving a number of other useful thermodynamic potentials.

SOME USEFUL THERMODYNAMIC POTENTIALS

New thermodynamic potentials can be generated by making Legendre transformations (Appendix 5) of $S(E,V,N)$ or $E(S,V,N)$. Whether we work with S or E, we shall obtain essentially the same results. For convenience, we choose to work with E. Since the characteristic variables of a Legendre transformation of a potential involve derivatives of the potential, it is helpful to assign a name and symbol to each of the derivatives of $E(S,V,N)$. We have already defined temperature T and pressure p by the relations

$$T \equiv \left(\frac{\partial E}{\partial S}\right)_{V,N} \tag{10.1}$$

$$p \equiv -\left(\frac{\partial E}{\partial V}\right)_{S,N} \tag{10.2}$$

The remaining derivative is assigned the letter μ and is called the *chemical potential;* thus

$$\mu \equiv \left(\frac{\partial E}{\partial N}\right)_{S,V} \tag{10.3}$$

There are seven possible Legendre transformations of $E(S,V,N)$. One of these, however, is identically zero. Therefore, six functions in addition to $E(S,V,N)$ contain the same information as $E(S,V,N)$. Of these, we shall be interested in the following three: $F(T,V,N)$, $G(T,p,N)$, and $H(S,p,N)$, where

$$F = E - \left(\frac{\partial E}{\partial S}\right)_{V,N} S = E - TS \tag{10.4}$$

$$\begin{aligned} G &= E - \left(\frac{\partial E}{\partial S}\right)_{V,N} S - \left(\frac{\partial E}{\partial V}\right)_{S,N} V \\ &= E - TS + pV \end{aligned} \tag{10.5}$$

$$H = E - \left(\frac{\partial E}{\partial V}\right)_{S,N} V = E + pV \tag{10.6}$$

F is called the Helmholtz free energy, G the Gibbs free energy, and H the enthalpy. The characteristic variables associated with each are (T,V,N), (T,p,N), and (S,p,N), respectively. Thus, if we know F as a function of T, V, and N, or G as a function of T, p, and N, or H as a function of S, p, and N, we then have a complete thermodynamic specification of the system.

All thermodynamic potentials, expressed as functions of their respective characteristic variables, for example, $E(S,V,N)$, $F(T,V,N)$, $G(T,p,N)$,

$H(S,p,N)$, and $S(E,V,N)$, contain the same information. At the present stage, the introduction of the potentials F, G, and H may appear to be quite arbitrary. However, as we learn more about the techniques of thermodynamics and begin to apply these techniques to specific problems, we shall find that use of one or another of these potentials greatly simplifies the analysis.

EXAMPLE

Problem. Obtain $G(T, p, N)$ for a system whose energy is given by $E = CS^3V^{-1}N^{-1}$, where C is a constant.

Solution. Given (1) $E = E(S,V,N)$, we can obtain by differentiation (2) $T = T(S,V,N)$ and (3) $p = p(S,V,N)$. These three equations, together with the defining equation (4) $G = E + pV - TS$, provide us with four equations in the seven unknowns: E, F, S, V, N, T, and p. We can use these equations to obtain any one of the unknowns as a function of any other three unknowns. Thus for (1) $E = CS^3V^{-1}N^{-1}$ we obtain (2) $T = 3 CS^2V^{-1}N^{-1}$ and (3) $p = CS^3V^{-2}N^{-1}$. If we use these equations, together with the Equation (4) $G = E + pV - TS$, we obtain $G = -T^3N/27Cp$.

PROBLEMS

10.1 There are seven possible Legendre transformations of $E(S,V,N)$. In the text we have derived three. Obtain the remaining four, and show that one of them vanishes identically.

10.2 Compare the Legendre transformations of $E(S,V,N)$ with the Legendre transformations of $S(E,V,N)$.

10.3 Determine the thermodynamic potential whose characteristic variables are (a) T, F, and N and (b) p,H, and N.

10.4 Obtain $F(T,V,N)$, $G(T,p,N)$, and $H(S,p,N)$ for a system whose entropy is given by $S = C(EVN)^{1/3}$, where C is a constant.

10.5 The entropy of a monatomic ideal gas is given by $S = NR \ln (E^{3/2}VN^{-5/2}) + NC$, where R and C are constants. Obtain $F(T,V,N)$, $G(T,p,N)$, and $H(S,p,N)$ for a monatomic ideal gas.

10.6 Use the expression given in the preceding problem for the entropy of an ideal monatomic gas and the definition $\mu = (\partial E/\partial N)_{S,V}$ to calculate $\mu(T,p)$. Use the results of the preceding problem to show that $G(T,p,N) = N\mu(T,p)$.

10.7 A gas that is initially enclosed in an adiabatic chamber at temperature T_1, pressure p_1, and volume V_1 is slowly forced by the pressure p_1, which is held constant, through a porous partition into a second adiabatic chamber that is maintained at a pressure p_2. In the final state, the gas is contained in the second chamber and has a temperature T_2, pressure p_2, and volume V_2. Show that the enthalpy of the initial state is equal to the enthalpy of the final state.

10.8   Show that when a system that is kept in contact with a heat reservoir is allowed to expand quasistatically, the amount of work done by the system is equal to the decrease in the Helmholtz free energy.

CHAPTER 11

First Derivatives
of the Thermodynamic Potentials

INTRODUCTION

For very few systems is it possible to obtain an analytical expression for one of the thermodynamic potentials as a function of its characteristic variables. We could, of course, in the absence of such an expression, tabulate a particular potential as a function of its characteristic variables. Although this tabulation would be a large undertaking, it would not be impossible. However, from a practical point of view, we are usually far more interested in values of the various derivatives of the thermodynamic potentials than we are in values of the potential itself. In the present chapter we shall consider the various first derivatives of the thermodynamic potentials. In the following chapter we shall consider the second derivatives.

THE FIRST DERIVATIVES

The three first derivatives of $E(S,V,N)$ have been discussed in the preceding chapter. They are:

$$T \equiv \left(\frac{\partial E}{\partial S}\right)_{V,N} \tag{11.1}$$

$$p \equiv -\left(\frac{\partial E}{\partial V}\right)_{S,N} \tag{11.2}$$

$$\mu \equiv \left(\frac{\partial E}{\partial N}\right)_{S,V} \tag{11.3}$$

These three derivatives can be easily remembered by simply substituting them in the expression for the differential of $E(S,V,N)$,

$$dE = \left(\frac{\partial E}{\partial S}\right)_{V,N} dS + \left(\frac{\partial E}{\partial V}\right)_{S,N} dV + \left(\frac{\partial E}{\partial N}\right)_{S,V} dN \tag{11.4}$$

When we do this, we obtain

$$dE = TdS - pdV + \mu dN \tag{11.5}$$

From Equation (11.5) it is a simple matter to write Equations (11.1), (11.2), and (11.3).

It is not necessary to introduce new symbols for the first derivatives of $S(E,V,N)$, $F(T,V,N)$, $G(T,p,N)$, and $H(S,p,N)$, since, as we shall see, all the first derivatives of these functions can be expressed in terms of S, V, T, p, and μ. To obtain the first derivatives of $F(T,V,N)$ as a function of these variables, we note that

$$dF = d(E - TS) = dE - TdS - SdT \tag{11.6}$$

Substituting Equation (11.5) in Equation (11.6), we obtain

$$dF = -SdT - pdV + \mu dN \tag{11.7}$$

The derivatives of $F(T,V,N)$ are thus $(\partial F/\partial T)_{V,N} = -S$, $(\partial F/\partial V)_{T,N} = -p$ and $(\partial F/\partial N)_{T,V} = \mu$. Similarly, we can derive the equations

$$dG = -SdT + Vdp + \mu dN \tag{11.8}$$

$$dH = TdS + Vdp + \mu dN \tag{11.9}$$

and by simply rearranging Equation (11.5),

$$dS = \frac{1}{T} dE + \frac{p}{T} dV - \frac{\mu}{T} dN \qquad (11.10)$$

From Equations (11.8), (11.9), and (11.10) we can obtain the first derivatives of G, H, and S in terms of S, V, T, p, and μ.

EQUATIONS OF STATE

A thermodynamic potential, when expressed as a function of its characteristic variables, contains a complete thermodynamic description of a system. As we shall now see, certain groups of functions also contain a complete thermodynamic description of a system. To show this, we note first that, since the internal energy is an extensive function, it is a homogeneous function of degree one in the variables S, V, and N, that is,

$$E(\lambda S, \lambda V, \lambda N) = \lambda E(S, V, N) \qquad (11.11)$$

Applying Euler's theorem (Appendix 6), we obtain

$$E(S,V,N) = \left(\frac{\partial E}{\partial S}\right)_{V,N} S + \left(\frac{\partial E}{\partial V}\right)_{S,N} V + \left(\frac{\partial E}{\partial N}\right)_{S,V} N$$
$$= TS - pV + \mu N \qquad (11.12)$$

It follows that if we know $T(S,V,N)$, $p(S,V,N)$, and $\mu(S,V,N)$, we can obtain $E(S,V,N)$. Thus knowledge of these three functions is equivalent to knowledge of the potential $E(S,V,N)$. It follows that if we know $T = T(S,V,N)$, $p = p(S,V,N)$, and $\mu = \mu(S,V,N)$ for a particular system, we know everything that can be known thermodynamically about the system. These three equations are called the equations of state in the energy representation.

We can similarly show that

$$S = \frac{1}{T} E + \frac{p}{T} V - \frac{\mu}{T} N \qquad (11.13)$$

$$F = -pV + \mu N \qquad (11.14)$$

$$G = \mu N \qquad (11.15)$$

$$H = TS + \mu N \qquad (11.16)$$

and, therefore, each of the following four groups of functions contains a complete thermodynamic description of a system: (1) $(1/T)(E,V,N)$, $(p/T)(E,V,N)$, and $(\mu/T)(E,V,N)$; (2) $p(T,V,N)$ and $\mu(T,V,N)$; (3) $\mu(T,p,N)$; and (4) $T(S,p,N)$, $\mu(S,p,N)$. Each of the above functions is the derivative of a thermodynamic potential with respect to one of its extensive variables, and each of the above groups of functions represents the complete set of such derivatives for a particular potential.

An equation in which one of the above derivatives is expressed as a function of the characteristic variables of the corresponding potential is called an *equation of state*, and the complete set of such equations for a particular potential is called the equations of state in the representation of this potential. If we know all the equations of state in a particular representation, we have a complete thermodynamic description. Note that there is only one equation of state for a one-component system in the Gibbs free energy representation, that is, $\mu = \mu(T,p,N)$, and thus $\mu(T,p,N)$ contains a complete thermodynamic description of a one-component system. As a matter of fact, it should be noted from Equation (11.15) that the chemical potential for a one-component system is merely the Gibbs free energy per mole.

Frequent reference is made in the literature to "the" equation of state of a system. What is usually meant is the relation between p, V, T, and N. The reason for singling out this relation will become more evident in Chapter 13.

THE GIBBS–DUHEM RELATION

The three intensive variables T, p, and μ are not independent. To prove this, we note first that Equations (11.1), (11.2), and (11.3) provide us with equations for T, p, and μ as functions of S, V, and N. We can use these three equations to obtain μ as a function of T, p, and N. Since μ, T, and p are intensive variables and N an extensive variable, the function $\mu(T,p,N)$ must be a homogeneous function of degree zero in the variable N, that is, $\mu(T,p,N) = \mu(T,p,\lambda N)$. Since μ is unchanged by changing N, while holding T and p fixed, it follows that μ is a function of T and p only, that is

$$\mu = \mu(T,p) \tag{11.17}$$

We can alternatively prove (11.17) as follows. From Euler's theorem we have

$$E = TS - pV + \mu N \tag{11.18}$$

Taking the differential of (11.18) we obtain

$$dE = TdS + SdT - pdV - Vdp + \mu dN + Nd\mu \tag{11.19}$$

If we now subtract the relation

$$dE = TdS - pdV + \mu dN \qquad (11.20)$$

from Equation (11.19), we get

$$SdT - Vdp + Nd\mu = 0 \qquad (11.21)$$

This is the Gibbs–Duhem Relation for a one-component system. According to Equation (11.21), variations in the temperature, pressure, and chemical potential are not independent. The variation of any one can be computed in terms of the variations of the other two. It follows that any one of the above variables can be expressed as a function of the other two.

In the entropy representation, the Gibbs–Duhem Relation takes the form

$$Ed\left(\frac{1}{T}\right) + Vd\left(\frac{p}{T}\right) - Nd\left(\frac{\mu}{T}\right) = 0 \qquad (11.22)$$

It follows from Equation (11.22) that any one of the variables $1/T$, p/T, or μ/T can be expressed as a function of the other two. This, of course, also follows from Equation (11.21).

EXAMPLE

Problem. An ideal monatomic gas satisfies the equations $E = 3\ NRT/2$ and $pV = NRT$, where R is a fundamental constant. Find $S(E,V,N)$.

Solution. If we know the three equations of state in the entropy representation, that is,

$$\frac{1}{T} = \frac{1}{T}(E,V,N) \qquad \frac{p}{T} = \frac{p}{T}(E,V,N) \qquad \frac{\mu}{T} = \frac{\mu}{T}(E,V,N)$$

then we can determine $S(E,V,N)$ from Equation (11.13). From the data given, we can immediately write the two equations of state:

$$\frac{1}{T} = \frac{3NR}{2E} \qquad \frac{p}{T} = \frac{NR}{V}$$

The third equation of state can be obtained by substituting these two equations in the Gibbs–Duhem Relation, Equation (11.22), and integrating. When we do this, we obtain

$$\frac{\mu}{T} = \frac{3}{2} R \ln \left(\frac{N}{E}\right) + R \ln \left(\frac{N}{V}\right) + B$$

where B is a constant of integration. Substituting the above three equations of state in Equation (11.13), we obtain

$$S = NR \ln (E^{3/2}VN^{-5/2}) + NC$$

where C is a constant.

PROBLEMS

11.1 The entropy of a monatomic ideal gas is given by $S = NR \ln (E^{3/2}VN^{-5/2}) + NC$, where R and C are constants. What are the equations of state in the (a) entropy representation, (b) enthalpy representation, (c) Gibbs free energy representation, and (d) Helmholtz free energy representation?

11.2 Prove that pV is a thermodynamic potential whose characteristic variables are T, V, and μ.

11.3 The Helmholtz free energy of one mole of a certain gas is given by $F = -aV^{-1} - RT \ln (V - b) + f(T)$, where a and b are constants and $f(T)$ a function of temperature only. Obtain $F(T,V,N)$ and $p(T,V,N)$.

11.4 The Gibbs free energy of one mole of a certain gas is given by $G = RT \ln p + A + Bp + Cp^2/2 + Dp^3/3$, where A, B, C, and D are functions of temperature only. Obtain $G(T,p,N)$ and $V(T,p,N)$.

11.5 For a certain gas it is found that $pV(1 - bp) = NRT$. Calculate the change in the Gibbs free energy when the gas undergoes an isothermal process from a pressure p_1 to a pressure p_2.

11.6 Assuming that the density of liquid mercury stays constant at 13.5 g cm^{-3}, calculate the change in the Gibbs free energy of one mole of mercury when the pressure is increased from one atm to 101 atm while the temperature is held constant at 25°C.

CHAPTER 12

Second Derivatives
of the Thermodynamic Potentials

INTRODUCTION

In the preceding chapter we investigated the first derivatives of $E(S,V,N)$, $F(T,V,N)$, $G(T,p,N)$, $H(S,p,N)$, and $S(E,V,N)$, and we saw that all the derivatives could be expressed in terms of the characteristic variables of E, and the first derivatives of E with respect to these variables, that is S, V, N, T, p, and μ. In the present chapter we wish to investigate the second derivatives of $E(S,V,N)$, $F(T,V,N)$, $G(T,p,N)$, $H(S,p,N)$, and $S(E,V,N)$. As we shall see, all the second derivatives can be expressed as functions of S, V, N, T, p, and μ, and the second derivatives of E with respect to S, V, and N. However, we shall find it more convenient to work with the second derivatives of $G(T,p,N)$ than with the second derivatives of $E(S,V,N)$.

THE SECOND DERIVATIVES OF THE GIBBS FREE ENERGY

Given $G(T,p,N)$, there are two first derivatives with respect to T and p, namely

$$\left(\frac{\partial G}{\partial T}\right)_{p,N} = -S \tag{12.1}$$

$$\left(\frac{\partial G}{\partial p}\right)_{T,N} = V \tag{12.2}$$

and there are four second derivatives

$$\left[\frac{\partial}{\partial T}\left(\frac{\partial G}{\partial T}\right)_{p,N}\right]_{p,N} = -\left(\frac{\partial S}{\partial T}\right)_{p,N} \tag{12.3}$$

$$\left[\frac{\partial}{\partial p}\left(\frac{\partial G}{\partial T}\right)_{p,N}\right]_{T,N} = -\left(\frac{\partial S}{\partial p}\right)_{T,N} \tag{12.4}$$

$$\left[\frac{\partial}{\partial T}\left(\frac{\partial G}{\partial p}\right)_{T,N}\right]_{p,N} = \left(\frac{\partial V}{\partial T}\right)_{p,N} \tag{12.5}$$

$$\left[\frac{\partial}{\partial p}\left(\frac{\partial G}{\partial p}\right)_{T,N}\right]_{T,N} = \left(\frac{\partial V}{\partial p}\right)_{T,N} \tag{12.6}$$

Of these four, only three are independent, since the two cross-derivatives must be equal, that is,

$$-\left(\frac{\partial S}{\partial p}\right)_{T,N} = \left(\frac{\partial V}{\partial T}\right)_{p,N} \tag{12.7}$$

For convenience, we define

$$c_p \equiv \frac{T}{N}\left(\frac{\partial S}{\partial T}\right)_{p,N} \tag{12.8}$$

$$\alpha \equiv \frac{1}{V}\left(\frac{\partial V}{\partial T}\right)_{p,N} \tag{12.9}$$

$$\beta \equiv -\frac{1}{V}\left(\frac{\partial V}{\partial p}\right)_{T,N} \tag{12.10}$$

where c_p is called the *specific heat at constant pressure*, α is called the *coefficient of thermal expansion*, and β is called the *isothermal compressibility*. Since $dQ = TdS$, the specific heat at constant pressure c_p is the quasistatic heat-flux per mole required to raise the temperature of the system one degree while holding the pressure and number of moles fixed. The coefficient of thermal expansion α represents the fractional increase in the volume per unit increase in temperature at constant pressure. The isothermal compressibility β represents the fractional decrease in the volume per unit increase in pressure at constant temperature. Of all possible second derivatives of F, G, H, E, and S, these three have been singled out because they are easy to measure.

REDUCTION OF SECOND DERIVATIVES

We shall in the present section show how, for a system in which N is held fixed, any derivative involving F, G, H, E, S, V, N, T, p, or μ can be reduced to an expression containing only the quantities S, V, N, T, p, c_p, α, and β.

Suppose we are given a derivative $(\partial X/\partial Y)_{Z,N}$. To reduce it, we carry out the following procedure:

Step I. Reduce the derivative to an expression containing only derivatives with respect to T, p, and N by using Theorem E in Appendix 1. Thus

$$\left(\frac{\partial X}{\partial Y}\right)_{Z,N} = \frac{\left(\frac{\partial X}{\partial T}\right)_{p,N}\left(\frac{\partial Z}{\partial p}\right)_{T,N} - \left(\frac{\partial X}{\partial p}\right)_{T,N}\left(\frac{\partial Z}{\partial T}\right)_{p,N}}{\left(\frac{\partial Y}{\partial T}\right)_{p,N}\left(\frac{\partial Z}{\partial p}\right)_{T,N} - \left(\frac{\partial Y}{\partial p}\right)_{T,N}\left(\frac{\partial Z}{\partial T}\right)_{p,N}} \tag{12.11}$$

Step II. If μ appears, replace it by G/N. Eliminate E, F, G, or H by making use of the following relations:

$$dE = TdS - pdV + \mu dN \tag{12.12}$$

$$dF = -SdT - pdV + \mu dN \tag{12.13}$$

$$dG = -SdT + Vdp + \mu dN \tag{12.14}$$

$$dH = TdS + Vdp + \mu dN \tag{12.15}$$

For example, using Equation (12.13) and the results of Appendix 1

$$\left(\frac{\partial F}{\partial p}\right)_{T,N} = -S\left(\frac{\partial T}{\partial p}\right)_{T,N} - p\left(\frac{\partial V}{\partial p}\right)_{T,N} + \mu\left(\frac{\partial N}{\partial p}\right)_{T,N} \tag{12.16}$$

$$= -p\left(\frac{\partial V}{\partial p}\right)_{T,N}$$

Step III. The remaining derivatives can now be eliminated by making use of the relations

$$\left(\frac{\partial S}{\partial T}\right)_{p,N} = \frac{Nc_p}{T} \tag{12.17}$$

$$\left(\frac{\partial V}{\partial p}\right)_{T,N} = -\beta V \tag{12.18}$$

$$\left(\frac{\partial V}{\partial T}\right)_{p,N} = \alpha V \tag{12.19}$$

$$\left(\frac{\partial S}{\partial p}\right)_{T,N} = -\alpha V \tag{12.20}$$

In the following section we shall illustrate an application of these steps.

THE SPECIFIC HEAT AT CONSTANT VOLUME

In addition to c_p, the specific heat at constant pressure, it is convenient to introduce another specific heat c_V, the specific heat at constant volume. The *specific heat at constant volume* is the quasistatic heat-flux per mole required to raise the temperature of a system one degree, while holding the volume and the number of moles fixed. Analytically, it is given by

$$c_V = \frac{T}{N}\left(\frac{\partial S}{\partial T}\right)_{V,N} \tag{12.21}$$

Since c_V occurs quite frequently in thermodynamic arguments, it will be helpful to derive the relation between c_V and c_p, α, and β. Following the technique outlined in the preceding section,

$$\left(\frac{\partial S}{\partial T}\right)_{V,N} = \frac{\left(\frac{\partial S}{\partial T}\right)_{p,N}\left(\frac{\partial V}{\partial p}\right)_{T,N} - \left(\frac{\partial S}{\partial p}\right)_{T,N}\left(\frac{\partial V}{\partial T}\right)_{p,N}}{\left(\frac{\partial V}{\partial p}\right)_{T,N}}$$

$$= \frac{\left(\frac{Nc_p}{T}\right)(-\beta V) - (-\alpha V)(\alpha V)}{-\beta V}$$

$$= \frac{Nc_p}{T} - \frac{\alpha^2 V}{\beta} \tag{12.22}$$

It follows that

$$c_V = c_p - \frac{\alpha^2 V T}{N\beta} \tag{12.23}$$

AN ALTERNATE TECHNIQUE FOR THE REDUCTION OF SECOND DERIVATIVES

The technique discussed earlier for the reduction of second derivatives to expressions containing only S, V, N, T, p, c_p, α, and β can be simplified if we exploit the properties of Jacobians (Appendix 2), as is done in the method below. In addition to being quicker and easier to remember than the previous method, the method to be described also has the advantage of first reducing the derivative in question to an expression containing not only the variables S, V, N, T, p, c_p, α, and β, but also the variable c_V. The resultant expression is usually considerably simpler than the expression that results when c_V is replaced by $c_p - (\alpha^2 V T/N\beta)$.

Suppose we are given a derivative $(\partial X/\partial Y)_{Z,N}$. To reduce it, we carry out the following procedure.

Step I. Reduce the derivative to an expression containing Jacobians in which the independent variables are T, p, and N. Thus

$$\left(\frac{\partial X}{\partial Y}\right)_{Z,N} = J\left(\frac{X,Z,N}{Y,Z,N}\right) = \frac{J\left(\frac{X,Z,N}{T,p,N}\right)}{J\left(\frac{Y,Z,N}{T,p,N}\right)} \tag{12.24}$$

Step II. If μ appears, replace it by G/N. Eliminate E, F, G, or H by making use of one of the following relations:

$$dE = TdS - pdV + \mu dN \tag{12.25}$$

$$dF = -SdT - pdV + \mu dN \tag{12.26}$$

$$dG = -SdT + Vdp + \mu dN \tag{12.27}$$

$$dH = TdS + Vdp + \mu dN \tag{12.28}$$

For example, using Equation (12.26) and the results of Appendix 2, we obtain

$$J\left(\frac{F,Z,N}{T,p,N}\right) = -SJ\left(\frac{T,Z,N}{T,p,N}\right) - pJ\left(\frac{V,Z,N}{T,p,N}\right) + \mu J\left(\frac{N,Z,N}{T,p,N}\right)$$

$$= -SJ\left(\frac{T,Z,N}{T,p,N}\right) - pJ\left(\frac{V,Z,N}{T,p,N}\right) \tag{12.29}$$

Step III. The remaining nonvanishing Jacobians can now be eliminated by making use of the relations

$$J\left(\frac{S,p,N}{T,p,N}\right) = \frac{Nc_p}{T} \tag{12.30}$$

$$J\left(\frac{T,V,N}{T,p,N}\right) = -\beta V \tag{12.31}$$

$$J\left(\frac{S,V,N}{T,p,N}\right) = J\left(\frac{S,V,N}{T,V,N}\right)J\left(\frac{T,V,N}{T,p,N}\right) = \left(\frac{Nc_V}{T}\right)(-\beta V) \tag{12.32}$$

$$J\left(\frac{V,p,N}{T,p,N}\right) = \alpha V \tag{12.33}$$

$$J\left(\frac{T,S,N}{T,p,N}\right) = J\left(\frac{p,V,N}{T,p,N}\right) = -\alpha V \tag{12.34}$$

$$J\left(\frac{T,p,N}{T,p,N}\right) = 1 \tag{12.35}$$

Step IV. Eliminate c_V by making use of the relation

$$c_V = c_p - \frac{\alpha^2 VT}{N\beta} \tag{12.36}$$

MAXWELL RELATIONS

In discussing the second derivatives of the Gibbs' free energy for a closed system, we found that although there are four second derivatives, only three are independent, since

$$\left[\frac{\partial}{\partial p}\left(\frac{\partial G}{\partial T}\right)_{p,N}\right]_{T,N} = \left[\frac{\partial}{\partial T}\left(\frac{\partial G}{\partial p}\right)_{T,N}\right]_{p,N} \tag{12.37}$$

From Equation (12.37) we obtained the result

$$\left(\frac{\partial S}{\partial p}\right)_{T,N} = -\left(\frac{\partial V}{\partial T}\right)_{p,N} \tag{12.38}$$

If we had taken the second derivatives of $F(T,V,N)$, $H(S,p,N)$, and $E(S,V,N)$, we would have similarly been able to equate the cross-derivatives and would have obtained the relations

$$\left(\frac{\partial S}{\partial V}\right)_{T,N} = \left(\frac{\partial p}{\partial T}\right)_{V,N} \tag{12.39}$$

$$\left(\frac{\partial T}{\partial p}\right)_{S,N} = \left(\frac{\partial V}{\partial S}\right)_{p,N} \tag{12.40}$$

$$\left(\frac{\partial T}{\partial V}\right)_{S,N} = -\left(\frac{\partial p}{\partial S}\right)_{V,N} \tag{12.41}$$

These relations are called *Maxwell relations*. For a system in which N varies, we would have had additional Maxwell relations involving the cross-derivatives containing N.

The four Maxwell relations given above can be expressed very concisely in terms of a single Jacobian relation. Consider Equation (12.38). Expressing both partial derivatives in Jacobian form, we obtain

$$J\left(\frac{S,T,N}{p,T,N}\right) = -J\left(\frac{V,p,N}{T,p,N}\right) \tag{12.42}$$

Multiplying both sides by $J(T,p,N/X,Y,Z)$ and noting that $J(S,T,N/p,T,N)$ $= J(T,S,N/T,p,N)$ and $-J(V,p,N/T,p,N) = J(p,V,N/T,p,N)$, we obtain

$$J\left(\frac{T,S,N}{T,p,N}\right)J\left(\frac{T,p,N}{X,Y,Z}\right) = J\left(\frac{p,V,N}{T,p,N}\right)J\left(\frac{T,p,N}{X,Y,Z}\right) \qquad (12.43)$$

which can be simplified to

$$J\left(\frac{T,S,N}{X,Y,Z}\right) = J\left(\frac{p,V,N}{X,Y,Z}\right) \qquad (12.44)$$

We shall obtain exactly the same result, starting with any one of the Maxwell relations. Thus Equation (12.44) contains all the Maxwell relations. To extract Equations (12.38), (12.39), (12.40), and (12.41) from Equation (12.44), we substitute (T,p,N), (T,V,N), (S,p,N), and (S,V,N), respectively, for (X,Y,Z).

A USEFUL MNEMONIC DIAGRAM

Many of the results employed in the preceding sections can be easily remembered by making use of the mnemonic diagram shown in Figure 12.1. The sides are labeled with the four potentials: E, F, G, and H, in alphabetical order, clockwise around the diagram. The two corners at the left are

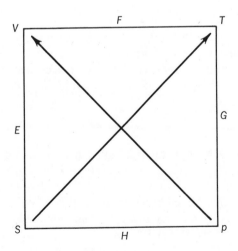

FIGURE 12.1

labeled with the extensive parameters V and S, and the two corners at the right are labeled with the intensive parameters T and p.

The diagram contains the following information: (1) the potentials are flanked by their respective characteristic variables (excluding N). (2) The differential expression for a particular potential as a function of its characteristic values, that is, $dE = TdS - pdV + \mu dN$, can be read off by noting that the coefficients of the differentials of the characteristic variables occupy the corners diagonally opposite to the variable in question, and the sign is indicated by the direction of the arrow. If the arrow points to the coefficient, it is positive. (3) The Maxwell relations can be read off by starting at adjacent corners, for example, the corners S and V, and proceeding from corner to corner as shown, for example, in Figure 12.2. For the situation illustrated we

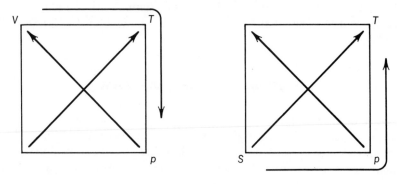

FIGURE 12.2

conclude $(\partial V/\partial T)_p = -(\partial S/\partial P)_T$. The sign is positive if the adjacent corners from which one starts both contain an arrowhead or both contain an arrowtail. The sign is negative if one of the corners from which one starts contains an arrowhead and the other contains an arrowtail.

EXAMPLE

Problem. A certain hypothetical substance is found to satisfy the equation $V = aT^3 N/p^2$, where a is a constant. It is also found that if one mole of the substance is maintained at a constant pressure, the amount of heat required to raise the temperature one degree is equal to $6aT^2/p$. Five moles of the substance are contained in a rigid, one-cubic-meter container at a pressure of 10^5 N/m². (a) How much heat is required to increase the pressure to 8×10^5 N/m²? (b) If the initial temperature is $100°K$, what is the final temperature?

Solution.

(a) From the data given we find that $\alpha = 3/T$; $\beta = 2/p$; and $c_p = 6aT^2/p$. Substituting these results in Equation (2.23), we obtain $c_V = 3aT^2/2p$. For the process described, $dQ = TdS$. We are, therefore, interested in the change in S for a given change in p, while holding V and N fixed. Considering S as a function of p, V, and N, we obtain for such a process $dQ = TdS = T(\partial S/\partial p)_{V,N}dp = (Nc_V\beta/\alpha)dp$. Substituting the above values of α, β, and c_V in this equation, we obtain $dQ =(NaT^3/p^2)dp = Vdp$. Integrating between $p = 10^5$ N/m² and $p = 8 \times 10^5$ N/m², while holding V fixed at 1 m³, we obtain $Q = 7 \times 10^5$ J.

(b) To determine the change in T for a given change in p, while holding V and N fixed, we note that for such a process $dT = (\partial T/\partial p)_{V,N}dp = (\beta/\alpha)dp$. Substituting the values determined above for α and β, we obtain $3dT/T = 2dp/p$. Integrating between $T = 100°K$, $p = 10^5$ N/m², and $T = T_f$, $p = 8 \times 10^5$ N/m², we obtain $T_f = 400°K$. We could, of course, have obtained the same result by noting from the data given that for a process in which V and N are held fixed, the quantity T^3/p^2 remains constant.

PROBLEMS

12.1   Prove the relation

$$\left(\frac{\partial T}{\partial V}\right)_{S,N} = - \frac{(\partial S/\partial V)_{T,N}}{(\partial S/\partial T)_{V,N}}$$

12.2   Reduce the following derivatives to expressions in terms of S, V, N, T, p, c_p, α, and β: (a) $(\partial\mu/\partial V)_{S,N}$, (b) $(\partial T/\partial p)_{S,N}$, (c) $(\partial p/\partial E)_{G,N}$, (d) $(\partial T/\partial p)_{V,N}$

12.3   Use the results of Appendix 1 to prove the theorems in Appendix 2.

12.4   Show that (a) $c_V = (1/N)(\partial E/\partial T)_{V,N}$ and (b) $c_p = (1/N)(\partial H/\partial T)_{p,N}$.

12.5   Show that the adiabatic compressibility $-(1/V)(\partial V/\partial p)_{S,N}$ and the isothermal compressibility $-(1/V)(\partial V/\partial p)_{T,N}$ are related as follows:

$$\frac{1}{V}\left(\frac{\partial V}{\partial p}\right)_{S,N} = \frac{c_V}{c_p}\left[\frac{1}{V}\left(\frac{\partial V}{\partial p}\right)_{T,N}\right]$$

12.6   Prove that $(\gamma - 1)(\partial p/\partial T)_{S,N} = \gamma(\partial p/\partial T)_{V,N}$ where $\gamma = c_p/c_V$.

12.7   Prove that $(\partial V/\partial T)_{p,N} = (1 - \gamma)(\partial V/\partial T)_{S,N}$, where $\gamma = c_p/c_V$.

12.8   Show that (a) $(\partial H/\partial p)_{T,N} = V - T(\partial V/\partial T)_{p,N}$ (b) $N(\partial c_p/\partial p)_{T,N} = -T(\partial^2 V/\partial T^2)_{p,N}$.

12.9   Show that

$$c_p - c_V = \frac{T}{N}\left\{\frac{\left[\dfrac{\partial^2 F(T,V,N)}{\partial T \partial V}\right]^2}{\dfrac{\partial^2 F(T,V,N)}{\partial V^2}}\right\}$$

12.10   (a) Express the second derivatives of $E(S,V,N)$ with respect to S and V in terms of the specific heat at constant volume c_V, the adiabatic coefficient of expansion $\alpha_S = (1/V)(\partial V/\partial T)_{S,N}$, and the adiabatic compressibility $\beta_S = -(1/V)(\partial V/\partial p)_{S,N}$. (b) Construct a scheme for reducing any derivative involving F, G, H, E, S, V, N, T, p, or μ to an expression containing only the quantities S, V, N, T, p, c_V, α_S, and β_S.

12.11   Prove for a closed system:
(a) $TdS = Nc_V dT + (\alpha T/\beta)dV$
(b) $TdS = Nc_p dT - \alpha VTdp$
(c) $TdS = (Nc_V \beta/\alpha)dp + (Nc_p/\alpha V)dV$.

12.12   Prove for a closed system $dH = Nc_p dT + V(1 - \alpha T)dp$.

12.13   Develop a general expression for the change in entropy for an isobaric change in the temperature of a substance in a range in which c_p is constant.

12.14   Show that for an ideal gas, that is, one obeying the equation of state $pV = NRT$, that $\alpha = 1/T$ and $\beta = 1/p$.

12.15   The coefficient of thermal expansion of water at 20°C and 1 atm is $2.1 \times 10^{-4}(°K)^{-1}$. Calculate approximately the work done by water when one mole of water is heated at atmospheric pressure from 15°C to 25°C. Use the information given in the preceding problem to compare this result with the work involved in heating one mole of an ideal gas from 15°C to 25°C.

12.16   The isothermal compressibility of water at 20°C is 49×10^{-6} atm^{-1} over the range 1–25 atm. Calculate the work required to compress 1 mole of water from a pressure of 1 atm to a pressure of 25 atm at 20°C. Compare this result with the work required to compress 1 mole of an ideal gas from 1 to 25 atm at 20°C.

12.17   The pressure on a block of copper at a temperature of 300°K is increased isothermally and quasistatically from 1 atm to 1001 atm. Assume that α, β, v (volume per mole), and c_p are approximately constant and equal, respectively, to $4.9 \times 10^{-5}(°K)^{-1}$, 7.8×10^{-7} atm^{-1}, 7.1 cm³ mole^{-1}, and 5.9 cal mole^{-1} $(°K)^{-1}$. Calculate (a) the work done on the copper per kilogram and (b) the heat evolved per kilogram. (c) How do you account for the fact that the heat evolved is greater than the work done?

12.18   The pressure on a block of copper is increased adiabatically and quasistatically from 1 atm to 1001 atm. The initial temperature is 300°K. Assume the values of α, β, v, and c_p given in the preceding problem. (a) What is the change in temperature? (b) What is the internal energy change per mole? (c) How much work is done on the copper per mole?

12.19 What additional hydrostatic pressure is produced in water by raising its temperature from 0°C to 50°C without permitting it to expand in volume? The density of water at 0°C is 0.9998 g cm^{-3}. The density of water at 50°C is 0.9881 g cm^{-3}. The isothermal compressibility of water may be assumed to be constant and equal to $5 \times 10^{-10}(N/m^2)^{-1}$.

12.20 The speed of a longitudinal wave in a material of density ρ is given by $v = [(\partial p/\partial \rho)_s]^{1/2}$. Show that $v = (\gamma/\beta \rho)^{1/2}$, where β is the isothermal compressibility and $\gamma = c_p/c_V$.

12.21 Using the results of the previous problem, show that the speed of sound in an ideal gas $[pV = NRT; E = E(T,N)]$ is a function of the temperature only.

12.22 The quantity $\gamma = c_p/c_V$ can be measured for an ideal gas as follows. The gas is confined within a vertical cylinder that is closed at the top by a freely moving piston of mass m. The piston and cylinder each have the same cross-sectional area A. The cylinder is immersed in the atmosphere whose pressure is p_0. The acceleration due to gravity is g. The initial volume of the gas is V_0. The piston is now displaced slightly from its position of equilibrium and is found to oscillate about this position with frequency v. The rate of oscillation is slow enough to allow the gas to remain in internal equilibrium but fast enough to prevent the gas from exchanging heat with the outside. Show that $\gamma = 4\pi^2 v^2 m V_0 (p_0 A^2 + mgA)^{-1}$.

12.23 The following method is sometimes used to find $\gamma = c_p/c_V$ for an ideal gas. A definite amount of gas, whose initial temperature, volume, and pressure are T_0, V_0, and p_0, respectively, is heated by a platinum wire, through which an electrical current passes for a definite period: first, at constant volume so that the gas reaches a temperature T_1 and pressure p_1 (volume V_0), second, at constant pressure so that the temperature becomes T_2 and the volume V_1 (pressure p_0). Show that $\gamma = (p_1 - p_0)V_0/(V_1 - V_0)p_0$. Assume c_p and c_V to be constant.

12.24 Show that if a system satisfies the relation $pV = NRT$, the energy can be expressed as a function of T and N only.

12.25 Show that the relation $\alpha = 1/T$ implies that c_p is independent of the pressure, that is, $(\partial c_p/\partial p)_{T,N} = 0$.

12.26 Express the coefficient of thermal expansion and the isothermal compressibility in terms of the density ρ and its partial derivatives.

12.27   In a particular ideal gas $(pV = NRT)$ of N moles, the specific heat is given by $c_p = A + BT + CT^2$, where A, B, and C are constants. The gas undergoes an adiabatic compression from a pressure p_1 and a temperature T_1 to a final temperature T_2. Show that for an adiabatic process $dT = (\alpha VT/Nc_p)dp$, and then use this result to calculate the final pressure.

12.28   Show that if $V(T,p,N)$ is a homogeneous function of degree zero in pressure and temperature, the energy of the substance must be a function of temperature and mole number only. (*Hint:* Use Euler's theorem.)

12.29   Show that if the pressure is a homogeneous function of degree zero with respect to the volume and temperature, the enthalpy must be a function of temperature and mole number only.

12.30   The internal energy of a certain gas obeys the relation $(\partial E/\partial V)_{T,N} = aN^2/V^2$ where a is a constant. Show that c_V depends only upon temperature and mole number.

12.31   Over a limited range of temperatures and pressures the equation of state of a liquid can be written $V = Nv_0[1 + a(T - T_0) - b(p - p_0)]$ where a and b are constants and v_0 is the volume of one mole of the liquid at $T = T_0$ and $p = p_0$.

(a) Obtain an expression for α, the coefficient of thermal expansion, and β, the isothermal compressibility.

(b) For water in the neighborhood of 20°C and 1 atm, $\alpha = 2.1 \times 10^{-4} (°K)^{-1}$ and $\beta = 49 \times 10^{-6}$ atm^{-1}. Calculate ΔS and ΔH when 1 mole of water is compressed at 20°C from 1 to 25 atm.

CHAPTER 13

The Experimental Determination
of the Properties
of a Thermodynamic System

THE MINIMUM EXPERIMENTAL INFORMATION NEEDED TO DETERMINE THE THERMODYNAMIC PROPERTIES OF A ONE-COMPONENT SYSTEM

If we are interested in the thermodynamic properties of a particular system and if we know one of the thermodynamic potentials as a function of its characteristic variables over some range R, then any thermodynamic property of the system can be found in this range. Although the thermodynamic potentials are very convenient and economical mathematical devices for storing thermodynamic information, they are not particularly easy to measure directly. Experimentally, one usually measures relationships among the pressure, volume, and temperature, or measures quantities, such as the coefficient of thermal expansion α, the isothermal compressibility β, or the specific heats c_p and c_V. In gathering such experimental information, it is important to know at what stage additional information is no longer needed, that is, when we have enough information to obtain a fundamental equation. In the present chapter, we shall prove the following theorem, which provides one answer to this question.

Theorem.   The thermodynamic properties of a one-component system are completely specified over a range R of temperatures and pressures, or temperatures and molar volumes, if we know: (1) the coefficient of thermal expansion α at all points in R, (2) the isothermal compressibility β at all points in R, (3) one of the specific heats c_p or c_V along a single path in R, provided that that path runs through all temperatures in R, (4) the temperature, pressure, and volume of a fixed number of moles at some point in R, (5) the value of the internal energy of a fixed number of moles at some point in R, and (6) the value of the entropy of a fixed number of moles at some point in R.

To prove the above theorem, let us suppose we are given a system consisting of a fixed number of moles N_0 of a certain substance, whose properties we wish to know over the range of temperatures and pressures indicated by the shaded region in Figure 13.1; this range we shall designate range R.

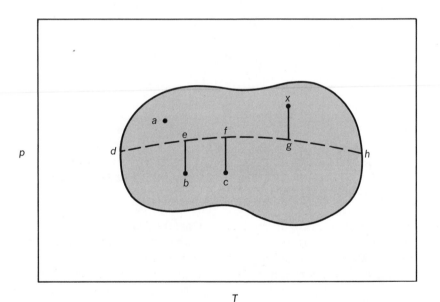

FIGURE 13.1

Let us further suppose that we know α and β at all points in R, the value of c_p along the dotted line *defgh*, the value of V at the point a, the value of E at the point b, and the value of S at the point c. If we could find the value of the Gibbs free energy G for all values of T and p falling within R, then we would have a complete thermodynamic description of the system over this range for the given number of moles N_0. Let x be an arbitrary point in R at which we wish to determine G. Since $G = E - TS + pV$, it follows that if we can determine E, S, and V at x, then we know G at x.

To determine V at x, we can integrate dV along any path joining a and x, noting that

$$dV = (\partial V/\partial T)_p dT + (\partial V/\partial p)_T dp$$
$$= \alpha V dT - \beta V dp \tag{13.1}$$

Since we know α and β at all points in R and the value of V at the point a, we have enough information to carry out the integration.

To determine E at x, we can integrate dE along the path $befgx$, noting that along the paths be and gx,

$$dE = \left(\frac{\partial E}{\partial p}\right)_T dp = (\beta V p - \alpha V T) dp \tag{13.2}$$

while along the path efg,

$$dE = \left(\frac{\partial E}{\partial T}\right)_p dT + \left(\frac{\partial E}{\partial p}\right)_T dp$$
$$= (N c_p - \alpha V p) dT + (\beta V p - \alpha V T) dp \tag{13.3}$$

Since we know α and β at all points in R, the value of c_p along the curve efg, and the value of E at the point b, and since we have calculated $V(T,p,N_0)$, we have enough information to carry out the integration.

Similarly, to determine S at x, we integrate dS along the path $cfgx$, noting that along the paths cf and gx

$$dS = \left(\frac{\partial S}{\partial p}\right)_T dp = -\alpha V dp \tag{13.4}$$

while along the path fg,

$$dS = \left(\frac{\partial S}{\partial T}\right)_p dT + \left(\frac{\partial S}{\partial p}\right)_T dp$$
$$= \left(\frac{N c_p}{T}\right) dT - \alpha V dp \tag{13.5}$$

As in the previous case, we are provided with all the information necessary to carry out the integration and to determine S at x.

Since, with the information given, we can determine $V(T,p,N_0)$, $E(T,p,N_0)$, and $S(T,p,N_0)$, we can, therefore, find $G(T,p,N_0)$ for the values of T and p falling within the range R. Finally, since $G(T,p,N)$ is a homogeneous function of degree one with respect to N, it follows that if we know $G(T,p,N_0)$, we can use the results of Appendix 6 to obtain $G(T,p,N)$. Since $G(T,p,N)$ contains a complete thermodynamic description of the system, the given information also contains a complete thermodynamic description of the system.

In a similar fashion it can be shown that if we are given the same information over a range R of temperatures and molar volumes, rather than temperatures and pressures, then we can determine $F(T,V,N)$; hence, the system is completely specified. This step completes the proof of the theorem.

There are situations in which it is not necessary to be provided explicitly with a particular value of E or S in the range R. When, for example, the range R includes a state in which the temperature vanishes, since we know from Postulate IV that in that state $S = 0$, we are automatically provided with the value of the entropy at a point in R. Or, if the system being studied is an elementary system, then, according to Corollary I, we can assign an arbitrary value to E in one state.

It should also be noted that many properties of a thermodynamic system do not depend on knowledge of the absolute values of the energy and entropy. If, for example, we are interested in the properties of a system in which the composition does not change, it is usually necessary to be able only to calculate changes in energy and entropy as the system goes from one state to another. In such cases we can arbitrarily assign a value to the energy in one state and the entropy in another state.

THE EQUATION OF STATE

As pointed out in Chapter 11, the equation that expresses the functional relationship between the pressure, volume, temperature, and mole number for a given system is generally referred to as *the* equation of state of the system.

If we know the equation of state for a system over a range of temperatures, pressures, and molar volumes, we can then calculate the coefficient of thermal expansion α and the isothermal compressibility β over this range. Conversely, if we know α and β over a range R of temperatures and pressures or temperatures and molar volumes, and if we also know the values of the temperature, pressure, and molar volume at one point in R, then, as shown in the preceding section, we can obtain the equation of state over the range R. It follows that knowledge of the equation of state over a range R of temperatures, pressures, and molar volumes is equivalent to knowledge of statements (1), (2), and (4) in the theorem of the preceding section. We could, therefore, have written the theorem in the following equivalent form.

Theorem. The thermodynamic properties of a one-component system are completely specified over a range R of temperatures and pressures or temperatures and molar volumes if we know: (1) the functional relationship between the pressure, volume, and temperature for a given number of moles over the range R, (2) one of the specific heats c_p or c_V along a single path in R, provided that the path runs through all temperatures in R, (3) the value of the internal energy at some point in R, and (4) the value of the entropy at some point in R.

As a concrete illustration of the relation between the pressure, volume, and temperature for a substance, see Table 13,* where the pressure–volume–temperature surface for water is shown.

CONCLUSION

The theorem derived above points out to us a set of readily measured quantities that can, in principle, be used to determine any other thermodynamic property of a given system. The set used above is not the only possible set. However, it is one of the most convenient and most often employed sets.

EXAMPLE

Problem. The coefficient of thermal expansion and the isothermal compressibility of a certain substance are given by $\alpha = 3/T$ and $\beta = 2/(p + b)$, respectively, where b is a constant. It is also found that when the pressure is zero, the temperature dependence of the specific heat is given by $c_p = 6aT^2/b$, where a is a constant, and when $T = 1$, $p = 0$, and $N = 1$, the volume is given by $V = a/b^2$. Assuming that $E = 0$ when $T = 0$, $p = 0$, and $N = 1$, find $G(T,p,N)$ for the substance.

Solution. We shall designate an arbitrary state of the system as (T, p, N). Integrating the equation $dV/V = \alpha dT - \beta dp$ from $(1,0,1)$ to $(T,0,1)$, while holding p fixed, and then from $(T,0,1)$ to $(T,p,1)$, while holding T fixed, we obtain $V(T,p,1) = aT^3/(p + b)^2$. Integrating the equation $dE = (Nc_p - \alpha Vp)dT + (\beta Vp - \alpha VT)dp$ from $(0,0,1)$ to $(T,0,1)$, while holding

*All tables appear at end of text.

p fixed, and from $(T,0,1)$ to $(T,p,1)$, while holding T fixed, we obtain $E(T,p,1) = aT^3(p + 2b)/(p + b)^2$. Integrating the equation $dS = (Nc_p/T)dT - \alpha V dp$ over the same path, noting that $S(0,0,1) = 0$, we obtain $S(T,p,1) = 3aT^2/(p + b)$.

Combining the results and using the relation $G = E - TS + pV$, we obtain $G(T,p,1) = -aT^3/(p + b)$. Since $G(T,p,N)$ is a homogeneous function of degree one with respect to N, it follows that $G(T,p,N) = NG(T,p,1)$; therefore, $G(T,p,N) = -aNT^3/(p + b)$, which is the desired result.

PROBLEMS

13.1   Show that if we know $p(T,V,N_0)$, $c_V(T,V_1,N_0)$, $E(T_2,V_2,N_0)$, and $S(T_3,V_3,N_0)$, we can then determine $F(T,V,N)$.

13.2   Determine as completely as possible the equation of state of a substance for which $\alpha = 3aNT^3/V$ and $\beta = bN/V$, where a and b are constants.

13.3   The coefficient of thermal expansion and the isothermal compressibility of a certain gas are, respectively, $\alpha = NR/pV$ and $\beta = (1/p) + (aN/V)$, where R and a are constants. Determine the equation of state. Note that you are given $\alpha(p,v)$ and $\beta(p,v)$, where v is the molar volume.

13.4   It is asserted that the equation of state of one mole of a certain system is given by $V = A - Bp + CT$, and the internal energy is given by $E = DT - CpT$, where A, B, C, and D are constants. Show that this assertion cannot be correct.

13.5   Over a certain range of values of temperature and pressure the coefficient of thermal expansion of a certain substance is given by $\alpha = 1/T$ and the isothermal compressibility by $\beta = 2/p$. The specific heat at unit pressure is given by $c_p = c$, where c is a constant. At a temperature T_0, pressure p_0, and mole number N_0, the volume is V_0, the energy E_0, and the entropy S_0. Find $G(T,p,N)$.

13.6   A certain substance has the following coefficient of thermal expansion, isothermal compressibility, and specific heat: $\alpha = 2bNT/V$, $\beta = aN/V$, and $c_V = cTV/N$, where a, b, and c are constants. Calculate $p(T,V,N)$, $E(T,V,N)$, $S(T,V,N)$, and $F(T,V,N)$. Find the necessary relation between a, b, and c.

13.7   Over a certain range of temperatures and pressures the coefficient of thermal expansion of a certain substance is given by $\alpha = 1/T$ and the isothermal compressibility by $\beta = 1/p$. The temperature dependence of the specific heat of 1 mole of the substance contained in a rigid container of unit volume is found to be $c_V = c/T^2$, where c is a constant. At a temperature T_0, pressure p_0, and mole number

N_0, the volume is V_0, the energy is E_0, and the entropy is S_0. Find $F(T,V,N)$.

13.8   Over a certain range of values of temperature and volume, 1 mole of a certain hypothetical substance is found to satisfy the equation $p = \exp(T - V)$ in MKS units. It is also found that if 1 mole of the substance is enclosed in a rigid, 1 m³ container, the amount of heat required to raise the temperature one degree Kelvin is equal to $T \exp T$ J. If 5 moles of the gas at a temperature of 100°K are compressed quasistatically and adiabatically from a volume of 2 m³ to a volume of 1 m³, what will the final temperature of the gas be?

13.9   Show that if $(\partial E/\partial V)_{T,N} = 0$, the equation of state of the substance must be of the form $p = Tf(V,N)$, in which $f(V,N)$ is some function of V and N.

13.10   Show that if $(\partial H/\partial p)_{T,N} = 0$, the equation of state of the substance must be of the form $V = Tg(p,N)$, where $g(p,N)$ is some function of p and N.

13.11   Show that if $(\partial E/\partial V)_{T,N} = 0$ and $(\partial H/\partial p)_{T,N} = 0$, then pV/NT is constant.

PART THREE

Some Consequences
of the Basic Principles
of Thermodynamics

In Part I the basic principles of
thermodynamics were established.
In Part II we developed certain
useful thermodynamic techniques
that will be of help to us in exploiting the basic principles. In
the present part we wish to consider some of the general consequences of the basic principles.
The results we obtain will be employed when we apply thermodynamics to particular thermodynamic systems.

CHAPTER 14

The Conditions
of Equilibrium

In the present chapter we wish to investigate some of the consequences of Postulate III.

THE CONDITIONS OF EQUILIBRIUM

Suppose we have an isolated composite system, consisting of two systems 1 and 2 that are separated by a rigid, adiabatic wall, as shown in Figure 4.1. The state of system 1 is uniquely determined if we know E_1, V_1, and N_1. The state of system 2 is uniquely determined if we know E_2, V_2, and N_2.

The entropy of system 1 is given by $S_1(E_1,V_1,N_1)$; the entropy of system 2 is given by $S_2(E_2,V_2,N_2)$; and the entropy of the composite system is given by

$$S_{12}(E_1,V_1,N_1,E_2,V_2,N_2) = S_1(E_1,V_1,N_1) + S_2(E_2,V_2,N_2) \quad (14.1)$$

If one or more of the constraining features of the internal wall are removed, the two systems will interact; the composite system will then usually proceed spontaneously and rapidly to a new equilibrium state.

Sometimes, however, the process may be very slow. At other times the process may be arrested in a state of metastable equilibrium. In these cases catalysis of the process in some manner may be necessary.

The new equilibrium state of the composite system can be obtained by maximizing S_{12}, subject to those internal constraints still operative.

Let us consider some concrete situations. Suppose we remove the insulation from the wall dividing the two systems described above. Energy can now be freely exchanged between the two systems. However, due to the rigidity and impermeability of the internal wall, neither matter nor volume can be exchanged. To find the equilibrium state, we must therefore maximize S_{12} subject to the conditions that V_1, V_2, N_1, N_2, and $E_1 + E_2$ are constant. This problem was solved in Chapter 5, where we obtained

$$\left(\frac{\partial S_1}{\partial E_1}\right)_{V_1,N_1} = \left(\frac{\partial S_2}{\partial E_2}\right)_{V_2,N_2} \tag{14.2}$$

or

$$\frac{1}{T_1} = \frac{1}{T_2} \tag{14.3}$$

Thus the composite system will be in equilibrium when the temperatures of its subsystems are equal.

If we replace the wall by a diathermal piston that is free to move, we can then determine the new equilibrium state by maximizing S_{12} while holding N_1, N_2, $V_1 + V_2$, and $E_1 + E_2$ constant. This problem was solved in Chapter 5, where we obtained

$$\left(\frac{\partial S_1}{\partial E_1}\right)_{V_1,N_1} = \left(\frac{\partial S_2}{\partial E_2}\right)_{V_2,N_2} \tag{14.4}$$

$$\left(\frac{\partial S_1}{\partial V_1}\right)_{E_1,N_1} = \left(\frac{\partial S_2}{\partial V_2}\right)_{E_2,N_2} \tag{14.5}$$

or

$$\frac{1}{T_1} = \frac{1}{T_2} \tag{14.6}$$

$$\frac{p_1}{T_1} = \frac{p_2}{T_2} \tag{14.7}$$

In this case the composite system will be in equilibrium when the temperatures and pressures of the subsystems are equal.

Finally, if the wall is held rigid but made permeable, then both matter and energy can be exchanged between the subsystems. Since we have restricted our analyses to one-component systems, we can at the present stage investigate the solution to this problem only for situations in which the two subsystems are chemically identical. We shall, therefore, assume we are dealing with such a situation. To find the equilibrium state, we must maximize S_{12}, while holding V_1, V_2, $N_1 + N_2$, and $E_1 + E_2$ constant. We obtain

$$\frac{1}{T_1} = \frac{1}{T_2} \tag{14.8}$$

$$\frac{\mu_1}{T_1} = \frac{\mu_2}{T_2} \tag{14.9}$$

In this case the composite system will be in equilibrium when the temperatures and chemical potentials of the subsystems are equal.

In all the cases considered above we have assumed that energy could be freely exchanged between the two subsystems. We might ask what would happen if the internal wall is replaced by a piston that is free to move but that is well insulated. Our first impulse is to maximize the entropy, while holding E_1, E_2, N_1, N_2, and $V_1 + V_2$ constant. This step would not be correct, because as the piston moves it does work on the subsystems, and, therefore, energy can be exchanged between the two subsystems. It follows that we cannot consider E_1 and E_2 to be constant. On the other hand, since this mechanism for energy transfer does not allow a *free* exchange of energy between the two subsystems, we cannot allow any value of E_1 or E_2 that is consistent with a fixed total energy, as we do when the wall is diathermal. We conclude that the problem is indeterminate. We need to have more information concerning the mechanism of energy transfer before we can determine what the final equilibrium state will be.

STABILITY

If the component systems in an isolated composite system are free to exchange energy, volume, and matter with one another, then, according to the analysis in the preceding section, they will be in equilibrium with one another only if $T_1 = T_2$, $p_1 = p_2$, and $\mu_1 = \mu_2$. These results follow from the fact that the entropy of the composite system, in equilibrium, will be a maximum. However, we would obtain exactly the same result if the entropy was a minimum, rather than a maximum, at equilibrium. We wish now to investigate some additional conditions that are imposed on the properties of the system by virtue of the fact that the entropy is a maximum rather than a minimum.

Let us consider an isolated composite system consisting of two systems

1 and 2 that are free to exchange matter, volume, and energy with one another. According to Postulate III, the equilibrium state will be the state for which

$$S_{12} \equiv S_1(E_1, V_1, N_1) + S_2(E_2, V_2, N_2) \qquad (14.10)$$

assumes its maximum value consistent with the constraints

$$E_1 + E_2 = E_{12} = \text{const} \qquad (14.11)$$

$$V_1 + V_2 = V_{12} = \text{const} \qquad (14.12)$$

$$N_1 + N_2 = N_{12} = \text{const} \qquad (14.13)$$

To find the equilibrium state we therefore maximize the function

$$\psi(E_1, V_1, N_1) = S_1(E_1, V_1, N_1) + S_2[E_2(E_1), V_2(V_1), N_2(N_1)] \qquad (14.14)$$

where $E_2(E_1) = E_{12} - E_1$; $V_2(V_1) = V_{12} - V_1$; and $N_2(N_1) = N_{12} - N_1$. If we set the first derivatives equal to zero, we obtain as necessary conditions for equilibrium: $T_1 = T_2$, $p_1 = p_2$, and $\mu_1 = \mu_2$. However, according to the results of Appendix 3, if $\psi(E_1, V_1, N_1)$ is to be a *maximum*, then the following conditions are also necessary

$$\frac{\partial^2 \psi(E_1, V_1, N_1)}{\partial E_1^2} \leq 0 \qquad (14.15)$$

$$\left[\frac{\partial^2 \psi(E_1, V_1, N_1)}{\partial E_1 \partial V_1} \right]^2 - \left[\frac{\partial^2 \psi(E_1, V_1, N_1)}{\partial E_1^2} \right]\left[\frac{\partial^2 \psi(E_1, V_1, N_1)}{\partial V_1^2} \right] \leq 0 \qquad (14.16)$$

If we substitute Equation (14.14) in Equations (14.15) and (14.16) and note that

$$\frac{\partial^2 S(E, V, N)}{\partial E^2} = \left[\frac{\partial}{\partial E}\left(\frac{1}{T}\right) \right]_{V,N} = -\frac{1}{T^2}\left(\frac{\partial T}{\partial E}\right)_{V,N} = -\frac{1}{N c_V T^2} \qquad (14.17)$$

$$\frac{\partial^2 S(E, V, N)}{\partial V \partial E} = \left[\frac{\partial}{\partial V}\left(\frac{1}{T}\right) \right]_{E,N} = -\frac{1}{T^2}\left(\frac{\partial T}{\partial V}\right)_{E,N}$$
$$= \frac{\alpha T - \beta p}{N c_V \beta T^2} \qquad (14.18)$$

$$\frac{\partial^2 S(E, V, N)}{\partial V^2} = \left[\frac{\partial}{\partial V}\left(\frac{p}{T}\right) \right]_{E,N} = \frac{1}{T}\left(\frac{\partial p}{\partial V}\right)_{E,N} - \frac{p}{T^2}\left(\frac{\partial T}{\partial V}\right)_{E,N}$$
$$= \frac{2\alpha p T V - c_p T N - \beta p^2 V}{N c_V \beta V T^2} \qquad (14.19)$$

$$\left[\frac{\partial^2 S(E, V, N)}{\partial E \partial V} \right]^2 - \left[\frac{\partial^2 S(E, V, N)}{\partial E^2} \right]\left[\frac{\partial^2 S(E, V, N)}{\partial V^2} \right] = -\frac{1}{N c_V \beta T^3 V} \qquad (14.20)$$

we obtain

$$\frac{1}{T^2}\left(\frac{1}{Nc_V}\right)_1 + \frac{1}{T^2}\left(\frac{1}{Nc_V}\right)_2 \geq 0 \qquad (14.21)$$

$$\frac{1}{T^3}\left(\frac{1}{Nc_V\beta V}\right)_1 + \frac{1}{T^3}\left(\frac{1}{Nc_V\beta V}\right)_2 \geq 0 \qquad (14.22)$$

where $T = T_1 = T_2$, and the subscripts indicate the system with which the parameters within the parentheses are respectively associated. Equations (14.21) and (14.22) are necessary conditions for the two systems 1 and 2 to be in equilibrium. If we consider the systems 1 and 2 to be different parts of the same system, then

$$(c_V)_1 = (c_V)_2 = c_V \qquad (14.23)$$

$$\beta_1 = \beta_2 = \beta \qquad (14.24)$$

In this case we conclude from Equation (14.21) that

$$c_V \geq 0 \qquad (14.25)$$

and from (14.25) and (14.22) that

$$\beta \geq 0 \qquad (14.26)$$

Furthermore, since from Equation (12.23) in Chapter 12, $c_p = c_V + (\alpha^2 VT/N\beta)$ it follows that

$$c_p \geq 0 \qquad (14.27)$$

Thus for a system to be intrinsically stable, c_V and β must be positive (or zero). If c_V and β are positive for each of two systems in contact, then Equations (14.21) and (14.22), the conditions for mutual stability, will also be satisfied.

THE ENTROPY CRITERION

An isolated composite system, consisting of two systems 1 and 2 that are free to exchange energy, matter, and volume with one another, will be in equilibrium only if $T_1 = T_2$, $p_1 = p_2$, $\mu_1 = \mu_2$, $(c_V)_1 \geq 0$, $(c_V)_2 \geq 0$, $\beta_1 \geq 0$, and $\beta_2 \geq 0$. Although the above equilibrium conditions have been derived for equilibrium between the component systems of an isolated composite system, they are equally valid if the two systems in contact with one another do not form an isolated system. To make this clear, we note that an imaginary observer, who is restricted to making observations at a single point within a simple system in equilibrium or at the boundary between two simple systems in equilibrium, cannot from the very definition of a simple system make any measurement that gives him information about the extent or shape of the systems. Consequently, the above equilibrium conditions which represent relations between the intensive variables of the two systems and which can be checked by our hypothetical observer cannot depend on the fact that the two systems in question form an isolated composite system. To bring out the generality of the equilibrium conditions, it is helpful to reword the entropy maximization principle as follows: If two simple one-component systems 1 and 2 that are free to exchange energy, volume, and matter with one another are in the states (E_1^*, V_1^*, N_1^*) and (E_2^*, V_2^*, N_2^*), respectively, then the two systems will be in equilibrium if and only if

$$\Delta S_{12} \equiv [S_1(E_1, V_1, N_1) + S_2(E_2, V_2, N_2)]$$

$$- [S_1(E_1^*, V_1^*, N_1^*) + S_2(E_2^*, V_2^*, N_2^*)]$$

$$\equiv S_1 + S_2 - S_1^* - S_2^* \leq 0 \tag{14.28}$$

for all values of E_1, V_1, N_1, E_2, V_2, and N_2 that satisfy the conditions

$$E_1 + E_2 = E_1^* + E_2^* \tag{14.29}$$

$$V_1 + V_2 = V_1^* + V_2^* \tag{14.30}$$

$$N_1 + N_2 = N_1^* + N_2^* \tag{14.31}$$

We shall refer to the above statement of the entropy maximization principle as simply the entropy criterion, and we shall abbreviate it by writing

$$(\Delta S)_{E,V,N} \leq 0 \tag{14.32}$$

where it is understood that S, E, V, and N refer to the total entropy, energy, volume, and mole number, respectively.

The above formulation is not restricted to isolated composite systems. However, in an isolated composite system the states available are physically restricted to those that satisfy the constraint conditions, and, therefore, the entropy of the composite system in equilibrium will assume the maximum value that is actually possible physically.

THE ENERGY CRITERION

In the present section we shall show that the following statement is equivalent to the entropy criterion: If two simple one-component systems 1 and 2 that are free to exchange energy, volume, and matter with one another are in the states $(S_1^*, V_1^* N_1^*)$ and (S_2^*, V_2^*, N_2^*), respectively, then the two systems will be in equilibrium if and only if

$$\Delta E_{12} \equiv [E_1(S_1, V_1, N_1) + E_2(S_2, V_2, N_2)]$$
$$-[E_1(S_1^*, V_1^*, N_1^*) + E_2^*(S_2^*, V_2^*, N_2^*)]$$
$$\equiv E_1 + E_2 - E_1^* - E_2^* \geq 0 \qquad (14.33)$$

for all the values of S_1, V_1, N_1, S_2, V_2, and N_2 that satisfy the conditions

$$S_1 + S_2 = S_1^* + S_2^* \qquad (14.34)$$

$$V_1 + V_2 = V_1^* + V_2^* \qquad (14.35)$$

$$N_1 + N_2 = N_1^* + N_2^* \qquad (14.36)$$

The above statement is called the energy criterion and is abbreviated as follows

$$(\Delta E)_{S,V,N} \geq 0 \qquad (14.37)$$

From (14.37) it follows that in a composite system in which the total entropy, volume, and mole number are held fixed, the equilibrium state will be the state that minimizes the internal energy.

To prove the equivalence of conditions (14.32) and (14.37), we shall show (1) that if condition (14.32) is false, then condition (14.37) is false, and (2) that if condition (14.37) is false, then condition (14.32) is false.

We note first that it is always possible to increase both the energy and the entropy of a system by adding heat to the system, or to decrease both by removing heat. Thus no matter what state a system is in, it is always possible by adding heat to, or removing it from, a system, to cause a change from the old state to a new state, in which the energy and entropy are both either larger or smaller, but in which the volume and mole number remain fixed.

Let us now suppose that condition (14.32) is false. It then follows that there exists a state that we shall label by primes, for which

$$S_1' + S_2' > S_1^* + S_2^* \tag{14.38}$$

$$E_1' + E_2' = E_1^* + E_2^* \tag{14.39}$$

$$V_1' + V_2' = V_1^* + V_2^* \tag{14.40}$$

$$N_1' + N_2' = N_1^* + N_2^* \tag{14.41}$$

By removing heat from either system 1 or system 2 or from both, while holding V_1', V_2', N_1', and N_2' fixed, we can bring the composite system to a new state, which we shall label with double primes, for which

$$S_1'' + S_2'' = S_1^* + S_2^* \tag{14.42}$$

$$E_1'' + E_2'' < E_1^* + E_2^* \tag{14.43}$$

$$V_1'' + V_2'' = V_1^* + V_2^* \tag{14.44}$$

$$N_1'' + N_2'' = N_1^* + N_2^* \tag{14.45}$$

But a state satisfying conditions (14.42), (14.43), (14.44), and (14.45) would violate (14.37). Thus, if condition (14.32) is false, then condition (14.37) is false. Conversely, if condition (14.37) is false, then there exists a state for which (14.42), (14.43), (14.44), and (14.45) are true. By adding heat to either system 1 or 2 or to both, we can bring the composite system to a state for which (14.38), (14.39), (14.40), and (14.41) are true. But this result represents a violation of (14.32). Therefore, if condition (14.37) is false, then condition (14.32) is false. This step completes the proof of the identity of conditions (14.32) and (14.37).

OTHER CRITERIA

Although either the energy criterion or the entropy criterion is sufficient to determine the conditions of equilibrium for any two systems in thermodynamic contact, a number of other criteria are useful when we are dealing with composite systems for which the temperatures or pressures of the subsystems are respectively equal.

We shall first show that if two simple one-component systems 1 and 2 that are free to exchange energy, volume, and matter with one another are in the states (T_1^*, V_1^*, N_1^*) and (T_2^*, V_2^*, N_2^*), respectively, and if $T_1^* = T_2^*$, then the two systems will be in equilibrium if and only if

$$\Delta F_{12} \equiv [F_1(T_1, V_1, N_1) + F_2(T_2, V_2, N_2)]$$
$$- [F_1(T_1^*, V_1^*, N_1^*) + F_2(T_2^*, V_2^*, N_2^*)]$$
$$\equiv F_1 + F_2 - F_1^* - F_2^* \geq 0 \qquad (14.46)$$

for all values of T_1, V_1, N_1, T_2, V_2, and N_2 that satisfy the conditions

$$T_1 = T_2 = T_1^* = T_2^* \qquad (14.47)$$

$$V_1 + V_2 = V_1^* + V_2^* \qquad (14.48)$$

$$N_1 + N_2 = N_1^* + N_2^* \qquad (14.49)$$

We shall refer to this condition as the Helmholtz free-energy criterion and abbreviate it as follows:

$$(\Delta F)_{T,V,N} \geq 0 \qquad (14.50)$$

From the Helmholtz free-energy criterion, it follows that in a composite system in which the total volume and mole number are held constant, and in which all component systems are in contact with a constant-temperature environment, the equilibrium state is that state which minimizes the Helmholtz free energy.

To prove (14.50), we first note that the energy criterion provides us with a necessary and sufficient condition for equilibrium under the above circumstances, namely,

$$(\Delta E)_{T,S,V,N} \geq 0 \qquad (14.51)$$

where the subscript T indicates restriction to states for which T is fixed.

We shall now show that (14.50) and (14.51) are equivalent. To prove this we shall show that if condition (14.51) is false, then condition (14.50) is false, and if condition (14.50) is false, then condition (14.51) is false. Supposing condition (14.51) to be false, there exists a state, which we designate by primes, for which

$$E_1' + E_2' < E_1^* + E_2^* \qquad (14.52)$$

$$S_1' + S_2' = S_1^* + S_2^* \qquad (14.53)$$

$$V_1' + V_2' = V_1^* + V_2^* \qquad (14.54)$$

$$N_1' + N_2' = N_1^* + N_2^* \qquad (14.55)$$

$$T_1' = T_2' = T_1^* = T_2^* = T \qquad (14.56)$$

Combining (14.52), (14.53), and (14.56), we obtain

$$E_1' - T_1'S_1' + E_2' - T_2'S_2' < E_1^* - T_1^*S_1^* + E_2^* - T_2^*S_2^* \tag{14.57}$$

or since $F \equiv E - TS$

$$F_1' + F_2' < F_1^* + F_2^* \tag{14.58}$$

Equations (14.54), (14.55), (14.56), and (14.58) constitute a violation of condition (14.50). Thus if condition (14.51) is false, condition (14.50) is false. Conversely, if condition (14.50) is false, then there exists a state, which we designate by primes, that satisfies Equations (14.54), (14.55), (14.56), and (14.58). By quasistatically adding or removing heat from the system, while T_1, T_2, $V_1 + V_2$, and $N_1 + N_2$ are held fixed, we can change the entropy by an amount $S_1^* + S_2^* - S_1' - S_2'$. As a result, the energy will change by an amount $T(S_1^* + S_2^* - S_1' - S_2')$. The resultant state, designated by a double prime, will be one for which

$$S_1'' + S_2'' = S_1' + S_2' + (S_1^* + S_2^* - S_1' - S_2') = S_1^* + S_2^* \tag{14.59}$$

$$\begin{aligned} E_1'' + E_2'' &= E_1' + E_2' + T(S_1^* + S_2^* - S_1' - S_2') \\ &= F_1' + F_2' + TS_1^* + TS_2^* \\ &< F_1^* + F_2^* + TS_1^* + TS_2^* \\ &= E_1^* + E_2^* \end{aligned} \tag{14.60}$$

$$V_1'' + V_2'' = V_1^* + V_2^* \tag{14.61}$$

$$N_1'' + N_2'' = N_1^* + N_2^* \tag{14.62}$$

$$T_1'' = T_2'' = T_1^* = T_2^* = T \tag{14.63}$$

Equations (14.59), (14.60), (14.61), (14.62), and (14.63) constitute a violation of condition (14.51). Thus if condition (14.50) is false, condition (14.51) will also be false. The proof of the equivalence of conditions (14.50) and (14.51) is now completed. In a similar fashion, we can derive the two following theorems:

If two simple one-component systems 1 and 2 that are free to exchange energy, volume, and matter with one another are in the states (S_1^*, p_1^*, N_1^*) and (S_2^*, p_2^*, N_2^*), respectively, and if $p_1^* = p_2^*$, then the two systems will be in equilibrium if and only if

$$(\Delta H)_{S,p,N} \geq 0 \tag{14.64}$$

Condition (14.64) is called the enthalpy criterion. From the enthalpy criterion, it follows that in a composite system in which the total entropy and mole number are held constant, and in which all component systems are in contact with a constant pressure environment, the equilibrium state is that state which minimizes the enthalpy.

If two simple one-component systems 1 and 2 that are free to exchange matter with one another are in the states (T_1^*, p_1^*, N_1^*) and (T_2^*, p_2^*, N_2^*), respectively, and if $T_1^* = T_2^*$ and $p_1^* = p_2^*$, then the two systems will be in equilibrium if and only if

$$(\Delta G)_{T,p,N} \geq 0 \qquad\qquad (14.65)$$

Condition (14.65) is called the Gibbs free-energy criterion. From the Gibbs free-energy criterion, it follows that in a closed composite system in which all component systems are in contact with a constant temperature and constant pressure environment, the equilibrium state is that state which minimizes the Gibbs free energy.

PROBLEMS

14.1 Show that two systems having the same pressure will be in equilibrium with one another if $(\Delta H)_{S,p,N} > 0$.

14.2 Use the equilibrium condition $(\Delta E)_{S,V,N} > 0$ to prove the conditions of stability, that is, $c_V \geq 0$ and $\beta \geq 0$.

14.3 Use the equilibrium condition $(\Delta F)_{T,V,N} > 0$ to prove that $\beta \geq 0$.

14.4 The entropy of an ideal monatomic gas is given by $S = NR \ln (E^{3/2}VN^{-5/2}) + NC$, where C is a constant. Show that the conditions of intrinsic stability are satisfied by this fundamental equation.

14.5 The van der Waals equation of state for a gas is given by $p = [NRT/(V - Nb)] - (aN^2/V^2)$, where a and b are positive constants. Are all states represented by this equation intrinsically stable? Prove your answer.

14.6 Show that the stability criteria imply that $(1/\alpha)(\partial T/\partial p)_{S,N} \geq 0$.

CHAPTER 15

According to the third law of thermodynamics, the entropy of any system vanishes in those states for which the temperature is zero.

In the present chapter we wish to investigate some consequences of this law.

THE NERNST POSTULATE

The statement of the third law given above is due to Planck. A weaker form of the third law was originally postulated by Nernst. According to Nernst, the entropy change in any isothermal quasistatic process approaches zero as the temperature at which the process occurs approaches zero.

Nernst's formulation of the third law can be derived immediately from Planck's formulation of the third law. Consider two states (T,V_1,N_1) and (T,V_2,N_2) of the same system. The change in the entropy of the system in going from the first state to the second is

$$\Delta S = S(T,V_2,N_2) - S(T,V_1,N_1) \tag{15.1}$$

But if both $S(T,V_2,N_2)$ and $S(T,V_1,N_1)$ approach zero as T approaches zero, then ΔS also approaches zero.

Nernst's formulation of the third law can be expressed mathematically as follows:

$$\left(\frac{\partial S}{\partial X}\right)_{T,Y}\Bigg]_{T=0} = 0 \tag{15.2}$$

where (T,X,Y) is any set of parameters that includes the temperature and that can be used to specify the state of a system.

THE COEFFICIENT OF THERMAL EXPANSION AT $T = 0$

By making use of Maxwell relations and Equation (15.2), a number of other quantities that vanish at $T = 0$ can be found. In particular,

$$\left(\frac{\partial V}{\partial T}\right)_{p,N}\Bigg]_{T=0} = -\left(\frac{\partial S}{\partial p}\right)_{T,N}\Bigg]_{T=0} = 0 \tag{15.3}$$

$$\left(\frac{\partial p}{\partial T}\right)_{V,N}\Bigg]_{T=0} = \left(\frac{\partial S}{\partial V}\right)_{T,N}\Bigg]_{T=0} = 0 \tag{15.4}$$

Since $(\partial V/\partial T)_{p,N} = \alpha V$, Equation (15.3) implies that

$$\alpha]_{T=0} = 0 \tag{15.5}$$

that is, the coefficient of thermal expansion vanishes at $T = 0$.

SPECIFIC HEATS AT $T = 0$

Another useful consequence of the third law is the fact that all specific heats vanish at $T = 0$. To prove this, we note first that since the entropy in the state (T,V,N) is zero when $T = 0$, the entropy when $T \neq 0$ can be written

$$S(T,V,N) = \int_{0,V,N}^{T,V,N} dS \tag{15.6}$$

Since S is a state function, the integration can be carried out along any path wished. Since the initial and final values of V and N are the same, the obvious process to choose is one in which V and N are held constant. For such a process,

$$dS = \left(\frac{\partial S}{\partial T}\right)_{V,N} dT = \frac{Nc_V}{T} dT \tag{15.7}$$

Substituting Equation (15.7) in (15.6), we obtain

$$S(T,V,N) = \int_0^T \frac{Nc_V}{T} \, dT \tag{15.8}$$

If c_V approaches a nonzero value as T approaches zero, then the integral in (15.8) will diverge for all values of T. But in the limit as T approaches zero, $S(T,V,N)$ approaches zero; therefore, the integral cannot diverge for all values of T. It is, therefore, a necessary consequence of the third law that

$$c_V]_{T=0} = 0 \tag{15.9}$$

We can similarly show

$$c_p]_{T=0} = 0 \tag{15.10}$$

THE UNATTAINABILITY OF ZERO TEMPERATURE

It can be shown that, as a consequence of the third law, it is impossible to reduce the temperature of any system to absolute zero in a finite number of operations.

To prove this statement, we note that if we wish to lower the temperature of a system we can do one of two things. We can remove energy from the system by allowing the system to transfer energy in the form of heat to a system at a lower temperature, or we can remove energy from the system by allowing the system to do work. In order to lower the temperature of a system to $T = 0$ by heat transfer, we would have to have a heat reservoir at $T = 0$. Since this condition assumes that we already have been successful in lowering the temperature of some system to $T = 0$, it begs the question. Therefore, since we have no reservoirs at $T = 0$, we obviously do not wish to consider any process in which heat is transferred.

On the other hand, if we attempt to lower the temperature of the system by an adiabatic process, the entropy of the system will either remain constant if the process is quasistatic, or will increase if the process is not quasistatic. But by the third law, at $T = 0$ the entropy is zero. Therefore, the only adiabatic process that could terminate at $T = 0$ is an adiabatic quasistatic process along the adiabat $S = 0$. But along this adiabat, $T = 0$. It is therefore impossible in a single process to reduce the temperature of a system from some finite nonzero temperature to zero. It follows that it is impossible in any finite number of operations to reduce the temperature of any system to absolute zero.

PROBLEMS

15.1 Show that c_p approaches zero as T approaches zero.

15.2 The specific heat at constant volume of many crystalline substances is given at low temperatures by the Debye formula $c_V = aT^3$, where a is a constant for a particular substance. Show that the entropy at low temperatures of one mole of a substance obeying Debye's formula is equal to one-third of its specific heat at constant volume.

15.3 The Debye–Sommerfeld equation for metals predicts the following temperature dependence for the specific heat at constant volume at low temperatures $c_V = aT^3 + bT$, where a and b are constants for a particular metal. Derive expressions for the energy and entropy of a substance that obeys the Debye–Sommerfeld equation.

15.4 Given the fundamental equation $S = C(EVN)^{1/3}$, where C is a constant,
(a) Show that this equation does not violate the third law of thermodynamics.
(b) Show that the value of α, the coefficient of thermal expansion derived from the above equation, does not vanish at zero temperature.
(c) Explain the paradox.

CHAPTER 16

An isolated one-component system that is in an equilibrium state is not necessarily a simple system. For example, if we half-fill an evacuated container with water at room temperature, seal the container, and allow the system to come to equilibrium, part of the container will contain water in liquid form and part of the container will contain water vapor. The system as defined by the walls of the container is not homogeneous, and is therefore not a simple system. It is possible, however, to divide such a system into subsystems that are homogeneous. Such homogeneous subsystems are called phases. It is not necessary that all parts of a phase be contiguous. For instance, a system consisting of water and ice is considered a two-phase system, whether the ice is in one lump or in many small pieces. A system in which several different phases are present at one time can be handled by the techniques previously discussed if we simply treat the system as a composite system in which the phases constitute the component systems. The boundary separating any two phases is then considered as a permeable, diathermal, and moveable wall.

PHASE DIAGRAM

Let us consider a closed one-component system in which two phases are present. If the two phases are to be in equilibrium, their temperatures, pressures, and chemical potentials must be equal, since the phases can freely exchange energy, matter, and volume with one another. We have shown, in discussing the Gibbs–Duhem relation, that only two of these three parameters are independent. It follows that if two phases that we label 1 and 2 coexist, then

$$T_1 = T_2 = T \tag{16.1}$$

$$p_1 = p_2 = p \tag{16.2}$$

$$\mu_1 = \mu_2 \tag{16.3}$$

$$\mu_1 = \mu_1(T_1, p_1) \tag{16.4}$$

$$\mu_2 = \mu_2(T_2, p_2) \tag{16.5}$$

We can reduce these equations to the equation

$$\mu_1(T, p) = \mu_2(T, p) \tag{16.6}$$

At best, the solution to Equation (16.6) will give us p as a function of T. It follows that the two phases 1 and 2 can coexist only for respective values of temperature and pressure along some curve $p = p(T)$. We call such a curve a *phase curve*.

For three phases 1, 2, and 3 to coexist, the temperature and pressure must satisfy the equations

$$\mu_1(T, p) = \mu_2(T, p) = \mu_3(T, p) \tag{16.7}$$

Since we have two equations in two unknowns, there is, at most, a finite number of values of T and p at which three phases can simultaneously coexist. A point at which three phases can simultaneously coexist is called a *triple point*.

If we examine the conditions for four phases to coexist simultaneously, we obtain three equations in two unknowns, and thus there are in general no points at which four phases can simultaneously coexist. The above result is a particular application of the Gibbs phase rule, which we shall take up when we discuss multicomponent systems.

If we plot the values of T and p at which more than one phase is present, we obtain a diagram that, over a given range of temperatures and pressures, might typically look like that shown in Figure 16.1. Such a diagram is called a *phase diagram*. As mentioned above, the curves are called phase curves. Along phase curve AO, phases 1 and 3 can coexist. Along phase curve OB, phases 1 and 2 can coexist. Along phase curve OC, phases 2 and 3 can coexist. A point at which a phase curve terminates is called a *critical point*. In Figure 16.1 the point C is a critical point. Point O is a triple point since phases 1, 2, and 3 can coexist at this point.

When a system undergoes a quasistatic process in which it "crosses" one of the phase curves, the system will pass from one phase to another phase, a *phase transition* occurring. Since it is possible for a system to

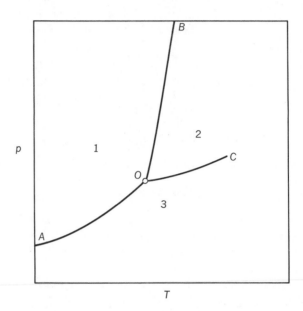

FIGURE 16.1

pass from one state to another state, as represented on the diagram, by different paths, the number of phase transitions that occur in passage from a given initial state to a given final state depends on the path. For example, a system could go from a state in region 2 to one in region 3 in Figure 16.1 without crossing any of the phase curves, hence undergoing no phase transition. Or from an initial state in region 2, it could go to a state in region 1 across line *OB*, and then from region 1 to region 3 across line *OA*. In this case, the system would undergo two phase transitions in going from region 2 to region 3.

As an example of a phase diagram, the phase diagram for water is given in Table 14.

LATENT HEAT

If a closed system of N moles of a one-component system undergoes a quasistatic phase transition from phase 1 to phase 2 at temperature T and pressure p, the amount of heat absorbed by the system is given by

$$Q_{12} = \int_1^2 T dS = T[S_2(T,p,N) - S_1(T,p,N)] \qquad (16.8)$$

If $|S_2(T,p,N) - S_1(T,p,N)| > 0$, then a finite amount of heat is required for the system to pass from the one phase to the other. This heat is called the *latent heat* and will be designated by L_{12}. Thus

$$L_{12}(T,p,N) = T[S_2(T,p,N) - S_1(T,p,N)] \qquad (16.9)$$

A more useful quantity is the *latent heat per mole* which we designate by ℓ_{12}. In terms of the latent heat per mole, Equation (16.9) becomes

$$\ell_{12}(T,p) = T[s_2(T,p) - s_1(T,p)] \qquad (16.10)$$

where s is the entropy per mole. A phase transition in which the latent heat is not zero is called a *first-order phase transition*.

The latent heat is frequently expressed in terms of enthalpy rather than entropy. From Equation (11.16), Chapter 11,

$$H = TS + \mu N \qquad (16.11)$$

and, therefore,

$$H_2(T,p,N) - H_1(T,p,N) = TS_2(T,p,N) + \mu_2 N - TS_1(T,p,N) - \mu_1 N \qquad (16.12)$$

Combining (16.6), (16.9), and (16.12), we obtain

$$L_{12}(T,p,N) = H_2(T,p,N) - H_1(T,p,N) \qquad (16.13)$$

Thus the latent heat is equal to the change in enthalpy. Similarly,

$$\ell_{12}(T,p) = h_2(T,p) - h_1(T,p) \qquad (16.14)$$

where $h_1(T,p)$ and $h_2(T,p)$ are the enthalpies per mole in phase 1 and phase 2, respectively.

THE CLAPEYRON EQUATION

We have seen earlier that if two phases are to coexist simultaneously, their chemical potentials must be equal, that is,

$$\mu_1(T,p) = \mu_2(T,p) \qquad (16.15)$$

If we take the differential of Equation (16.15), we obtain

$$d\mu_1(T,p) = d\mu_2(T,p) \qquad (16.16)$$

But from the Gibbs–Duhem relation, Equation (11.21),

$$d\mu = -\frac{S}{N}\,dT + \frac{V}{N}\,dp \equiv -s\,dT + v\,dp \qquad (16.17)$$

where s and v are the entropy per mole and the volume per mole, respectively. Making use of Equation (16.17) in Equation (16.16), we obtain

$$-s_1\,dT + v_1\,dp = -s_2\,dT + v_2\,dp \qquad (16.18)$$

From Equation (16.18) it follows that the slope of the phase curve is given by

$$\frac{dp}{dT} = \frac{s_2 - s_1}{v_2 - v_1} \qquad (16.19)$$

We see that, as long as the slope of the phase curve is neither zero nor infinity, a change in the molar volume implies a change in the molar entropy, and a change in the molar entropy implies a change in the molar volume. In a first-order phase transition, we therefore expect both the molar entropy and the molar volume to simultaneously undergo a change.

If we express Equation (16.19) in terms of the latent heat per mole ℓ_{12}, we obtain

$$\frac{dp}{dT} = \frac{\ell_{12}}{T(v_2 - v_1)} \qquad (16.20)$$

This equation is known as the *Clapeyron equation*. It is frequently easier to measure dp/dT, T, and $v_2 - v_1$ than to measure the latent heat per mole directly. In these cases the Clapeyron equation can be used to calculate the latent heat per mole. Conversely, knowledge of the latent heat per mole can be useful in describing the behavior of the pressure p as a function of T along a phase curve. For example, since heat is required to vaporize a liquid or a solid, and since the volume of a given mass of the vapor is much greater than the volume of the same mass of liquid or solid, it follows that $dp/dT > 0$ for the phase curve separating the solid or liquid phase from the vapor phase; therefore, vapor pressure increases with increasing temperature.

The phase diagram for water is given in Table 14. One very interesting and unusual feature of the low-pressure diagram is that the slope of the curve separating the ice and water phases is negative. Since heat is required to melt ice, it follows from Clapeyron's equation that the molar volume of ice must be larger than the molar volume of water. This property of ice is the property that allows ice to float.

EXAMPLE

Problem. The boiling point of water at a pressure of one atm is 100°C. The latent heat of vaporization of water at 100°C is 4.07×10^4 J(mole)$^{-1}$. Determine the approximate boiling point of water at 2 atm.

Solution. The *boiling point of a liquid* is defined as the temperature at which the vapor pressure is equal to the external pressure. From the given data it follows that (1) water undergoes a phase transition from the liquid to the gaseous state at a pressure of 1 atm and a temperature of 100°C, and (2) the latent heat for this transformation is $\ell = 4.07 \times 10^4$ J(mole)$^{-1}$. From the Clapeyron equation,

$$\frac{dp}{dT} = \frac{\ell}{T(v_g - v_\ell)}$$

where v_ℓ and v_g are the molar volumes of liquid water and water vapor, respectively, at a pressure of 1 atm and a temperature of 100°C. We shall assume that the molar volume of the liquid can be neglected, compared to the molar volume of the vapor, and that the water vapor behaves like an ideal gas, that is, $pv = RT$, where $R = 8.31$ J. It follows that

$$v_g - v_\ell \approx v_g \approx \frac{RT}{p}$$

Substituting this result in the Clapeyron equation and rearranging, we obtain

$$\frac{dp}{p} = \frac{\ell dT}{RT^2}$$

This equation is known as the *Clausius–Clapeyron equation*. Assuming that ℓ remains constant and integrating from T_1, p_1 to T_2, p_2, we obtain

$$\ln \frac{p_2}{p_1} = \frac{\ell}{R}\left[\frac{1}{T_1} - \frac{1}{T_2}\right]$$

Letting $p_1 = 1$ atm, $p_2 = 2$ atm, $T_1 = 373°K$, $\ell = 4.07 \times 10^4$ J(mole)$^{-1}$, and $R = 8.31$ J(mole)$^{-1}$(°K)$^{-1}$, we obtain

$$T_2 = 394°K$$

for the boiling point of water at 2 atm, which value agrees with the experimental value.

PROBLEMS

16.1   A sealed vessel of 50 cm³ capacity contains 10 cm³ of water at room temperature. The remaining space contains only water vapor. Discuss what happens as the vessel is heated, and draw rough curves showing the variation with temperature of (a) the pressure in the vessel and (b) the thermal capacity of the system as a whole. Values of the density ρ of saturated water vapor at different temperatures are given below:

$T(°C)$	350	360	370	380
ρ(g cm^{-3})	0.11	0.15	0.21	0.37

16.2   Show that the latent heat of vaporization of a liquid obeys the equation $\ell = RT^2 d(\ln p)/dT$, provided that the vapor pressure is small.

16.3   Show that the temperature variation of the latent heat of vaporization of a liquid obeys the equation $d\ell/dT = (c_p)_{vapor} - (c_p)_{liquid}$, provided that the vapor pressure is small and the coefficient of thermal expansion of the liquid may be taken to be zero. Compute $d\ell/dT$ using the following data: c_p for water vapor = 1.9 J(°K)$^{-1}$g^{-1}; c_p for liquid water = 4.2 J(°K)$^{-1}$g^{-1}.

16.4   A mass m of pure substance is placed in a tube of constant volume V. If two phases are present, show that: (a) The volume occupied by one phase will be $V_1 = (m - \rho_2 V)/(\rho_1 - \rho_2)$, where ρ_1, ρ_2, V_1 and V_2 are the densities and volumes, respectively, of the two phases. (b) The condition that V_1 will not change as the temperature is increased is given by $V_1/V_2 = -(d\rho_2/dT)/(d\rho_1/dT)$.

16.5   (a) The entropy of saturated water at 100°C is 0.31 cal/g deg, and that of saturated steam at the same temperature is 1.76 cal/g deg. What is the heat of vaporization per gram at this temperature? (b) The enthalpy of saturated steam at 100°C is 640 cal/g. From (a) calculate the enthalpy of saturated water at this temperature. (c) Calculate the Gibbs function of saturated water and of saturated vapor at 100°C, and verify the fact that the two are equal.

16.6 A liquid and vapor in equilibrium undergo a change of temperature dT and a change of pressure dp. Assuming that $v_{vapor} \equiv v_g \gg v_{liquid} \equiv v_\ell$ and that the vapor behaves like an ideal gas, show that the expansivity at constant saturation is $(1/v_g)(dv_g/dT) = (1/T)[1 - (\ell/RT)]$.

16.7 The vapor pressure of mercury at 399°K and at 401°K is found to be 0.988 mm and 1.084 mm of mercury, respectively. Calculate the latent heat of vaporization of liquid mercury at 400°K.

16.8 The vapor pressures of many liquids are well represented by the equation $\ln p = B - (A/T)$, where A/T is always greater than 5. (a) Assuming that the saturated vapor obeys the ideal gas equation, what is the equation of the liquid-vapor phase curve on a p-V diagram?
(b) Show that the magnitude of the slope of this curve is greater than that of an isotherm of an ideal gas, but less than that of an adiabatic curve of an ideal gas for which $\gamma \equiv c_p/c_V = 1.25$.

16.9 In the vicinity of the triple point the vapor pressure, in millimeters of mercury, of solid ammonia is given by $\ln p = 23.03 - (3754/T)$ and that of liquid ammonia by $\ln p = 19.49 - (3063/T)$.
(a) What is the temperature of the triple point?
(b) What are the latent heats of sublimation and vaporization?
(c) What is the latent heat of fusion at the triple point?

16.10 Assuming that the evaporation of electrons from a hot wire (thermionic effect) is thermodynamically equivalent to the sublimation of a solid, show that the pressure of the electron gas in equilibrium with a metal is given by $p = aT^{5/2}e^{-\ell_0/RT}$, provided that the electrons outside the metal constitute an ideal monatomic gas and also that the electrons inside the metal contribute nothing to the heat capacity of the metal. The quantity ℓ_0 is the latent heat at absolute zero.

16.11 Derive the Clapeyron equation by considering a Carnot cycle for a system consisting of a liquid and its saturated vapor.

16.12 One mole of ethyl alcohol C_2H_5OH is allowed to boil off at 78.4°C and 1 atm. If the heat of vaporization is observed to be 205 cal/g, what heat would you expect to be absorbed for evaporation into a perfect vacuum?

CHAPTER 17

Engines
and Refrigerators

It is not possible, according to the second law of thermodynamics, to change the universe in such a way that the only effect is a transfer of a positive amount of energy from a low-temperature heat reservoir to a high-temperature heat reservoir, or from a single heat reservoir to a work reservoir. Each of these processes involves only two reservoirs. If we consider processes in which more than two reservoirs are involved, in particular, processes in which two heat reservoirs and a work reservoir are involved, then it is possible for a process to take place in which the only effect is: (1) a positive amount of energy is surrendered by a high-temperature heat reservoir; (2) a portion of the energy surrendered is received by a low-temperature heat reservoir; and (3) the remainder of the energy surrendered appears as energy in a work reservoir. As a result of such a process, a net amount of energy in the form of heat has disappeared from the universe, being replaced by an equivalent amount of energy in the form of work. Heat has been converted into work. A device that permits continuous transformation of heat into work without the device, itself, undergoing any permanent change is called a *heat engine*.

In a similar fashion, it is possible for a process to take place in which the only effect is: (1) a positive amount of energy is extracted from a low-temperature reservoir; (2) a positive amount of energy is surrendered by a work reservoir; and (3) the energy from the low-temperature reservoir and the work reservoir is received by a high-temperature reservoir. As a result of such a process, energy can be transferred from a low-temperature reservoir to a high-temperature reservoir at the expense of work. A device that permits continuous extraction of heat from a low-temperature reservoir without itself undergoing any permanent change is called a *refrigerator*.

ENGINES

Let us assume we have a low-temperature heat reservoir 1, a high-temperature heat reservoir 2, a work reservoir R, and a complete supply of auxiliary mechanical devices, such as pistons, valves, and so forth. The reservoirs, together with the auxiliary devices, can be used to take a system X through a variety of cyclic processes. If such a process is quasistatic and if the system is a one-component system, the cycle can be plotted on a p-V diagram, as shown in Figure 17.1. During the cycle the system X receives a certain amount of heat Q_{2X} from heat reservoir 2, surrenders a certain amount of heat Q_{X1} to heat reservoir 1, and does work. If the work is stored in reservoir R, the increase of energy in the reservoir is given by

$$W_{XR} = \oint p\,dV \qquad (17.1)$$

The integral on the right-hand side of Equation (17.1) is equal to the area enclosed by the curve in Figure 17.1. If the process is executed in a clockwise fashion, the area is positive, and the net amount of work delivered to the reservoir is positive. It follows that when the cycle is executed in a clockwise fashion, as shown on a p-V diagram, the system X, together with the auxiliary mechanical devices needed to produce the cycle, constitute a heat engine.

A steam engine is an example of an engine that closely approximates the type of engine described above. The working substance is water, which receives heat at a high temperature, exhausts it at low temperature, and does work. Although the cycle through which the water is taken is not strictly quasistatic, it is possible to approximate the behavior of a steam engine by a particular quasistatic cycle, called a *Rankine cycle*. An ordinary gasoline engine is another example of a heat engine. In this case, however, the departure from the type of engine described in the preceding paragraph is considerable. Heat is *not* supplied by a high-temperature heat reservoir; but by the combustion of gasoline within the engine; the working substance does not progress through a cycle but is admitted in one state and exhausted in another; and, finally, as in the case of a steam engine, the process is not

quasistatic. Nevertheless, it is possible to approximate many of the properties of a gasoline engine by an idealized engine, in which air is taken
through a particular quasistatic cycle called an *Otto cycle*. By analyzing the

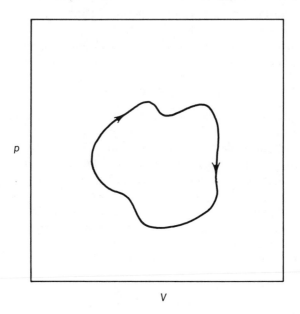

FIGURE 17.1

behavior of the Otto cycle, we can determine the influence of various factors
on its performance, and hence obtain some information about the effect of
these same factors on the behavior of gasoline engines. In a similar fashion,
we can study the properties of other heat engines by constructing idealized
quasistatic cycles that approximate the behavior of these engines. A detailed
analysis of such cycles can be found in any good book on engineering
thermodynamics.

In the present text we shall not consider the numerous thermodynamic
cycles encountered in the design of engines, but will restrict our attention
to a few general properties of such cycles.

ENGINE EFFICIENCY

If a system X undergoes a cycle in which a positive amount of heat Q_{2X} is
received from a high-temperature reservoir 2, an amount of heat Q_{X1} is
surrendered to a low-temperature reservoir 1, and a positive amount of

work W_{XR} is delivered to a work reservoir R, then the efficiency of the cycle is defined as

$$\eta = \frac{W_{XR}}{Q_{2X}} \qquad (17.2)$$

From the conservation of energy

$$W_{XR} = Q_{2X} - Q_{X1} \qquad (17.3)$$

Since the entropy of the universe cannot decrease, and since the only entropy changes that take place as a result of the cycle are the entropy changes of the two heat reservoirs, the sum of the entropy changes of the two heat reservoirs must be greater than, or equal to, zero, that is,

$$\frac{Q_{X1}}{T_1} + \frac{Q_{X2}}{T_2} \geq 0 \qquad (17.4)$$

We note from relation (17.4) that if Q_{2X} is positive, then $Q_{X2} = -Q_{2X}$ is negative, and therefore, Q_{X1} must be positive. If we substitute (17.3) and (17.4) in Equation (17.2), we obtain

$$\eta \leq 1 - \frac{T_1}{T_2} \qquad (17.5)$$

If the process is reversible, the entropy change of the universe as given by (17.4) is zero, and the efficiency is given by

$$\eta^* = 1 - \frac{T_1}{T_2} \qquad (17.6)$$

It follows that the most efficient heat engine that can operate between two heat reservoirs is a reversible engine, that is, an engine in which the working substance is taken through a reversible cycle. Furthermore, since no mention was made in the above argument of a particular type of reversible cycle, all reversible engines operating between the same two heat reservoirs have the same efficiency, namely, that given by Equation (17.6).

It should be carefully noted that even though a substance is taken through a quasistatic cycle, the cycle is not necessarily reversible. As a matter of fact, although the number of possible quasistatic cycles that can be carried out with the aid of two heat reservoirs and a work reservoir is infinite, it is difficult to think of many such cycles that are reversible. For a transfer of heat between a system and a heat reservoir to take place reversibly, the difference between their respective temperatures must be infinitesimal. It would, therefore, appear that the only reversible cycle that can be carried out with the aid of a reservoir at temperature T_1 and a reservoir at T_2 is a Carnot cycle, that is, a cycle consisting of two isotherms at temperatures T_1 and T_2, respectively, and two adiabats connecting the two isotherms to form a cycle. However, it is possible, by introducing, in addition to the reservoirs at temperatures T_1 and T_2, auxiliary reservoirs that absorb heat during one portion of the cycle and give up the same amount of heat during another portion of the cycle, to construct reversible cycles other than a Carnot cycle, in which the only net energy changes are in the two heat reservoirs at temperatures T_1 and T_2 and in a work reservoir.

Since a reversible cycle is the most efficient cycle that can operate between two reservoirs, it might appear that all engines ought to be constructed to operate in reversible cycles. However, there are many factors other than the thermal efficiency of a cycle that determine the practicality of a given engine. The cost of construction, ease of operation, and so forth, all affect the particular design chosen.

REFRIGERATORS

If a system X is taken through a cyclic process with the aid of a low-temperature reservoir 1, a high-temperature reservoir 2, a work reservoir R, and needed auxiliary mechanical devices, and if, as a result, a positive amount of heat is extracted from the low-temperature reservoir, then the system X, together with the auxiliary mechanical devices, constitute a refrigerator. If we let Q_{1X} represent the heat removed from reservoir 1, Q_{X2} the heat delivered to reservoir 2, and W_{RX} the work surrendered by reservoir R, then the coefficient of performance ω of the refrigerator is defined by the relation

$$\omega = \frac{Q_{1X}}{W_{RX}} \qquad (17.7)$$

From the first law of thermodynamics or Postulate I,

$$W_{RX} = Q_{X2} - Q_{1X} \qquad (17.8)$$

From the second law of thermodynamics or Postulate III,

$$\frac{Q_{X1}}{T_1} + \frac{Q_{X2}}{T_2} \geq 0 \qquad (17.9)$$

Substituting (17.8) and (17.9) in Equation (17.7), we obtain

$$\omega \leq \frac{T_1}{T_2 - T_1} \qquad (17.10)$$

If the process is reversible, the coefficient of performance is given by

$$\omega^* = \frac{T_1}{T_2 - T_1} \tag{17.11}$$

It follows that a reversible refrigerator uses the least amount of work to remove a given amount of heat from a low-temperature reservoir.

EXAMPLE

Problem.   A gasoline engine can be represented approximately by an idealized cycle, called an Otto cycle, consisting of: (1) a quasistatic adiabatic compression from a volume V_a to a volume V_b, corresponding to the compression of the air and gasoline mixture; (b) a quasistatic constant volume increase in pressure, corresponding to the explosion of the mixture; (c) a quasistatic adiabatic expansion from volume V_b to volume V_a, corresponding to the expansion of the air and the products of the combustion, during which the engine does useful work; and (d) a quasistatic constant volume decrease in the pressure to the original state, corresponding to the replacement of the consumed mixture by a fresh mixture of air and gasoline. Assume that the air and gasoline mixture can be treated as a gas, for which $pV = NRT$, and for which c_V is a constant. Calculate the efficiency of the engine in terms of V_a, V_b, and c_V.

Solution.   We designate the system by the letter X; the state of the system at the beginning of each stage by the letters a, b, c, and d, respectively. We assume that: (1) all work done on or by the system comes from, or goes to, a work reservoir R; (2) all heat transferred to the system comes from a high-temperature heat reservoir 2; and (3) all heat transferred from the system goes to a low-temperature heat reservoir 1. If a gas for which $pV = NRT$ undergoes an adiabatic process, then during the process,

$$\frac{dT}{T} = \left(\frac{\partial T}{\partial V}\right)_{S,N} \frac{dV}{T} = -\left(\frac{R}{c_V}\right)\left(\frac{dV}{V}\right)$$

Integrating, we obtain

$$TV^{R/c_V} = \text{const}$$

It follows that along the path $(a \rightarrow b)$,

$$T = T_b V_b^{R/c_V} V^{-R/c_V}$$

while along the path $(c \rightarrow d)$,

$$T = T_c V_c^{R/c_V} V^{-R/c_V}$$

The only work done on or by the system is done during the processes $(a \to b)$ and $(c \to d)$. Since $dW_{XR} = pdV = (NRT/V)dV$, it follows that along the path $(a \to b)$

$$dW_{XR} = NRT_b V_b{}^{R/c_V} V^{-(R+1)/c_V} dV$$

while along the path $(c \to d)$

$$dW_{XR} = NRT_c V_c{}^{R/c_V} V^{-(R+1)/c_V} dV$$

Integrating to obtain the work done by the system during these two processes, noting that $V_c = V_b$ and $V_d = V_a$, we obtain

$$W_{XR} = Nc_V(T_c - T_b)\left[1 - \left(\frac{V_b}{V_a}\right)^{R/c_V}\right]$$

The only heat transferred *to* the system is transferred in the process $(b \to c)$, during which

$$dQ_{2X} = TdS = T\left(\frac{\partial S}{\partial T}\right)_{V,N} dT = Nc_V dT$$

Integrating, we obtain

$$Q_{2X} = Nc_V (T_c - T_b).$$

The efficiency of the engine is thus given by

$$\eta = \frac{W_{XR}}{Q_{2X}} = 1 - \left(\frac{V_b}{V_a}\right)^{R/c_V}$$

PROBLEMS

17.1 A Carnot engine is operating between two reservoirs at temperatures T_1 and T_2, where $T_1 > T_2$. Which is the more effective way to increase the efficiency of the engine: to increase T_1, keeping T_2 constant, or to decrease T_2, keeping T_1 constant?

17.2 In a certain engine, working between the limits of 180°C and 10°C, the efficiency is 20 percent. If the heat supplied is 90 cal, what is the increase in the entropy of the universe per cycle?

17.3 Compare the efficiency of a heat engine in which a monatomic ideal gas $[S = NR \ln (E^{3/2} V N^{-5/2}) + NC]$ is taken through a quasistatic cycle, consisting of alternating constant temperature processes and

constant pressure processes with the efficiency of a Carnot engine
operating between the same temperature limits.

17.4   An ideal monatomic gas $[S = NR \ln(E^{3/2}VN^{-5/2}) + NC]$ undergoes
a cycle composed of two constant pressure processes at pressures
p_1 and p_2, respectively, and two constant volume processes at
volumes V_1 and V_2, respectively. Find the efficiency of this cycle when
used as a heat engine.

17.5   A substance undergoes a cyclic process represented on a T-S diagram
by a triangle as shown in Figure 17.2 below. What is the efficiency of
this cycle in terms of T_1 and T_2?

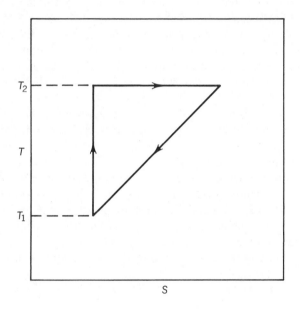

FIGURE 17.2

17.6   Three hundred watts of power are required to drive a Carnot refrigerator that is being used to maintain a certain substance at a constant
temperature T, and 500 W are rejected as heat by the refrigerator
into the surroundings at a temperature of 300°K. What is the
temperature of the substance?

17.7   Two identical bodies for which $E = NCT$, where C is a constant,
are initially at temperatures T_1 and T_2, respectively. The two bodies are
brought to a common temperature by using them as a source and sink
for a heat engine. (Assume that the volume changes of the two bodies

during the process are negligible.) What is the maximum amount of work which the heat engine is capable of performing? What is the minimum final temperature attainable in this fashion?

17.8 Suppose that an object of constant specific heat $c_V = c$ were to be cooled from a temperature of T_1 to a temperature T_2 by use of a reversible refrigerating machine whose expansion coils are always at the temperature of the object and whose compressor is at a constant temperature T_0.

(a) Show that if the substance were cooled at constant volume, the work expended in operating the refrigerator would be $W = NcT_0 \ln (T_1/T_2) - Nc(T_1 - T_2)$.

(b) Show that the work required to reduce the temperature to absolute zero would be infinite.

(c) Actually all specific heats approach zero as the temperature approaches absolute zero. Taking this fact into account, show that the work expended in operating the refrigerator and cooling the substance to absolute zero would be $W = -E(T_1,V,N) + E(0,V,N) + T_0 S(T_1,V,N)$.

(d) Does the fact that W is finite in Problem 17.8(c) violate the unattainability of zero aspect of the third law? Explain your answer.

17.9 A diesel engine can be represented approximately by an idealized cycle (called a diesel cycle) in which an ideal gas of constant specific heat is taken through a cyclic process consisting of: (1) a quasistatic adiabatic compression from a temperature T_a and a volume V_a to a volume V_b; (2) a quasistatic constant pressure expansion from the volume V_b to a volume $V_c < V_a$; (3) a quasistatic adiabatic expansion from the volume V_c to the volume V_a; and (4) a quasistatic constant volume cooling to the temperature T_a. Calculate the efficiency of the engine in terms of V_a, V_b, V_c, and c_V.

CHAPTER 18

Maximum Work

INTRODUCTION

It is possible to use two or more thermodynamic systems that are not in equilibrium to do work. For example, if two systems are at different temperatures, they can be used as a source and sink to drive a heat engine; or if two systems are at different pressures, the pressure difference, itself, can be used to do work directly. The amount of work that can be obtained in a particular situation depends on the initial and final states of the respective systems involved and also on the processes by which the systems pass between these two states. In the present chapter we wish to determine the maximum amount of work that can be obtained under various circumstances. For convenience, we shall state the results in a series of theorems.

MAXIMUM WORK

Theorem A. If a process takes place in which the only changes in the universe are: (1) a closed system passes from a state 1 to a state 2, (2) an amount of heat Q flows into a heat reservoir, and (3) an amount of work

141

W flows into a work reservoir, then W will be a maximum and Q a minimum when the process is carried out reversibly; and the respective values of W and Q will be the same for all reversible processes between the given states.

Proof.   Let us designate the system by the letter X; the heat reservoir by the letter I and its temperature by T_I; the work reservoir by the letter R; the heat flow to the heat reservoir by Q_{XI}; the work flow to the work reservoir by W_{XR}; the entropy change of the system X by ΔS_X; the entropy change of the heat reservoir by ΔS_I; and the energy change of the system X by ΔE_X. The total energy of the universe is conserved, and therefore

$$W_{XR} + Q_{XI} + \Delta E_X = 0 \qquad (18.1)$$

The total entropy of the universe remains constant in a reversible process and increases in an irreversible process; therefore,

$$\Delta S_X + \Delta S_I = 0 \qquad \text{(Reversible process)} \qquad (18.2a)$$

$$\Delta S_X + \Delta S_I > 0 \qquad \text{(Irreversible process)} \qquad (18.2b)$$

Since all processes taking place inside a heat reservoir are quasistatic, it follows that

$$Q_{XI} = T_I \Delta S_I \qquad (18.3)$$

Combining Equations (18.1), (18.2), and (18.3), we obtain

$$W_{XR} = T_I \Delta S_X - \Delta E_X \qquad \text{(Reversible process)} \qquad (18.4a)$$

$$W_{XR} < T_I \Delta S_X - \Delta E_X \qquad \text{(Irreversible process)} \qquad (18.4b)$$

The temperature T_I is fixed, and since the system X passes between a given initial and a given final state, the quantities ΔS_X and ΔE_X are also fixed. The right-hand sides of (18.4a) and (18.4b) are therefore fixed quantities. It follows that W_{XR} is maximum for a reversible process and is the same for any reversible process between the given states. From (18.1) it further follows that when W_{XR} is at a maximum, Q_{XI} must be at a minimum. This step completes the proof of the theorem.

Theorem B.   If a process takes place in which the only changes in the universe are: (1) a composite system that is enclosed in a rigid and impermeable container passes from a given state 1, in which the component systems are not in mutual equilibrium, to a state 2 in which the component systems are in mutual equilibrium and (2) an amount of work W flows into a work reservoir, then W will be a maximum when the component systems are brought to equilibrium reversibly, and the value of W will be the same for all such reversible processes.

Proof. Let us designate the system by the letter X; the work reservoir by the letter R; the work flow to the work reservoir by W_{XR}; the initial and final energies and entropies of the system X by $E_X(1)$, $E_X(2)$, $S_X(1)$, and $S_X(2)$, respectively. The total energy of the universe remains constant, and therefore,

$$W_{XR} = E_X(1) - E_X(2) \tag{18.5}$$

The total entropy of the universe remains constant in a reversible process and increases in an irreversible process; therefore,

$$S_X(2) = S_X(1) \quad \text{(Reversible process)} \tag{18.6a}$$

$$S_X(2) > S_X(1) \quad \text{(Irreversible process)} \tag{18.6b}$$

The quantities $E_X(1)$ and $S_X(1)$ are fixed. The quantities $E_X(2)$ and $S_X(2)$ are not fixed, since there are many different final states of the composite system that satisfy the conditions of the theorem, that is, for which the component systems are in mutual equilibrium and in which the only transfer of energy occurs with a work reservoir. It therefore follows from Equation (18.5) that the work W_{XR} will be a maximum when $E_X(2)$ is a minimum. But when the component systems are in equilibrium, the value of $(\partial E/\partial S)_{V,N} \equiv T$, for each of the component systems will be equal and positive, hence, $E_X(2)$ will be a minimum when $S_X(2)$ is a minimum. From Equation (18.6), $S_X(2)$ is a minimum when the process is reversible, and thus the work W_{XR} will be a maximum when the process is reversible. Since the system is contained in a rigid and impermeable container, knowledge of the initial state of the system, together with knowledge of $E_X(2)$ or $S_X(2)$, is sufficient to determine the final state. For a reversible process $S_X(2) = S_X(1)$. Thus the final state, and hence W_{XR}, are unique for a reversible process. This step completes the proof of the theorem.

FREE ENERGY

We are frequently interested in processes that begin and end with a system in thermal equilibrium with a constant temperature environment, such as the atmosphere, and in which the only heat reservoir available is this same environment. The following theorem is applicable to such situations.

Theorem C. If a process takes place in which (1) a system passes from a state 1 in which it is at a temperature T to a state 2 in which it is also at temperature T, (2) an amount of heat Q flows into a heat reservoir at temperature T, and (3) an amount of work W flows into a work reservoir, then the maximum value of W is equal to the difference between the Helmholtz free energy in the state 1 and the Helmholtz free energy in state 2.

Proof. Let us designate the system by the letter X; the heat reservoir by the letter I; the work reservoir by the letter R; the initial and final states of each by the numbers 1 and 2, respectively; and the work and heat delivered to the reservoirs by W_{XR} and Q_{XI}, respectively. We note first that

$$W_{XR} = E_X(1) - E_X(2) - Q_{XI}$$
$$= E_X(1) - E_X(2) - T_I[S_I(2) - S_I(1)] \tag{18.7}$$

The maximum amount of work will be delivered to the work reservoir if the system passes from the state 1 to the state 2 by a reversible process. For a reversible process, the total entropy change of the universe is zero, that is,

$$[S_X(2) - S_X(1)] + [S_I(2) - S_I(1)] = 0 \tag{18.8}$$

Furthermore, from the conditions of the theorem

$$T_I = T_X(1) = T_X(2) \tag{18.9}$$

Combining Equations (18.7), (18.8), and (18.9), we obtain

$$W_{XR} = [E_X(1) - T_X(1)S_X(1)] - [E_X(2) - T_X(2)S_X(2)] \tag{18.10}$$

But $[E_X(1) - T_X(1)S_X(1)]$ and $[E_X(2) - T_X(2)S_X(2)]$ are simply the values of the Helmholtz free energy in the initial and final states, respectively, and therefore,

$$W_{XR} = F_X(1) - F_X(2) \tag{18.11}$$

that is, the maximum work obtainable is equal to the decrease in the Helmholtz free energy of the system. The Helmholtz free energy thus represents the energy of a system that can be freed to do work in a process beginning and ending with the system in thermal equilibrium with a heat reservoir, and in which process the heat reservoir is the only heat source used. This is the origin of the designation "free energy."

If the system begins and ends in thermal equilibrium with a constant temperature environment, and also in mechanical equilibrium with a constant pressure environment, then the following theorem is applicable.

Theorem D. If a process takes place in which (1) a system passes from a state 1 in which it is at a temperature T, pressure p, and volume V_1 to a state 2 in which it is at a temperature T, pressure p, and volume V_2, (2) an amount of heat Q flows into a heat reservoir, at temperature T, (3) due to the change in volume of the system, an amount of work $p(V_2 - V_1)$ flows into the environment, which is at a constant pressure p, and (4) an additional amount of work W flows into a work reservoir, then the maximum value of W is equal to the difference between the Gibbs free energy in state 1 and the Gibbs free energy in state 2.

Proof. Let us designate the system by the letter X; the heat reservoir by the letter I; the constant pressure environment by the letter P; the work reservoir by the letter R; the initial and final states of each by the numbers 1 and 2, respectively; the work delivered to the work reservoir and the constant pressure environment by W_{XR} and W_{XP}, respectively; and the heat delivered to the heat reservoir by Q_{XR}. We note first that

$$W_{XR} = [E_X(1) - E_X(2)] - W_{XP} - Q_{XR}$$

$$= [E_X(1) - E_X(2)] - p_P[V_P(1) - V_P(2)] - T_I[S_I(2) - S_I(1)] \quad (18.12)$$

But for a reversible process,

$$S_I(2) - S_I(1) = S_X(1) - S_X(2) \quad (18.13)$$

and from the conditions of the problem,

$$V_P(1) - V_P(2) = V_X(2) - V_X(1) \quad (18.14)$$

$$T_I = T_X(1) = T_X(2) \quad (18.15)$$

$$p_P = p_X(1) = p_X(2) \quad (18.16)$$

Combining these results, we obtain

$$W_{XR} = [E_X(1) + p_X(1)V_X(1) - T_X(1)S_X(1)]$$

$$- [E_X(2) + P_X(2)V_X(2) - T_X(2)S_X(2)] \quad (18.17)$$

and therefore,

$$W_{XR} = G_X(1) - G_X(2) \quad (18.18)$$

The Gibbs free energy thus represents the energy of a system that can be freed to do useful work in a process that begins and ends with the system in thermal and mechanical equilibrium with a constant temperature and constant pressure environment, and in which process this environment is the only heat reservoir. This is the origin of the designation "free energy."

AVAILABILITY

We are frequently interested in the maximum amount of work W that can be extracted from a system in passing from some arbitrary initial state to a state in which it is in thermal and mechanical equilibrium with the atmosphere. The following theorem applies to such a situation.

Theorem E.   If a process takes place in which (1) a system passes from an arbitrary state 1 in which the energy is E, the volume V, and the entropy S, to a state 0 in which the energy is E_0, the volume V_0, the entropy S_0, and in which it is in thermal and mechanical equilibrium with the atmosphere at a temperature T_0 and pressure p_0, (2) an amount of heat Q flows to the atmosphere, (3) an amount of work $p_0(V_0 - V)$ flows to the atmosphere due to the change in volume of the system, and (4) an additional amount of work W flows into a work reservoir, then the maximum value of W is equal to the availability A, which is defined for an arbitrary state as follows:

$$A \equiv (E + p_0V - T_0S) - (E_0 + p_0V_0 - T_0S_0) \qquad (18.19)$$

Proof.   The loss of energy from the system is $E - E_0$; the flow of work to the work reservoir is W; the flow of work to the atmosphere is $-p_0(V - V_0)$; and if the process is reversible, the flow of heat to the atmosphere is $T_0(S - S_0)$. Since the total energy of the universe is conserved,

$$E - E_0 = T_0(S - S_0) - p_0(V - V_0) + W \qquad (18.20)$$

Solving for W, we obtain

$$W = A \qquad (18.21)$$

where A is the availability, which is defined by Equation (18.19). The availability thus represents the maximum amount of work that can be delivered to a work reservoir, other than the atmosphere, when a system passes from its initial state to the dead state, that is, the state in which it is in equilibrium with the atmosphere.

EXAMPLE

Problem.   Two identical bodies 1 and 2 are initially at known temperatures T_1' and T_2', respectively. What is the maximum amount of work that can be extracted in a process in which the two bodies are brought to a common temperature T''? Assume that no heat reservoirs are available and that the bodies are maintained at a constant volume.

Solution.   The maximum amount of work will be obtained if we bring the two bodies to equilibrium with one another by a reversible process. By using the two bodies as a heat source and a heat sink, respectively, for a Carnot engine, we can bring them to equilibrium reversibly. If we let Q_{1X} and Q_{2X} be the respective heat flows from bodies 1 and 2 to the engine; W_{XR} the work flow from the engine to the work reservoir; and $C_V \equiv Nc_V$ the heat capacity at constant volume of the bodies 1 and 2; then at any stage in the operation of the engine,

$$dW_{XR} = dQ_{1X} + dQ_{2X} = -C_V dT_1 - C_V dT_2$$

$$dS_1 + dS_2 = \frac{C_V dT_1}{T_1} + \frac{C_V dT_2}{T_2} = 0$$

Integrating both equations between the initial and the final states, we obtain

$$W_{XR} = C_V(T_1' - T'') + C_V(T_2' - T'')$$

$$(T'')^2 = T_1' T_2'$$

Solving for W_{XR}, we obtain

$$W_{XR} = C_V[T_1' + T_2' - 2(T_1' T_2')^{1/2}]$$

PROBLEMS

18.1   A system has a heat capacity at constant volume of $C_V = aT^2$. The system is originally at a temperature T_1, and a heat reservoir at a temperature T_0 is available. What is the maximum amount of work that can be recovered as the system is cooled down to the temperature of the reservoir?

18.2 What is the maximum amount of work that can be obtained by any means from an ideal monatomic gas which goes from a state (E_1, V_1, N_1) to a state (E_2, V_2, N_1) when the only reservoirs available are a work reservoir at a pressure p_0 and a heat reservoir at a temperature T_0. The fundamental equation for an ideal monatomic gas is $S = NR \ln (E^{3/2}VN^{-5/2}) + NC$.

18.3 Each of three identical bodies has an equation of state $E = NCT$. Their initial temperatures are T_1, T_2, and T_3, respectively. What is the maximum amount of work that can be extracted in a process in which these three bodies are brought to a final common temperature. Assume that any changes in the volume of the three bodies can be neglected.

18.4 Each of two identical bodies has a heat capacity at constant volume given by $C_V = a + 2bT$, where a and b are constants. The two bodies are initially at temperatures T_1 and T_2, respectively, and a reversible work source is available. Assuming that the volumes of the two bodies remain constant,

(a) What is the maximum amount of work that can be transferred to the reversible work source?

(b) What is the minimum final temperature to which the two bodies can be brought?

18.5 A lead ball of mass m falls from a height h in a vacuum, strikes a lead plate of mass M and sticks. Let the specific heat of lead be equal to c J(kg)$^{-1}$(°K)$^{-1}$, and assume: (1) no heat is lost to the surroundings, (2) the volume change of the lead is negligible, (3) the initial temperatures of the ball and plate are T_0, and (4) the increase ΔT in the temperature of the ball and the plate is small compared to T_0.

(a) Calculate the entropy change of the system consisting of the lead ball and the lead plate.

(b) Calculate the increase in availability of the two masses due to the increase in temperature.

18.6 Show that the minimum amount of useful work that must be used to accomplish a process is equal to the increase in availability (in the absence of all reservoirs except the atmosphere).

PART FOUR

Applications
of Thermodynamics
to Some Simple Systems

The principles and techniques discussed in the preceding chapters can be used to study the thermodynamic behavior of simple one-component systems. We are now in a position to apply these results to a number of simple systems.

CHAPTER 19

THE NATURE OF AN IDEAL GAS

At sufficiently low densities, gases are found to have the following properties:

(1) If the temperature is held fixed, the pressure is directly proportional to the density, and the constant of proportionality for a given temperature is the same for all gases.

(2) If the gas is allowed to expand freely in a rigid, impermeable, and well-insulated container, the temperature of the gas remains constant.

A gas which has these two properties is called an ideal gas. Property (1) can be stated mathematically as

$$p = f(T)\frac{N}{V} \qquad (19.1)$$

where $f(T)$, the proportionality constant, is some yet undetermined function of T. Property (2) can be stated mathematically as

$$\left(\frac{\partial T}{\partial V}\right)_{E,N} = 0 \qquad (19.2)$$

151

To verify property (1), we can put a known mass of the gas in an impermeable but diathermal container that is in contact with a heat reservoir, as shown in Figure 19.1. If condition (1) is satisfied, the product pV will

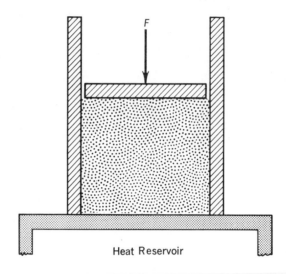

Heat Reservoir

FIGURE 19.1

remain constant as the gas is compressed, and pV/N will be the same for all such gases in contact with the same heat reservoir. To verify property (2), we can initially confine the gas to a limited region within a rigid, impermeable, and adiabatic container, as shown in Figure 19.2. If condition (2) is satisfied, then the gas will undergo no change in temperature when the partition is removed.

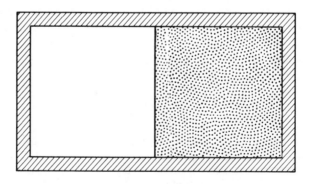

FIGURE 19.2

Although not essential to our analysis, it is sometimes helpful to consider an ideal gas from a microscopic point of view. From such a view, an ideal gas consists of a collection of molecules that are moving around rapidly and randomly, and which are separated by such large distances that the effect of the finite size of the molecules and also the effect of intermolecular forces can be neglected. It can be shown that the temperature of an ideal gas is directly proportional to the average translational kinetic energy of a molecule, and, in addition, the pressure of an ideal gas is directly proportional to the density of molecules and to the average magnitude of the momentum of a molecule. Furthermore, the average magnitude of the momentum of a molecule is proportional to the square root of the product of the mass of a molecule and its average translational kinetic energy. Thus if the temperature is held constant, the average kinetic energy and, therefore, the average magnitude of the momentum of a molecule will also be held constant; consequently, the pressure will be proportional to the density. Furthermore, if the gas is allowed to expand freely with no loss in total energy, the average translational kinetic energy will remain constant; therefore, the temperature will remain constant.

THE IDEAL GAS LAW

In the present section we wish to determine the exact form of the function $f(T)$ in Equation (19.1). We start with Equation (19.2), which by the methods of Chapter 12 can be written in the form

$$\left(\frac{\partial T}{\partial V}\right)_{E,N} = \frac{p - (\alpha/\beta)T}{Nc_V} = 0 \tag{19.3}$$

From Equation (19.3), we conclude

$$p = \frac{\alpha}{\beta} T \tag{19.4}$$

But from Equation (19.1) or property (1) of an ideal gas,

$$p = \frac{N}{V} f(T) \tag{19.5}$$

and

$$\left(\frac{\alpha}{\beta}\right) \equiv \frac{\frac{1}{V}\left(\frac{\partial V}{\partial T}\right)_{p,N}}{-\frac{1}{V}\left(\frac{\partial V}{\partial p}\right)_{T,N}} \equiv \left(\frac{\partial p}{\partial T}\right)_{V,N} = \frac{N}{V} f'(T) \tag{19.6}$$

Substituting Equations (19.5) and (19.6) in Equation (19.4), we obtain

$$\frac{f'(T)}{f(T)} = \frac{1}{T} \tag{19.7}$$

Integrating, we obtain

$$\ln f = \ln T + \text{const} \equiv \ln T + \ln R \equiv \ln RT \tag{19.8}$$

where R is a constant. From Equation (19.8), we obtain

$$f(T) = RT \tag{19.9}$$

Combining Equations (19.9) and (19.1), we obtain

$$pV = NRT \tag{19.10}$$

Equation (19.10) is called the ideal gas law. To determine R, we experi-mentally measure pV for a given number of moles N of some gas at a given temperature T. The only unknown is R, which we find to be

$$R = 8.3143 \text{ J}(°K)^{-1}(\text{mole})^{-1} \tag{19.11}$$

The quantity R is called the gas constant. If the amount of matter in the gas had been expressed in molecules, rather than in moles, the value of the proportionality constant would have been $k = R/A = 1.38054 \times 10^{-23}$ J$(°K)^{-1}(\text{molecule})^{-1}$, where A is Avogadro's number. The constant k is called Boltzmann's constant.

Starting from Equation (19.10), we can reverse the argument to prove Equation (19.2). Thus if Equations (19.1) and (19.2) are true, then Equation (19.10) is true; and conversely, if Equation (19.10) is true, Equations (19.1) and (19.2) are true. It follows that an ideal gas can be defined simply as a gas that satisfies the ideal gas law, Equation (19.10).

From Equation (19.10) it follows that we can verify the ideality of a gas simply by measuring the dependence of its pressure and volume on tem-perature. However, the method indicated in the preceding section does not involve the use of a calibrated thermometer. To prove property (1), it was only necessary to be able to measure pressure, volume, and mass. To prove property (2), we needed only to be able to detect a change in temperature. Thus, the ideal gas provides us with a system that, in principle, can be used to measure absolute temperatures, obviating the necessity of resorting experimentally to the use of Carnot cycles.

THE COEFFICIENTS OF COMPRESSION AND EXPANSION OF AN IDEAL GAS

From the ideal gas law Equation (19.10), we obtain

$$\alpha \equiv \frac{1}{V}\left(\frac{\partial V}{\partial T}\right)_{p,N} = \frac{1}{T} \tag{19.12}$$

$$\beta \equiv -\frac{1}{V}\left(\frac{\partial V}{\partial p}\right)_{T,N} = \frac{1}{p} \tag{19.13}$$

According to the third law of thermodynamics, the coefficient of thermal expansion α should vanish at $T = 0$. It follows that no substance behaves like an ideal gas when the temperature is sufficiently low.

THE INTERNAL ENERGY OF AN IDEAL GAS

From Equation (19.2) it follows that the temperature of an ideal gas is a function of the internal energy and mole number only; therefore, the internal energy is a function of the temperature and mole number only, that is,

$$E = E(T,N) \tag{19.14}$$

Since $E(T,N)$ is a homogeneous function of degree one with respect to the variable N, we can show, using the results of Appendix 6, that

$$E(T,N) = NE(T,1) = N\epsilon(T) \tag{19.15}$$

where $\epsilon(T)$ is the internal energy per mole. The internal energy per mole of an ideal gas is, therefore, a function of temperature only. The exact dependence of the internal energy on the temperature will depend on the gas.

THE SPECIFIC HEAT OF AN IDEAL GAS

From Equations (19.14) and (19.15), we obtain for an ideal gas

$$c_V \equiv \frac{T}{N}\left(\frac{\partial S}{\partial T}\right)_{V,N} \equiv \frac{1}{N}\left(\frac{\partial E}{\partial T}\right)_{V,N} = \frac{d\epsilon}{dT} = c_V(T) \tag{19.16}$$

and from Equations (19.12) and (19.13),

$$c_p \equiv c_V + \frac{\alpha^2 VT}{N\beta} = c_V + \frac{pV}{NT} = c_V + R = c_p(T) \tag{19.17}$$

Thus the specific heats of an ideal gas are functions of temperature only.

The specific heat of a monatomic gas over a wide range of temperatures is given by

$$c_p - R = c_V = \tfrac{3}{2}R \tag{19.18}$$

The specific heat of many polyatomic gases over a wide range of temperatures can be represented by the first few terms in a power series in the temperature, that is,

$$c_p = A + BT + CT^2 \tag{19.19}$$

Coefficients A, B, and C for various gases are given in Table 4.

THE FUNDAMENTAL EQUATION FOR AN IDEAL GAS

Let us assume that we have a certain gas about which we know the following facts: (1) the gas obeys the ideal gas law $pV = NRT$ and (2) the specific heat c_V is known as a function of the temperature.

As long as the gas is not subject to any chemical reactions or change in chemical composition, we can assign respective, arbitrary values to the internal energy and to the entropy in some state. Let us assign the values E_0 and S_0 to the energy and entropy, respectively, in the state T_0, V_0, N_0, which we shall refer to as the "reference state."

If we integrate the equation,

$$dS = \frac{1}{T}dE + \frac{p}{T}dV - \frac{\mu}{T}dN \tag{19.20}$$

between the state T_0, V_0, N_0, and the state T, V, N_0, along a path of constant N, noting that

$$dE = d(N_0\epsilon) = N_0\,d\epsilon = N_0 c_V(T)dT \tag{19.21}$$

$$\frac{p}{T} = \frac{N_0 R}{V} \tag{19.22}$$

$$dN = 0 \tag{19.23}$$

we obtain

$$\int_{S_0}^{S} dS = N_0 \int_{T_0}^{T} \frac{c_V(T)}{T} dT + N_0 R \int_{V_0}^{V} \frac{dV}{V} \qquad (19.24)$$

and therefore,

$$S(T,V,N_0) = S_0 + N_0 \int_{T_0}^{T} \frac{c_V(T)}{T} dT + N_0 R \ln \left(\frac{V}{V_0} \right) \qquad (19.25)$$

Since $S(T,V,N)$ is homogeneous of degree one with respect to the variables V and N, we obtain from the results of Appendix 6

$$S(T,V,N) = \frac{N}{N_0} S_0 + N \int_{T_0}^{T} \frac{c_V(T)}{T} dT + NR \ln \left(\frac{V}{V_0} \frac{N_0}{N} \right) \qquad (19.26)$$

Similarly, if we integrate Equation (19.21), we obtain

$$E(T,N) = \frac{N}{N_0} E_0 + N \int_{T_0}^{T} c_V(T) dT \qquad (19.27)$$

From Equation (19.27) it is possible, in principle, to solve for $T(E,N)$, which can then be substituted in Equation (19.26) to obtain $S(E,V,N)$. Equations (19.26) and (19.27), therefore, contain a complete thermodynamic description of the system. This fact can also be seen by combining Equations (19.26) and (19.27) and obtaining the Helmholtz free energy $F \equiv E - TS$, as a function of its characteristic variables T, V, N. Thus,

$$F(T,V,N) = \frac{N}{N_0} E_0 + N \int_{T_0}^{T} c_V(T) dT$$
$$- \frac{N}{N_0} TS_0 - NT \int_{T_0}^{T} \frac{c_V(T)}{T} dT - NRT \ln \left(\frac{V}{V_0} \frac{N_0}{N} \right) \qquad (19.28)$$

If c_V is constant, and if we choose $E_0 = N_0 c_V T_0$, then Equations (19.26) and (19.27) give

$$S = \frac{N}{N_0} S_0 + NR \ln \left[\left(\frac{E}{E_0} \right)^{c_V/R} \left(\frac{V}{V_0} \right) \left(\frac{N_0}{N} \right)^{(c_V+R)/R} \right] \qquad (19.29)$$

In particular, for a monatomic gas $c_V = 3R/2$, and

$$S = \frac{N}{N_0} S_0 + NR \ln \left[\left(\frac{E}{E_0} \right)^{3/2} \left(\frac{V}{V_0} \right) \left(\frac{N_0}{N} \right)^{5/2} \right]$$
$$\equiv NR \ln \left[E^{3/2} V N^{-5/2} \right] + NC \qquad (19.30)$$

where C is a constant that statistical mechanical arguments and experiments show to be $(5R/2) + (3R/2) \ln (4m\pi/3h^2)$, where m is the mass of an atom and h is Planck's constant.

EXAMPLE

Problem. Show that if an ideal gas, for which the specific heats are constant, undergoes an adiabatic quasistatic process, then the quantity pV^{c_p/c_V} remains constant.

Solution. If an ideal gas undergoes a quasistatic adiabatic change in volume, then

$$dp = \left(\frac{\partial p}{\partial V}\right)_{S,N} dV = -\left(\frac{c_p}{c_V \beta V}\right) dV$$

For an ideal gas $\beta = 1/p$, and therefore,

$$\frac{dp}{p} + \left(\frac{c_p}{c_V}\right)\left(\frac{dV}{V}\right) = 0$$

If c_p and c_V are constant, we can integrate and obtain

$$pV^{c_p/c_V} = \text{const}$$

We could have obtained the same result by using Equation (19.29) to obtain $S = S(p,V,N)$ and then setting $S = \text{const}$.

PROBLEMS

19.1   Calculate the entropy change that occurs when an ideal gas at 25°C undergoes a free expansion within a rigid, impermeable, and adiabatic container to three times its original volume.

19.2   An ideal monatomic gas of N moles is heated quasistatically from T_1 to T_2 along a path governed by the equation $V = a \exp (bT)$, in which a and b are constants. Derive expressions for the work done on the gas and the heat transferred to the gas during the process.

19.3   Prove that if an ideal gas undergoes a quasistatic change in volume $dQ = (c_p p/R)dV + (c_V V/R)dp$. Show directly that dQ is not an exact differential.

19.4   One mole of an ideal gas (not necessarily monatomic) is subjected to the following sequence of steps: (1) it is heated at constant volume from 300°K to 400°K, (2) it is expanded freely into a vacuum to double its volume, and (3) it is cooled reversibly at constant pressure to 300°K. Calculate ΔE, ΔH, Q, and W for the overall process (1) + (2) + (3).

19.5   According to the Gibbs theorem, the entropy of a mixture of two different ideal gases filling the volume V is equal to the sum of the entropies of the two gases separately, evaluated on the assumption that each of them occupies the whole volume V. How must this theorem be modified if the gases are identical?

19.6   A rigid, impermeable, and adiabatic container is divided into two equal compartments by a rigid, impermeable, and adiabatic partition. Initially one compartment contains 0.5 mole of helium ($c_V = 3R/2$) at 100°C, and the other contains 1.0 mole of oxygen (for which you may assume $c_V = 5R/2$) at 0°C. If the partition is removed and the gases behave like ideal gases, what will the final temperature be?

19.7   One of the most accurate experimental methods for the determination of the ratio $\gamma = c_p/c_V$ is the measurement of the velocity of sound in the gas investigated. The velocity of propagation of longitudinal waves in an elastic medium is equal to $(\epsilon/\rho)^{1/2}$, where ϵ is the modulus of elasticity and ρ the density. The rapidity of compression and rarefaction of an elastic medium in which sound is propagating is so large that no heat exchange occurs in the time of one oscillation.
(a) Express the velocity of sound as a function of γ, ρ, and β, where β is the isothermal compressibility.
(b) Determine the velocity of sound at 300°K in hydrogen (2.0159 g/mole) and in nitrogen (28.0134 g/mole). Assume that both gases behave as ideal gases. Use the specific heats given in Table 4.

CHAPTER 20

The van der Waals Equation

In the present chapter we shall consider what happens to a gas when the range wherein the ideal gas law begins to break down is reached.

More than 150 different equations, either empirical or derived on the basis of microscopic theory, have been used to describe the relationships among p, V, and T in the region in which the ideal gas law breaks down. We shall investigate one of the simpler of these equations.

VAN DER WAALS' EQUATION

In the discussion of the microscopic theory of an ideal gas, it was assumed that we could ignore the volume occupied by the molecules and the effect of intermolecular forces. As the density of a gas increases, however, both factors become more and more significant. One of the simplest and most frequently used expressions that attempts to include these effects is the van der Waals equation.

$$p = \frac{NRT}{V - bN} - a\left(\frac{N}{V}\right)^2 \tag{20.1}$$

where a and b are positive constants that are different for each gas. Values of a and b for a number of gases are given in Table 8.

The term bN is introduced to account for the fact that a particular molecule is not free to roam throughout the volume V, but, due to the finite volume occupied by the other molecules, is restricted to some volume smaller than V. The effective volume occupied by the other molecules will be proportional to N; therefore, we subtract a quantity bN from the original volume.

The second term $- a(N/V)^2$ is introduced to account for the effect of intermolecular forces on the pressure. As the molecules get closer and closer together, there is, in addition to the kinetic pressure due to the motion of the molecules tending to drive the molecules apart, a static contribution due to the attractive forces between molecules tending to draw them together. The effect of the intermolecular forces is negligible at low densities but becomes more and more important as the density increases. Since the ordinary kinetic pressure NRT/V is linear in the density, the simplest way to

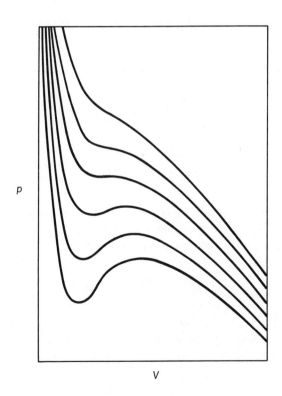

FIGURE 20.1

include such an effect is to introduce a pressure term that is quadratic in the density. At low densities, this pressure term is small compared to the linear term NRT/V, but at high densities it becomes the dominant term.

A few isotherms for van der Waals' equation are shown in Figure 20.1.

THE INTERNAL ENERGY AND SPECIFIC HEAT

Using the techniques of Chapter 12, we find

$$\left(\frac{\partial E}{\partial V}\right)_{T,N} = T\left(\frac{\partial S}{\partial V}\right)_{T,N} - p\left(\frac{\partial V}{\partial V}\right)_{T,N}$$

$$= T\left(\frac{\partial p}{\partial T}\right)_{V,N} - p \tag{20.2}$$

From the van der Waals equation,

$$\left(\frac{\partial p}{\partial T}\right)_{V,N} = \frac{NR}{V - bN} = \frac{1}{T}\left[p + a\left(\frac{N}{V}\right)^2\right] \tag{20.3}$$

Substituting Equation (20.3) in Equation (20.2), we obtain

$$\left(\frac{\partial E}{\partial V}\right)_{T,N} = a\left(\frac{N}{V}\right)^2 \tag{20.4}$$

Integrating, we get

$$E = -a\frac{N^2}{V} + f(T,N) \tag{20.5}$$

where $f(T,N)$ is an unknown function of T and N. If we hold T and N fixed and increase V, the density will decrease, and $E(T,N) \to f(T,N)$. Since we expect the gas to approach the behavior of an ideal gas in this limit, we conclude that

$$f(T,N) = E_I(T,N) = N\epsilon_I(T) \tag{20.6}$$

where $E_I(T,N)$ and $\epsilon_I(T)$ are, respectively, the internal energy and the internal energy per mole of the system in the range in which the system behaves like an ideal gas. The internal energy of a van der Waals gas is thus

$$E = -a\frac{N^2}{V} + N\epsilon_I(T) \tag{20.7}$$

From Equation (20.7), we obtain for the specific heat

$$c_V = \frac{1}{N}\left(\frac{\partial E}{\partial T}\right)_{V,N} = \frac{d\epsilon_I(T)}{dT} \tag{20.8}$$

The specific heat at constant volume is a function of temperature only and is the same as the specific heat in the ideal gas range.

THE JOULE EFFECT

If a real gas is allowed to expand freely from a volume V_1 to a volume V_2 within a rigid, adiabatic container, the temperature will usually change. Since the energy and number of moles of the gas remain constant during the process, it follows that if the initial state of the gas is (E_1,V_1,N_1), the final state will be (E_1,V_2,N_1). Thus if we know $T(E,V,N)$, we can calculate the final temperature. Alternatively, if we know the initial temperature and the derivatives of $T(E,V,N)$, we can calculate the final temperature by integrating the equation,

$$dT = \left(\frac{\partial T}{\partial E}\right)_{V,N} dE + \left(\frac{\partial T}{\partial V}\right)_{E,N} dV + \left(\frac{\partial T}{\partial N}\right)_{E,V} dN \tag{20.9}$$

along some path from the initial to the final state. If we choose a path of constant E and constant N, then

$$dT = \left(\frac{\partial T}{\partial V}\right)_{E,N} dV \tag{20.10}$$

If we define a quantity

$$\eta \equiv N\left(\frac{\partial T}{\partial V}\right)_{E,N} \tag{20.11}$$

which we shall call the Joule coefficient, then Equation (20.10) can be written

$$dT = \frac{\eta}{N} dV \tag{20.12}$$

Using the techniques of Chapter 12, we can write the Joule coefficient as

$$\eta = \frac{p - (\alpha/\beta)T}{c_V} \tag{20.13}$$

For a van der Waals gas

$$\frac{\alpha}{\beta} = \left(\frac{\partial p}{\partial T}\right)_{V,N} = \frac{NR}{V - Nb} = \frac{p + a(N/V)^2}{T} \tag{20.14}$$

and therefore,

$$\eta = -\frac{aN^2}{c_V V^2} \tag{20.15}$$

For an ideal gas, $a = 0$ and therefore, $\eta = 0$. It follows that an ideal gas will undergo no temperature change in a free expansion. We have already noted this result in the preceding chapter. For a real gas, $a > 0$ and there-fore, $\eta < 0$. It follows that a real gas will undergo a decrease in temperature in a free expansion. Microscopically, the cooling is to be expected, since the molecules must overcome attractive forces in a free expansion, conse-quently losing kinetic energy. This effect is known as the Joule effect.

THE JOULE–KELVIN EFFECT

The Joule effect can be used to measure the deviation of a gas from ideal behavior. A related effect called the Joule–Kelvin, or Joule–Thomson, effect can also be used. In the Joule–Kelvin experiment, a gas that is initially enclosed in an adiabatic chamber at temperature T_1, pressure p_1, and volume V_1 is slowly forced by the pressure p_1, which is held constant, through a porous partition into a second adiabatic chamber that is main-tained at a lower pressure p_2. In the final state, the gas is contained in the second chamber and has a temperature T_2, pressure p_2, and volume V_2. The situation is illustrated in Figure 20.2. Since the outer walls and pistons are

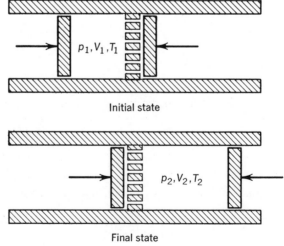

Initial state

Final state

FIGURE 20.2

insulated, the net heat-flow to the system is zero, and therefore, the change in internal energy is equal to the work done on the system, that is,

$$E_2 - E_1 = W \tag{20.16}$$

The work done by the left-hand piston is $+p_1V_1$, and the work done by the right-hand piston is $-p_2V_2$, therefore,

$$W = p_1V_1 - p_2V_2 \tag{20.17}$$

Combining Equations (20.16) and (20.17), we get

$$E_1 + p_1V_1 = E_2 + p_2V_2 \tag{20.18}$$

But $E + pV$ is simply the enthalpy; therefore,

$$H_1 = H_2 \tag{20.19}$$

It follows that if the initial state of the gas is (H_1,p_1,N_1), the final state will be (H_1,p_2,N_1). Thus if we know $T(H,p,N)$, we can calculate the final temperature. Alternatively, if we know the initial temperature and the derivatives of $T(H,p,N)$, we can calculate the final temperature by integrating the equation,

$$dT = \left(\frac{\partial T}{\partial H}\right)_{p,N} dH + \left(\frac{\partial T}{\partial p}\right)_{H,N} dp + \left(\frac{\partial T}{\partial N}\right)_{H,p} dN \tag{20.20}$$

along some path joining the initial and final states. If we choose a path of constant H and constant N, then

$$dT = \left(\frac{\partial T}{\partial p}\right)_{H,N} dp \tag{20.21}$$

If we define a quantity μ, not to be confused with the chemical potential, as

$$\mu \equiv \left(\frac{\partial T}{\partial p}\right)_{H,N} \tag{20.22}$$

which we shall call the Joule–Kelvin coefficient, then Equation (20.21) can be written

$$dT = \mu dp \tag{20.23}$$

Using the techniques of Chapter 12, we can write the Joule–Kelvin coefficient as

$$\mu = \frac{\alpha VT - V}{Nc_p} \tag{20.24}$$

Since $p_2 < p_1$, it follows that if the path joining the initial and final states lies in a region for which $\alpha T > 1$, then the temperature will decrease; but if the path joining the initial and final states lies in a region for which $\alpha T < 1$, then the temperature will increase. If the path lies partially in a region for which $\alpha T < 1$ and partially in a region for which $\alpha T > 1$, then we cannot say whether the temperature will increase or decrease without studying the circumstances in greater detail. The locus of points on a p-T diagram for which $\alpha T = 1$ is called the inversion curve. The inversion curve for nitrogen is shown in Table 12.

For a van der Waals gas

$$(\alpha V)^{-1} = \left(\frac{\partial T}{\partial V}\right)_{p,N} = \frac{RTV^3 - 2aN(V - bN)^2}{RV^3(V - bN)} \qquad (20.25)$$

and therefore,

$$\mu = \frac{-bRTV^3 + 2aV(V - bN)^2}{c_p[RTV^3 - 2aN(V - bN)^2]} \qquad (20.26)$$

If the departure from ideal gas behavior is small, then $Nb \ll V$ and $a(N/V)^2 \ll NRT/(V - Nb) \approx NRT/V$, and therefore,

$$\mu \approx \frac{2a - bRT}{RTc_p} \qquad (20.27)$$

For a van der Waals gas, the inversion curve is simply the constant temperature curve $T = 2a/bR \equiv T_i$. The temperature $T_i \equiv 2a/bR$ is called the inversion temperature. For $T < T_i$, $\mu > 0$, and therefore, the gas undergoes a decrease in temperature in this region. For $T > T_i$, $\mu < 0$, and the gas undergoes an increase in temperature.

The Joule–Kelvin effect is utilized in the commercial liquefaction of gases. The Joule–Kelvin coefficient has the largest positive values at low temperatures and low pressures, and hence the greatest cooling effect will be obtained in these regions.

PHASE CHANGE

We have seen in the preceding section that the van der Waals equation accounts qualitatively for a nonzero temperature change in the Joule and Joule–Kelvin effects. The most significant feature of the van der Waals equation, however, is that it predicts a phase transformation from the gaseous to the liquid state. In the present section we shall investigate this aspect of the van der Waals equation.

Let us consider a typical isotherm of a van der Waals gas, as shown for example in Figure 20.3. We note first that in the region B-C

$$\beta \equiv -\frac{1}{V}\left(\frac{\partial V}{\partial p}\right)_{T,N} < 0 \qquad (20.28)$$

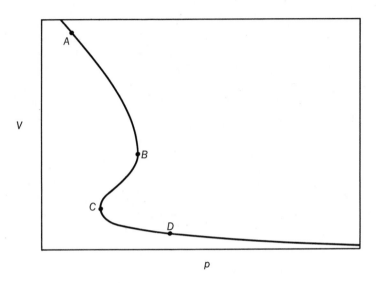

FIGURE 20.3

which is a violation of one of our stability criteria. The van der Waals equation, as it stands, cannot therefore correctly represent the transition of the system from the region A to the region D. We shall see, however, that a closer look at the equation will nevertheless enable us to predict how the gas will make the transition.

We note first that for a process in which T and N are held fixed,

$$dG = \left(\frac{\partial G}{\partial p}\right)_{T,N} dp = V\,dp \qquad (20.29)$$

It follows that if we know the equation $V = V(p)$ of an isotherm on a p-V diagram, we can obtain the corresponding isotherm $G = G(p)$ on a G-p diagram within a constant simply by integrating Equation (20.29). Graphically, we can obtain the curve $G = G(p)$ by noting from Equation (20.29) that the slope of the curve $G = G(p)$ is equal to $V(p)$.

In Figure 20.4 we have schematically plotted the isotherm $G(p)$, corresponding to the isotherm $V(p)$ shown in Figure 20.3. Since the volume is progressively decreasing along the path $ABCD$ in Figure 20.3, the slope of the curve in Figure 20.4 must, as shown, also be progressively decreasing along the path $ABCD$.

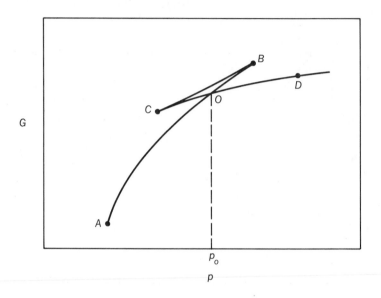

FIGURE 20.4

The Gibbs free energy of a system that is maintained at a constant T and p will, in equilibrium, assume the minimum value possible consistent with the constraints. The states represented by points along the path $OBCO$ are, therefore, not equilibrium states, since along this path lower values of the Gibbs free energy are possible. It follows that if we take the system from A to D, while consistently maintaining it in equilibrium, it must move along the path AOD. Along this path there is a discontinuity in the derivative of the Gibbs free energy, that is, the volume, and hence, by the Clapeyron equation, a discontinuity in the entropy. We thus have a first-order phase transition. Physically, this corresponds to the transition from the gaseous to the liquid state.

On a p-V diagram the path AOD corresponds to the solid line shown in Figure 20.5. To determine the pressure p_0 at which the transition takes place, we note first that

$$0 = \int_X^Z dG = \int_X^Z V\,dp$$

$$= \int_X^C V\,dp + \int_C^Y V\,dp + \int_Y^B V\,dp + \int_B^Z V\,dp \qquad (20.30)$$

and therefore,

$$\int_C^Y V dp - \int_C^X V dp = \int_Z^B V dp - \int_Y^B V dp \qquad (20.31)$$

The quantity on the left-hand side of Equation (20.31) is equal to the vertically shaded area in Figure 20.5, while the quantity on the right-hand side is equal to the horizontally shaded area. The value of p_0 at which the transition takes place is, consequently, the value at which these two areas become equal.

THE LEVER RULE

When a system obeying van der Waals' equation is in the transition region between phase 1 and phase 2 at a temperature T, as represented, for example, by point (p_0, V_3) in Figure 20.6, a certain fraction x_1 of the system

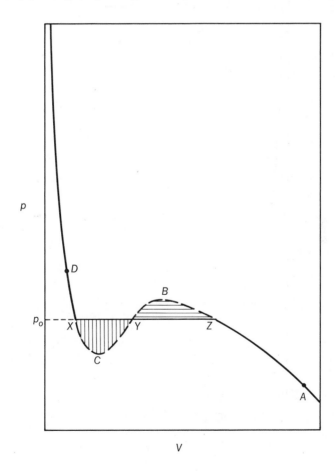

FIGURE 20.5

will be in phase 1, and a certain fraction x_2 will be in phase 2. The values of x_1 and x_2 for a given value of V_3 can be found by noting that

$$x_1 + x_2 = 1 \tag{20.32}$$

$$x_1 V_1 + x_2 V_2 = V_3 \tag{20.33}$$

Knowing V_1, V_2, and V_3, we can solve for x_1 and x_2.

THE LATENT HEAT

In Figure 20.7 we have plotted two neighboring isotherms at temperatures T and $T + dT$ for a system obeying van der Waals' equation. We shall now

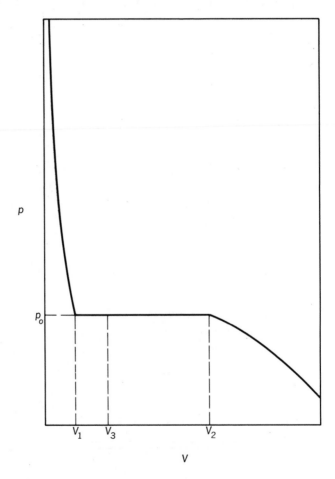

FIGURE 20.6

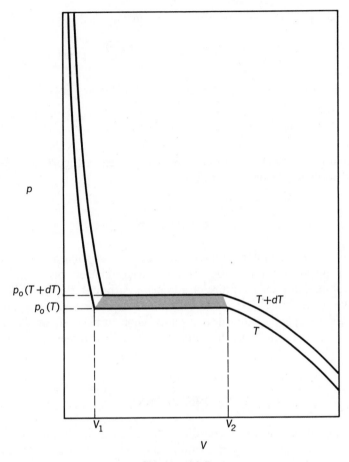

FIGURE 20.7

show that the shaded area in Figure 20.7 is approximately equal to the product of the latent heat and the quantity dT/T.

The latent heat L_{12} for the transition from phase 1 to phase 2 is given by

$$L_{12} = T(S_2 - S_1) = T \int_{V_1}^{V_2} \left(\frac{\partial S}{\partial V}\right)_{T,N} dV \qquad (20.34)$$

But from Maxwell's relations

$$\left(\frac{\partial S}{\partial V}\right)_{T,N} = \left(\frac{\partial p}{\partial T}\right)_{V,N} \qquad (20.35)$$

and therefore,

$$L_{12} = T \int_{V_1}^{V_2} \left(\frac{\partial p}{\partial T}\right)_{V,N} dV \qquad (20.36)$$

But between V_1 and V_2, $(\partial p/\partial T)_{V,N}$ is a constant and is given by

$$\left(\frac{\partial p}{\partial T}\right)_{V,N} \approx \frac{p_0(T + dT) - p_0(T)}{dT} = \text{const} \qquad (20.37)$$

Substituting Equation (20.37) in Equation (20.36), we obtain

$$L_{12} = \left(\frac{T}{dT}\right)\{[p_0(T + dT) - p_0(T)][V_2 - V_1]\} \qquad (20.38)$$

The quantity in braces is simply the shaded area in Figure 20.7. We have proved what we set out to prove.

CONCLUSION

In the present chapter we have seen how it is possible to extract a great deal of physical information from a given relation between the pressure, volume, and temperature of a system. Although the analysis was, for the sake of simplicity, carried out in terms of van der Waals' equation, the techniques employed are equally valid when applied to any one of the numerous other equations that link the pressure, volume, and temperature of a system.

PROBLEMS

20.1 Curves of p as a function of V at constant T for a van der Waals gas exhibit either: (1) a maximum and a minimum, (2) an inflection point, that is, a point at which the slope is zero but which is neither a maximum nor a minimum, or (3) neither a maximum nor minimum. The value of T for which the p versus V curve has simply an inflection point is called the critical temperature and is designated T_c. The values of the pressure p and molar volume v at which the inflection point occurs are called the critical pressure and critical molar volume and are designated p_c and v_c, respectively.
(a) Express a and b in terms of T_c and v_c.
(b) Express p_c in terms of T_c and v_c.
(c) Write the van der Waals equation in terms of the dimensionless variables $T' = T/T_c$, $v' = v/v_c$, and $p' = p/p_c$.
20.2 Obtain an expression for the entropy of a van der Waals gas as a function of T, V, and N. Assume that c_V is known.
20.3 Show that when a van der Waals gas for which c_V is constant undergoes a quasistatic, adiabatic change, $T(V - Nb)^{R/c_V}$ will be constant.

20.4   A van der Waals gas of volume V_0 is compressed quasistatically and isothermally to half its volume. Calculate ΔE, ΔH, and ΔS. Compare these values with those obtained for an ideal gas.

20.5   Prove that for a van der Waals gas

$$c_P - c_V = R\left[1 - \left(\frac{2aN}{RTV}\right)\left(\frac{V - Nb}{V}\right)^2\right]^{-1}$$

20.6   Show by integrating the equation $dE = TdS - pdV$ that if it were possible for a cyclic isothermal process to be carried out along the path represented by $XYZBYCX$ in Figure 20.5, then the vertically shaded area would be equal to the horizontally shaded area.

20.7   A tube of uniform cross section is equipped with a porous plug and provided with a frictionless piston on one side and a fixed end on the other. The space between the plug and the fixed end is initially evacuated, and the space between the plug and the piston contains a large quantity of an ideal gas at temperature T_1 and pressure p. The gas is allowed to effuse through the plug, and the pressure on the piston is maintained at the constant value p. When the pressure of the gas between the plug and the fixed end reaches p, the experiment is terminated. Assuming that the system is insulated so that the process takes place adiabatically, and neglecting any heat conduction through the plug, show that the final temperature of the gas between the plug and the fixed end is given by $T_2 = c_p T_1 / c_V$.

20.8   (a) Assuming that the Joule–Kelvin coefficient, which we designate μ (not to be confused with the chemical potential), is constant, prove that the enthalpy must be given by a function of $T - \mu p$. (b) Assuming that both μ and c_p are constant, prove that $H = Nc_p T - \mu Nc_p p + CN$, where C is a constant.

INTRODUCTION

Liquids and homogeneous isotropic solids acted upon by hydrostatic pressure constitute simple systems, and their thermodynamic properties can be handled by the techniques previously discussed. In the following sections we shall consider the equation of state and the specific heat for such systems.

THE EQUATION OF STATE

To obtain the equation of state

$$V = V(T,p,N) = NV(T,p,1) \equiv Nv(T,p) \tag{21.1}$$

of a solid or a liquid we start with the relation

$$dv = \left(\frac{\partial v}{\partial T}\right)_p dT + \left(\frac{\partial v}{\partial p}\right)_T dp$$

$$= \alpha v dT - \beta v dp \tag{21.2}$$

where $v(T,p)$ is the volume per mole. If we integrate Equation (21.2) first from T_0,p_0 to T,p_0, while holding p fixed, and second from T,p_0 to T,p while holding T fixed, we obtain

$$v(T,p) = v(T_0,p_0) + \int_{T_0}^{T} \alpha(T,p_0)v(T,p_0)dT - \int_{p_0}^{p} \beta(T,p)v(T,p)dp \quad (21.3)$$

Substituting Equation (21.3) in Equation (21.1), we obtain

$$V(T,p,N) = Nv(T_0,p_0) + N\int_{T_0}^{T} \alpha(T,p_0)v(T,p_0)dT$$

$$- N\int_{p_0}^{p} \beta(T,p)v(T,p)dp \quad (21.4)$$

The volume of a liquid or a solid does not vary greatly with temperature or pressure, and consequently, the second and third terms on the right-hand side of Equation (21.4) are small compared to the first term. We can, therefore, make the approximations

$$v(T,p) \approx v(T,p_0) \approx v(T_0,p_0) \equiv v_0 \quad (21.5)$$

in the integrals in Equation (21.4). Furthermore β does not depend strongly on pressure, and therefore we can assume

$$\beta(T,p) \approx \beta(T,p_0) \quad (21.6)$$

Substituting Equations (21.5) and (21.6) in Equation (21.4), we obtain

$$V(T,p,N) \approx Nv_0\left[1 + \int_{T_0}^{T} \alpha(T,p_0)dT - \beta(T,p_0)(p - p_0)\right] \quad (21.7)$$

Equation (21.7) provides us with an approximate equation of state for a liquid or a solid. In dealing with solids the coefficient of linear expansion,

$$\alpha_L \equiv \frac{1}{L}\left(\frac{\partial L}{\partial T}\right)_p \quad (21.8)$$

is usually tabulated rather than the coefficient of volume expansion α. The relation between the two for an isotropic solid can be readily obtained by noting

$$\alpha \equiv \frac{1}{V}\left(\frac{\partial V}{\partial T}\right)_p = \frac{1}{L^3}\left[\frac{\partial}{\partial T}(L^3)\right]_p = \frac{3}{L}\left(\frac{\partial L}{\partial T}\right)_p \equiv 3\alpha_L \quad (21.9)$$

For most practical purposes we can treat $\beta(T,p_0)$ in Equation (21.7) as a constant. Values of α and β for a number of liquids and solids are given in Tables 6 and 7 respectively.

SPECIFIC HEATS

In dealing with solids and liquids it is easier to measure c_p than c_V. On the other hand, if one is attempting to derive a theoretical expression for the specific heat on the basis of a model, it is easier to work with c_V than with c_p. The connection between the two specific heats is given by the relation

$$c_V = c_p - \frac{\alpha^2 VT}{\beta N} \tag{21.10}$$

which was derived in Chapter 12. It follows that as long as we know the equation of state, we can move freely between the two. If numerical values are substituted for α and β in Equation (21.10), it is found that for most solids and liquids the differences between the respective specific heats is of the order of a few percent so that no great error is committed if one is used in the place of the other.

The specific heats of many liquids, such as water and mercury, are practically independent of temperature. On the other hand, the specific heat of liquids, such as benzene and ether, are strongly dependent on temperature. In Table 5, the specific heats of a number of liquids are listed.

For many solids the temperature dependence of the specific heat can be approximated by the following equation, which was derived theoretically by Debye.

$$c_V = \frac{9R}{y^3} \int_0^y \frac{x^4 dx}{(e^x - 1)(1 - e^{-x})} \tag{21.11}$$

where

$$y \equiv \frac{\theta(v)}{T} \tag{21.12}$$

The quantity $\theta(v)$, called the Debye temperature, is a function of the molar volume and is different for different solids. In Figure 21.1 we have plotted c_V/R as a function of y.

The derivation of Equation (21.11) requires a knowledge of quantum statistical mechanics. From our point of view, it may be considered simply as a useful analytical expression for conveniently describing some of the experimental data. As long as we are not interested in the properties of a solid that involve changes in the composition of the solid, knowledge of the equation of state, together with knowledge of the specific heat c_V at some molar volume v_0, is sufficient to determine the properties of the solid.

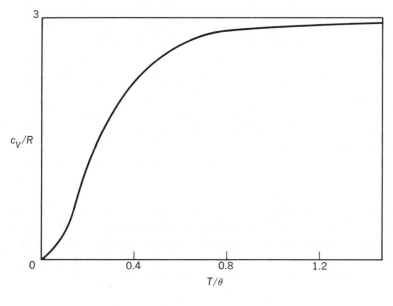

FIGURE 21.1

It follows that if we know the equation of state of the solid, and if we know that its specific heat obeys the Debye law, Equation (21.11), then we do not need to know $y \equiv \theta(v)/T$ as a function of v, but simply its value at one value of v. In Table 9 values of θ are given for a number of solids.

THE GRUNEISEN CONSTANT

On the basis of empirical data Gruneisen has suggested that

$$\theta = \text{constant } v^{-\gamma} \tag{21.13}$$

where γ is a constant, called the Gruneisen constant. The value of γ is given for several metals in Table 10. In principle, if we know the equation of state and the specific heat at some fixed volume, then, except for situations in which the system undergoes a chemical change, we have a complete description of the system. The additional information contained in Equation

(21.13) should, therefore, make some of the information contained in the equation of state unnecessary. Let us consider a Debye solid for which Equation (21.11) is true. For such a solid the entropy per mole $s(v,T)$ can be written as a function of y. If, in addition, Equation (21.13) is true, then

$$\left(\frac{\partial s}{\partial v}\right)_T = \frac{ds}{dy}\left(\frac{\partial y}{\partial v}\right)_T = \frac{ds}{dy}\left[\frac{\gamma T}{v}\left(\frac{\partial y}{\partial T}\right)_v\right]$$

$$= \frac{\gamma T}{v}\left(\frac{\partial s}{\partial T}\right)_v = \frac{\gamma c_V}{v}$$

(21.14)

But

$$\left(\frac{\partial s}{\partial v}\right)_T \equiv \left(\frac{\partial S}{\partial V}\right)_{T,N} \equiv \frac{\alpha}{\beta}$$

(21.15)

and therefore,

$$\frac{\alpha v}{\beta c_V} = \gamma$$

(21.16)

Equation (21.13) thus provides us with a relation that connects α and β. It follows that if we have a Debye solid, and if we know α or β, the Gruneisen constant γ, and the Debye temperature θ at some molar volume v, we can then determine all the physical properties of the solid except those depending on a change in the composition of the solid.

CHAPTER 22

Radiation

As another example of the application of thermodynamics to simple systems, we shall consider the properties of the electromagnetic radiation that is present inside a cavity bounded by opaque walls maintained at a uniform temperature. We shall call this radiation *cavity radiation*.

Experimentally, cavity radiation is found to have the following two properties: (1) the pressure exerted by the radiation on the walls of the container is equal to one-third of the energy per unit volume and (2) the thermodynamic state of the radiation is uniquely determined by the temperature of the container and its volume. In the following sections we shall consider these two properties in greater detail and show that they are sufficient, together with the value of the pressure at some temperature other than zero, to determine a fundamental equation.

RADIATION PRESSURE

According to property (1) above

$$p = \frac{1}{3}\left(\frac{E}{V}\right) \tag{22.1}$$

Thermodynamically, this relation is an experimental fact. It is possible,

179

however, to derive this result from classical electromagnetic theory. It can also be derived, as we shall show, from the particle picture of radiation, in which the radiation is considered to be made up of particles, called photons, all moving with the velocity of light c.

Consider a particle contained in a cubic box whose dimensions are $L \times L \times L$ and whose sides are perpendicular to a set of Cartesian axes. Let $|v_x|$ and $|\pi_x|$ be the magnitudes of the x components of the velocity and momentum, respectively, of one particle. The particle will strike each of the two walls, which are perpendicular to the x axis, $|v_x|/2L$ times a second, and with each collision will impart an impulse $2 |\pi_x|$ to the wall in an outward perpendicular direction. The average force exerted by the particle on each of these walls is, therefore, $|v_x||\pi_x|/L$ in an outward perpendicular direction, and the average pressure is $|v_x||\pi_x|/L^3$. If there are N particles in the box, and if the velocity of a particle is in the same direction as its momentum, then the average pressure exerted by the N particles is

$$p = \frac{N \overline{|\pi_x||v_x|}}{L^3} = \frac{N \overline{\pi_x v_x}}{L^3} = \frac{N \overline{\pi_x v_x}}{V} \tag{22.2}$$

where a bar over a quantity stands for the average value of the quantity. If the distribution of the particles in velocity and momentum is isotropic, and the velocity of a particle is in the same direction as the momentum, then

$$\overline{\pi_x v_x} = \overline{\pi_y v_y} = \overline{\pi_z v_z} = \tfrac{1}{3}(\overline{\pi_x v_x} + \overline{\pi_y v_y} + \overline{\pi_z v_z})$$
$$= \tfrac{1}{3}\overline{(\pi_x v_x + \pi_y v_y + \pi_z v_z)}$$
$$= \tfrac{1}{3}\overline{\boldsymbol{\pi} \cdot \mathbf{v}} = \tfrac{1}{3}\overline{\pi v} \tag{22.3}$$

where π is the magnitude of the momentum and v the magnitude of the velocity. Substituting Equation (22.3) in (22.2), we obtain

$$p = \frac{N \overline{\pi v}}{3V} \tag{22.4}$$

The speed of a photon is c and its energy $\epsilon = \pi c$. It follows that the pressure due to the radiation in a cavity is given by

$$p = \frac{N \overline{\epsilon}}{3V} = \frac{E}{3V} \tag{22.5}$$

which agrees with Equation (22.1).

ENERGY AND ENTROPY

When we experimentally examine the equilibrium properties of the radiation contained in an opaque cavity, we find, as stated at the beginning of this chapter, that the state of the radiation is completely determined if the temperature of the container and its volume are known. In particular, the equilibrium properties do not depend on the shape of a container or the material out of which it is made. Every thermodynamic property of the radiation can therefore be expressed as a function of the temperature and volume. Thus for the energy, we have

$$E = E(T,V) \tag{22.6}$$

Furthermore, since $E(T,V)$ is a homogeneous function of degree one with respect to V, we can write

$$E = VE^*(T) \tag{22.7}$$

where $E^*(T)$ is the energy per unit volume. From Equation (22.6) it follows that the chemical potential $\mu = (\partial E/\partial N)_{T,V} = 0$, and therefore,

$$dE = TdS - pdV \tag{22.8}$$

From Equations (22.7) and (22.8) it follows that

$$E^* = \left(\frac{\partial E}{\partial V}\right)_T = T\left(\frac{\partial S}{\partial V}\right)_T - p \tag{22.9}$$

From Equation (22.5)

$$p = \tfrac{1}{3}E^* \tag{22.10}$$

From Maxwell's relations and Equation (22.10), we obtain

$$\left(\frac{\partial S}{\partial V}\right)_T = \left(\frac{\partial p}{\partial T}\right)_V = \frac{1}{3}\frac{dE^*}{dT} \tag{22.11}$$

Substituting Equations (22.10) and (22.11) in (22.9), we obtain

$$\frac{dE^*}{dT} = \frac{4E^*}{T} \tag{22.12}$$

Solving (22.12), we obtain

$$E^* = bT^4 \tag{22.13}$$

where b is a constant of integration that can be evaluated if we know the value of E^* or, what is equivalent, the value of the pressure at some temperature other than zero. Experimentally, b is found to have the value 7.56 $\times$ 10^{-16} J($^\circ$K)$^{-4}$m^{-3}. Substituting (22.13) in (22.7), we obtain

$$E = bVT^4 \tag{22.14}$$

In a similar fashion, noting that

$$S = S(T,V) = VS^*(T) \tag{22.15}$$

where S^* is the entropy per unit volume, we obtain

$$S^* = \left(\frac{\partial S}{\partial V}\right)_T = \left(\frac{\partial p}{\partial T}\right)_V = \frac{1}{3}\frac{dE^*}{dT} = \frac{4}{3}\frac{E^*}{T} \tag{22.16}$$

and therefore,

$$S = \tfrac{4}{3}bVT^3 \tag{22.17}$$

THE FUNDAMENTAL EQUATION

The Helmholtz free energy is given by

$$F = E - TS \tag{22.18}$$

Substituting the results of the previous section into (22.18), we obtain

$$F = -\tfrac{1}{3}bVT^4 \tag{22.19}$$

As stated in the preceding section, the constant b can be evaluated experimentally by determining a particular value of some property of the radiation that depends explicitly on b, such as the pressure or energy density. It can also be evaluated theoretically by using the techniques of quantum statistical mechanics. In either case, we find

$$b = \frac{8\pi^5 k^4}{15h^3c^3} = 7.56 \times 10^{-16} \text{ J}(°\text{K})^{-4}\text{m}^{-3} \tag{22.20}$$

where k is Boltzmann's constant, h is Planck's constant, and c is the speed of light.

Equation (22.19) is a fundamental equation and, consequently, contains a complete thermodynamic description of cavity radiation.

THE STEFAN–BOLTZMANN LAW

A body at a temperature T will emit radiation. The total radiant energy emitted per unit area of the surface is called the *radiant emittance R*. The value of R will depend on the nature and temperature of the surface. In the present section we wish to determine this dependence.

We note first that if a given material is used to construct a cavity and heated to a temperature T, then when the radiant energy inside the cavity has reached equilibrium, the energy that is absorbed by the surface of the cavity must be equal to the energy being emitted by the surface. Let us designate the energy per unit area incident on the surface of the cavity by the letter I, and define the ratio of the energy absorbed to the incident energy as the absorptivity a. Equating the energy emitted per unit area to the energy absorbed, we obtain

$$R = aI \qquad (22.21)$$

To determine R, we need to know a and I. The absorptivity a is a constant that depends on the nature of the surface; it must be obtained by experiment. The value of I will be shown to be given by

$$I = \tfrac{1}{4}cbT^4 \qquad (22.22)$$

where c is the speed of light and b is given by Equation (22.20). To prove Equation (22.22), let us consider a large box of volume V, which contains a particle moving with a speed v. Suppose a small sphere of radius r is placed in the box. Let us ask ourselves how many times a second on the average the particle will strike the sphere. This problem is equivalent to that of finding the number of times a second a sphere of radius r, moving with speed v, will strike a particle that is at rest, as can be seen by switching to a reference system in which the particle is at rest and the sphere is moving. A sphere of radius r and speed v will sweep out a volume $\pi r^2 v$ in one second. If the particle is somewhere in the volume V, the probability per second that the sphere will hit the particle is just $\pi r^2 v/V$. The number of times a second a particle moving with speed v inside a box will, on the average, hit a sphere of radius r that is at rest inside the box is, therefore, $\pi r^2 v/V$. If there are N particles moving with an average speed $\bar{v}$ inside the box, the sphere will be hit $N\pi r^2\bar{v}/V$ times a second. Finally, since the surface area of the sphere is $4\pi r^2$, the number of particles hitting a unit area of the surface of the sphere is simply J, where

$$J = \frac{N\pi r^2 \bar{v}/V}{4\pi r^2} = \frac{\bar{v}N}{4V} \qquad (22.23)$$

Since any unit surface in the box will be struck on the average the same number of times a second, Equation (22.23) gives us the average rate at which the particles in a box strike a unit surface area. All the photons in the cavity are moving with the same speed c. If we let $\bar{\epsilon}$ be their average energy, the energy incident per unit time on a unit area is

$$I = J\bar{\epsilon} = \left(\frac{cN}{4V}\right)\bar{\epsilon} = \frac{cE}{4V} \qquad (22.24)$$

If we substitute the value for E/V from Equation (22.14) in Equation (22.24) we obtain Equation (22.22), the relationship we set out to prove.

Finally, if we substitute Equation (22.22) in Equation (22.21), we obtain

$$R = a\sigma T^4 \qquad (22.25)$$

where

$$\sigma = \tfrac{1}{4}bc = 5.67 \times 10^{-8} \text{ J (sec)}^{-1}(°\text{K})^{-4}\text{m}^{-2} \qquad (22.26)$$

Equation (22.25) is called the Stefan–Boltzmann Law, and the constant σ is called the Stefan–Boltzmann constant. From Equation (22.25), it is seen that the energy radiated from a surface is directly proportional to the absorptivity a and to the fourth power of the temperature. The better absorber a body is, the better radiator it also is. Therefore, the most radiation is provided by a black body for which $a = 1$. We can construct a perfect black surface by making a small hole in a cavity. Any radiation that falls on the hole will pass into the cavity and be effectively absorbed by the hole. Conversely, if the temperature of the radiation in the cavity is T, the radiation emitted by the hole will correspond to the radiation emitted by a perfectly black surface at a temperature T.

PROBLEMS

22.1   Show that the amount of heat required to maintain a constant temperature inside a cavity whose volume is reversibly changed by an amount ΔV is given by $Q = (4bT^4/3)\Delta V$.

22.2   A quantity of cavity radiation at a temperature of 10,000°K is expanded adiabatically and reversibly. How much must its volume increase in order for its temperature to fall to 1000°K? How much will its pressure decrease in the process?

22.3   The surface temperature of the sun is 5500°K; the radius of the sun is 7×10^8 m; the radius of the earth is 6.37×10^6 m; the average distance between the earth and sun is 1.5×10^{11} m. Assume that: (1) the earth and sun absorb all electromagnetic radiation incident upon them, respectively, and (2) the earth has reached a steady state so that its mean temperature T does not change in time. Calculate the temperature of the earth.

PART FIVE

Thermodynamics
of Multicomponent Systems

In the preceding sections our attention
has been directed toward simple one-
component systems. In the present section we wish to extend our analysis to
multicomponent systems.

CHAPTER 23

Multicomponent Systems

INTRODUCTION

A multicomponent system is a system consisting of a mixture of two or more chemical species. For example, air is a mixture of nitrogen, oxygen, hydrogen, and small quantities of other chemical species, and is therefore a multicomponent system. We shall initially restrict our attention to simple multicomponent systems. The definition of a simple system was given in Chapter 1.

If we are given an n-component system, containing N_1 moles of species 1, N_2 moles of species 2, $\cdots$, and N_n moles of species n, the composition of the system is said to be fixed if the relative concentrations N_i/N_j of the various species remain fixed. If we restrict our attention to multicomponent systems of fixed composition, the techniques of Part 1 are directly applicable. If we wish to consider systems of variable composition, we must extend these techniques. This will be the object of Part 5.

THE BASIC POSTULATES

With only a few minor modifications the basic postulates given in Part 1 can be extended as follows from one-component systems to multicomponent systems.

Postulate I. For every system there exists a quantity E, called the internal energy, that has the following properties:

(a) A unique value of the internal energy is associated with each state of the system.

(b) The internal energy of a closed system has a lower bound but no upper bound.

(c) The difference between the internal energy in one state and the internal energy in another state of a closed system is equal to the work required to bring the system, while adiabatically enclosed, from the one state to the other.

Postulate II. There exists a state of an isolated, simple n-component system, called the equilibrium state, that is uniquely determined by the internal energy E, volume V, and the numbers of moles N_1, $N_2, \cdots, N_n$, respectively, of the components 1, 2, $\cdots$, n.

Postulate III. For every system there exists a state function S, called the entropy, that has the following properties:

(a) For a simple n-component system, S is a single-valued function of E, V, N_1, $\cdots$, and N_n.

(b) The entropy of a composite system is equal to the sum of the entropies of its component systems.

(c) If an internal constraint is removed from an isolated composite system, consisting of m simple n-component systems 1, 2, $\cdots$, m, and the system is allowed to come to an equilibrium state, then the values assumed by the extensive variables, E_1, V_1, N_{11}, $\cdots$, N_{n1}, E_2, V_2, N_{12}, $\cdots$, N_{n2}, $\cdots$, E_m, V_m, N_{1m}, $\cdots$, N_{nm}, where N_{ij} is the number of moles of species i in system j, will be those values, consistent with the remaining internal and external constraints, that maximize the entropy of the composite system.

(d) During a quasistatic, adiabatic change in volume of a simple system, the entropy of the system remains constant.

Postulate IV. The temperature $(\partial E/\partial S)_{V_1, N_1, \cdots, N_n}$ and entropy S of a closed system of fixed volume vanish in the state of minimum energy and are greater than zero in all other states.

A number of questions immediately arise when attention shifts from a one-component system to an n-component system. How, for instance, can we measure the difference in the energies between two states of *different* composition? To answer this question, we note that (1) if we start off with n one-component systems 1, 2, $\cdots$, and n, such that system 1 contains N_1 moles of species 1, system 2 contains N_2 moles of species 2, and so forth, and (2) if we mix the systems in a rigid adiabatic container, we then obtain an n-component system containing N_1 moles of species 1, N_2 moles of species 2, and so forth. Furthermore, since the mixing was carried out in a rigid adiabatic container, the final energy of the n-component system will be equal to the sum of the initial energies of the one-component systems. In this way it is possible to relate states of arbitrary composition to the states of a set of one-component systems. Using the techniques of Part 1, we can measure the energies of one-component systems and the differences in energies between states of the same composition; therefore, we can use the above approach, together with the techniques of Part 1, to relate any state of arbitrary composition to any other state of arbitrary composition.

A similar problem arises when we attempt to measure the difference in entropy between two states of different composition. In this case we can either measure the entropy of each state with reference to the zero entropy state at $T = 0$, and then take the difference, or we can start with n one-component systems in known states and devise some means of mixing them reversibly. In the latter case the total entropy of the universe remains constant, and the entropy of the n-component system in the final state can be related to the entropies of the n one-component systems in their respective initial states.

THE INTENSIVE VARIABLES

Given $S(E,V,N_1,\cdots,N_n)$, we define the temperature T, pressure p, and chemical potential of species i as follows:

$$T \equiv \frac{\partial E(S,V,N_1,\cdots,N_n)}{\partial S} \tag{23.1}$$

$$p \equiv -\frac{\partial E(S,V,N_1,\cdots,N_n)}{\partial V} \tag{23.2}$$

$$\mu_i \equiv \frac{\partial E(S,V,N_1,\cdots,N_n)}{\partial N_i} \tag{23.3}$$

Note that in an n-component system a chemical potential is associated with each species. For a quasistatic change, we have

$$dE = TdS - pdV + \sum_{i=1}^{n} \mu_i dN_i \qquad (23.4)$$

THE GIBBS–DUHEM RELATION

The energy of a simple n-component system is a homogeneous function of degree one in the variables S, V, N_1, $\cdots$, and N_n. From Euler's theorem (Appendix 6), it follows that

$$E = TS - pV + \sum_i \mu_i N_i \qquad (23.5)$$

Taking the differential of Equation (23.5), we obtain

$$dE = TdS + SdT - pdV - Vdp + \sum_i N_i d\mu_i + \sum_i \mu_i dN_i \qquad (23.6)$$

Subtracting Equation (23.4) from (23.6), we obtain

$$SdT - Vdp + \sum_i N_i d\mu_i = 0 \qquad (23.7)$$

Relation (23.7) is known as the Gibbs–Duhem relation. From (23.7) it follows that the intensive variables T, p, μ_1, $\cdots$, and μ_n are not independent. We can express this fact by saying that there exists a relation

$$\phi(T,p,\mu_1,\cdots,\mu_n) = 0 \qquad (23.8)$$

connecting the intensive variables.

CHAPTER 24

Nonreacting
Multicomponent Systems

In the present chapter we shall consider systems in which the composition can vary but in which chemical reactions can be ignored.

THE CONDITIONS OF EQUILIBRIUM

Suppose we have an isolated composite system consisting of two n-component systems X and Y that are separated by a rigid adiabatic wall. The state of system X is completely determined if we know $E_X, V_X, N_{1X}, \cdots,$ and N_{nX}. The state of system Y is completely determined if we know $E_Y, V_Y, N_{1Y}, \cdots,$ and N_{nY}.

The entropy of system X is given by $S_X(E_X, V_X, N_{1X}, \cdots, N_{nX})$, the entropy of system Y is given by $S_Y(E_Y, V_Y, N_{1Y}, \cdots, N_{nY})$, and the entropy of the composite system is given by

$$S_{XY}(E_X, V_X, N_{1X}, \cdots, N_{nX}, E_Y, V_Y, N_{1Y}, \cdots, N_{nY})$$
$$= S_X(E_X, V_X, N_{1X}, \cdots, N_{nX}) + S_Y(E_Y, V_Y, N_{1Y}, \cdots, N_{nY}) \quad (24.1)$$

If one or more of the constraining features of the internal wall are removed, thus enabling the two systems X and Y to interact, the new equilibrium state can be obtained by maximizing S_{XY}, subject to whatever internal constraints are still operative. If the insulation is removed from the dividing wall, energy can be freely exchanged between the two systems. To find the new equilibrium state, we maximize S_{XY}, subject to the conditions that $V_X, V_Y, N_{1X}, N_{1Y}, \cdots, N_{nX}, N_{nY}$, and $E_X + E_Y$ are constant. The details of the calculation are identical with those of Chapter 5, and we obtain as a condition of equilibrium

$$T_X = T_Y \tag{24.2}$$

If the wall is replaced by a diathermal piston, the equilibrium state will be the state for which S_{XY} is a maximum, subject to the conditions that $N_{1X}, N_{1Y}, \cdots, N_{nX}, N_{nY}, V_X + V_Y$, and $E_X + E_Y$ are constant. Maximizing S_{XY}, subject to these constraints, we obtain

$$T_X = T_Y \tag{24.3}$$

$$p_X = p_Y \tag{24.4}$$

If the wall is replaced by a rigid wall that is permeable to species i and impermeable to the remaining species, the equilibrium state will be that state for which S_{XY} is a maximum, subject to the conditions that $V_X, V_Y,$ $N_{1X}, N_{1Y}, \cdots, N_{iX} + N_{iY}, \cdots, N_{nX}, N_{nY}$, and $E_X + E_Y$ are constant. Maximizing S_{XY}, subject to these constraints, we obtain

$$T_X = T_Y \tag{24.5}$$

$$\mu_{iX} = \mu_{iY} \tag{24.6}$$

Although the above equilibrium conditions have been derived for equilibrium between the component systems of an isolated composite system, they are, by the arguments on page 114, equally valid if the two systems that are in contact with one another do not form an isolated system. From Equation (24.6) it therefore follows that if two systems X and Y are able to freely exchange molecules of a certain component i, then, when the systems are in equilibrium, the chemical potential associated with component i in system X will be equal to the chemical potential associated with component i in system Y.

THE APPROACH TO EQUILIBRIUM

From the fact that the entropy of an isolated system can only increase, it is possible not only to predict what the final equilibrium state will be when two systems are brought into thermodynamic contact, but also to say something about how they establish equilibrium.

Consider an isolated composite system consisting of two subsystems X and Y that are separated by a rigid adiabatic wall. Since the system is isolated,

$$E_X + E_Y \equiv \mathbb{E} = \text{const} \tag{24.7}$$

$$V_X + V_Y \equiv \mathbb{V} = \text{const} \tag{24.8}$$

$$N_{iX} + N_{iY} \equiv \mathbb{N}_i = \text{const} \tag{24.9}$$

The entropy of the composite system can therefore be expressed as a function of $N_{1X}, \cdots, N_{nX}, E_X$, and V_X, that is,

$$\begin{aligned} S_{XY}(E_X,V_X,N_{1X},\cdots,N_{nX}) = {} & S_X(E_X,V_X,N_{1X},\cdots,N_{nX}) \\ & + S_Y(\mathbb{E} - E_X, \mathbb{V} - V_X, \mathbb{N}_1 - N_{1X}, \cdots, \mathbb{N}_n - N_{nX}) \end{aligned} \tag{24.10}$$

If one or more of the internal constraints, that is, the insulation, rigidity, and impermeability of the partition separating the subsystems, are momentarily relaxed, the entropy of the composite system will *increase* by an infinitesimal amount or remain constant. Thus

$$\begin{aligned} dS_{XY} = {} & \left(\frac{1}{T_X} - \frac{1}{T_Y}\right)dE_X + \left(\frac{p_X}{T_X} - \frac{p_Y}{T_Y}\right)dV_X \\ & - \sum_i \left(\frac{\mu_{iX}}{T_X} - \frac{\mu_{iY}}{T_Y}\right)dN_{iX} \geq 0 \end{aligned} \tag{24.11}$$

From (24.11), it follows that if $p_X = p_Y$, $\mu_{iX} = \mu_{iY}$ for all i, and $T_X > T_Y$, then $dE_X \leq 0$, that is, energy tends to flow from the high-temperature system to the low-temperature system. Similarly, if $T_X = T_Y$, $\mu_{iX} = \mu_{iY}$ for all i and $p_X > p_Y$, then $dV_X \geq 0$, that is, the volume of the high-pressure system tends to expand at the expense of the low-pressure system. Finally, if $T_X = T_Y$, $p_X = p_Y$, $\mu_{jX} = \mu_{jY}$ for $j \neq i$, and $\mu_{iX} > \mu_{iY}$, then $dN_{iX} \leq 0$, that is, molecules of component i tend to diffuse from the system in which the component i has the higher chemical potential into that in which it has the lower chemical potential.

CHAPTER 25

Chemical Reactions

In the preceding chapter we considered multicomponent systems in which chemical reactions could be ignored. In the present chapter we shall consider situations in which chemical reactions are possible.

CHEMICAL REACTIONS

For the sake of simplicity, let us suppose we wish to study a reaction in which two species M_1 and M_2, which we call the reactants, are capable of interacting and producing two different species M_3 and M_4, which we call the products. The generalization to reactions in which there are a different number of reactants or a different number of products involved is straightforward.

The actual process of beginning with a set of independent reactants and ending up with a set of independent products is usually a complicated multistage process. If, for example, we mix the reactants in a container and allow them to react, the resultant system will be a mixture of species M_1, M_2, M_3, and M_4; therefore, to obtain a set of independent products, it is necessary to devise a scheme for separating M_3 and M_4 from the mixture.

Thus, in an actual reaction, we have to consider the initial mixing process, the chemical interaction, and the final separation process.

To avoid the necessity of discussing the intermediate details of a particular reaction, we shall consider an arrangement which, though of limited practical importance, is theoretically very convenient. Let us suppose that we have four cylinders, each of which contains a different one of the above four species, and each of which is connected, by a membrane permeable only to the species that it contains, to a rigid box containing a mixture of all four species, as shown in Figure 25.1. We shall label the systems in the cylinders as 1, 2, 3, and 4, respectively, and the system in the box as X; we shall assume that the systems are all simple systems in known phases (liquid, solid, gas) that we label ϕ_1, ϕ_2, ϕ_3, ϕ_4, and ϕ_X, respectively. In equilibrium,

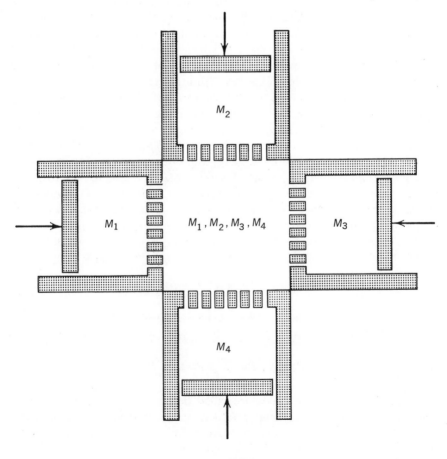

FIGURE 25.1

the systems 1, 2, 3, and 4 have a common temperature T but may have differing pressures p_1, p_2, p_3, and p_4. Since the volume of system X is fixed, and since its temperature is T and the chemical potentials of the species M_1, M_2, M_3, and M_4 in the mixture are equal to the respective chemical potentials of M_1, M_2, M_3, and M_4 in the systems 1, 2, 3, and 4, with which system X is in equilibrium, the state of system X will be uniquely fixed by the parameters T, p_1, p_2, p_3, and p_4.

If the whole system is maintained at a constant temperature T by keeping it in contact with a heat bath at a temperature T, and if the volumes of systems 1, 2, 3, and 4 are varied in such a way that the pressures p_1, p_2, p_3, and p_4 remain fixed, it will be found that the change in the number of moles of species M_1, M_2, M_3, and M_4 in systems 1, 2, 3, and 4, respectively, will bear a fixed ratio to one another. For example, if ν_1 moles of species M_1 disappear from system 1, a fixed number of moles ν_2 will disappear from system 2, a fixed number of moles ν_3 will appear in system 3, and a fixed number of moles ν_4 will appear in system 4. In standard terminology we say that a chemical reaction has taken place in which ν_1 moles of species M_1 in the state (T,p_1,ϕ_1) have combined with ν_2 moles of species M_2 in the state (T,p_2,ϕ_2), to form ν_3 moles of species M_3 in the state (T,p_3,ϕ_3) and ν_4 moles of species M_4 in the state (T,p_4,ϕ_4). We can further extend the generality of the initial and final states by assuming that we start off with ν_1 moles of species M_1 in a state (T_1,p_1,ϕ_1) and ν_2 moles of species M_2 in a state (T_2,p_2,ϕ_2), which are brought to the states (T,p_1,ϕ_1) and (T,p_2,ϕ_2) and allowed to interact, as described above, to produce ν_3 moles of species M_3 in the state (T,p_3,ϕ_3) and ν_4 moles of species M_4 in the state (T,p_4,ϕ_4); the products are then taken to a pair of final states (T_3,p_3,ϕ_3) and (T_4,p_4,ϕ_4). We describe this reaction by saying that ν_1 moles of species M_1 in the state (T_1,p_1,ϕ_1) have combined with ν_2 moles of species M_2 in the state (T_2,p_2,ϕ_2) to form ν_3 moles of species M_3 in the state (T_3,p_3,ϕ_3) and ν_4 moles of species M_4 in the state (T_4,p_4,ϕ_4), and we express it symbolically by writing

$$\nu_1 M_1 + \nu_2 M_2 \rightarrow \nu_3 M_3 + \nu_4 M_4 \tag{25.1}$$

$$\begin{array}{cccc} \phi_1 & \phi_2 & \phi_3 & \phi_4 \\ T_1 & T_2 & T_3 & T_4 \\ p_1 & p_2 & p_3 & p_4 \end{array}$$

The coefficients ν_1, ν_2, ν_3, and ν_4 are called *stoichiometric coefficients*. When the states of the reactants and products are clear from the context, the terms ϕ_i, T_i, and p_i can be dropped. An example of the above notation is given in Example 2 at the end of this chapter.

In the following sections we shall discuss two aspects of chemical reactions, looking first at the thermodynamic changes that have taken place as a result of the chemical reaction and then investigating the nature of the equilibrium situation that exists when species capable of reacting are mixed together in a container as was, for example, the case with system X above.

THE STANDARD STATE FOR PURE SUBSTANCES

In studying chemical reactions in which a set of independent reactants combines completely, forming a set of independent products, it is frequently necessary to be able to calculate the differences between the values of E, F, G, H, and S for the products and the corresponding values of E, F, G, H, and S for the reactants. If we had a table that provided values of the molar energy ϵ, the molar Helmholtz free energy f, the molar Gibbs free energy g, the molar enthalpy h, and the molar entropy s for any substance at any temperature and pressure, it would be a simple matter to calculate any of the above quantities. Such a complete table would be impractical and is unnecessary, as we shall see in the present and following chapters. In the present section, before considering the nature of the tabulated data that are usually available, we shall define a few terms.

A solid, liquid, or an ideal gas is said to be in its standard state for a temperature T_0 when it is in its most stable form under a standard pressure p_0. The pressure p_0 is practically always chosen to be 1 atm. The temperature T_0 most often used in tabular data in the United States is 298.15°K. We shall refer to the state (T_0, p_0) as the reference state. The properties of a real gas approach those of an ideal gas in the limit of zero pressure. Therefore, it is possible, in principle, to determine a particular property of a real gas at a temperature T_0 and pressure p_0, if we know the same property of the corresponding ideal gas in the same state, simply by taking the real gas from pressure p_0 to zero pressure, and then taking the corresponding ideal gas from zero pressure to pressure p_0. Thus it is not necessary to define an additional standard state for a real gas. As an example, suppose we know the value of the molar Gibbs free energy of an ideal gas in the state (T_0, p_0) and we wish to find the value of the molar Gibbs free energy of the corresponding real gas in the state (T_0, p_0). We shall designate the values of the molar Gibbs free energies of the real gas and the ideal gas in the state (T_0, p_0) as $g(T_0, p_0)$ and $g^*(T_0, p_0)$, respectively. To obtain the relation between $g(T_0, p_0)$ and $g^*(T_0, p_0)$, we note first that

$$g(T_0, p_0) - g(T_0, 0) = \int_{T_0, 0}^{T_0, p_0} dg \qquad (25.2)$$

and

$$g^*(T_0, p_0) - g^*(T_0, 0) = \int_{T_0, 0}^{T_0, p_0} dg^* \qquad (25.3)$$

Subtracting (25.3) from (25.2) and noting that $g(T_0,0) = g^*(T_0,0)$, we obtain

$$g(T_0,p_0) = g^*(T_0,p_0) + \int_{T_0,0}^{T_0,p_0} dg - \int_{T_0,0}^{T_0,p_0} dg^* \qquad (25.4)$$

The integration from $(T_0,0)$ to (T_0,p_0) may be carried out along any path. If the integration is carried out along a constant temperature path, then

$$\int_{T_0,0}^{T_0,p_0} dg = \int_{T_0,0}^{T_0,p_0} \left(\frac{\partial g}{\partial p}\right)_T dp = \int_0^{p_0} v(T_0,p)dp \qquad (25.5)$$

where v is the molar volume of the real gas. Similarly,

$$\int_{T_0,0}^{T_0,p_0} dg^* = \int_0^{p_0} v^*(T_0,p)dp \qquad (25.6)$$

where $v^* = RT_0/p$ is the molar volume of the corresponding ideal gas. Substituting (25.5) and (25.6) in (25.4) we obtain

$$g(T_0,p_0) = g^*(T_0,p_0) - \int_0^{p_0} [v^*(T_0,p) - v(T_0,p)]dp \qquad (25.7)$$

Thus if we know $g^*(T_0,p_0)$ and $v(T,p)$, we can calculate $g(T_0,p_0)$. One can obtain similar expressions for $\epsilon(T_0,p_0,)$, $f(T_0,p_0)$, $h(T_0,p_0)$, and $s(T_0,p_0)$. In particular

$$s(T_0,p_0) = s^*(T_0,p_0) + \int_0^{p_0} \frac{\partial}{\partial T_0} [v^*(T_0,p) - v(T_0,p)]dp \qquad (25.8)$$

$$h(T_0,p_0) = h^*(T_0,p_0) - \int_0^{p_0} [v^*(T_0,p) - v(T_0,p)]dp$$

$$+ T_0 \int_0^{p_0} \frac{\partial}{\partial T_0} [v^*(T_0,p) - v(T_0,p)]dp \quad (25.9)$$

We shall designate the values of ϵ, f, g, h, and s of a particular substance in its standard state for a temperature T_0 as $\epsilon°(T_0)$, $f°(T_0)$, $g°(T_0)$, $h°(T_0)$, and $s°(T_0)$, respectively. We shall refer to these quantities, respectively, as the standard molar energy for a temperature T_0, the standard molar Helmholtz free energy for a temperature T_0, the standard molar Gibbs free energy for a temperature T_0, the standard molar enthalpy for a temperature T_0, and the standard molar entropy for a temperature T_0. For liquids, solids, and ideal gases, $\epsilon°(T_0) = \epsilon(T_0,p_0)$; $f°(T_0) = f(T_0,p_0)$; $g°(T_0) = g(T_0,p_0)$; $h°(T_0) =$

$h(T_0,p_0)$; and $s°(T_0) = s(T_0,p_0)$. Since for real gases the standard state for a temperature T_0 is a hypothetical state, it does not correspond to a unique and universal real state (T_0,p_0), as in the above cases.

In many situations only differences in the values of a particular thermodynamic potential need be known and not absolute values. When this is true, we are free to assign an arbitrary value to the potential for one state of each elementary system, measuring all other states with respect to this choice. It is customary, in these cases, to assign a value of zero to the potential of each of the chemical elements in its standard state at the reference temperature T_0. The value of a potential with respect to this reference is called the *potential of formation* and will be designated by a subscript f. For example, the molar Gibbs free energy of formation $g_f(T,p)$ is the molar Gibbs free energy of a substance in the state (T,p), on the assumption that the standard Gibbs free energy of the chemical elements for the temperature T_0 is zero. The value of a particular potential of formation in its standard state is called the *standard potential of formation*. For example, the standard molar Gibbs free energy of formation for a temperature T_0, written $g_f°(T_0)$, is the molar Gibbs free energy of formation of a substance in its standard state for a temperature T_0.

In summary: $g(T,p)$ is the molar Gibbs free energy for a substance in an arbitrary state; $g(T_0,p_0)$ is the molar Gibbs free energy for a substance in the reference state (T_0,p_0); $g°(T_0)$, called the standard molar Gibbs free energy for a temperature T_0, is the molar Gibbs free energy of a substance in its standard state at a temperature T_0; $g_f(T,p)$, called the molar Gibbs free energy of formation, is the molar Gibbs free energy for a substance in an arbitrary state on the assumption that the standard Gibbs free energy of each of the chemical elements is zero at temperature T_0; $g_f(T_0,p_0)$ is the molar Gibbs free energy of formation of a substance in the reference state (T_0,p_0); and $g_f°(T_0)$, called the standard molar Gibbs free energy of formation for the temperature T_0, is the molar Gibbs free energy of formation of a substance in its standard state for a temperature T_0.

We can define similar quantities for the potentials E, F, H, and S. The most commonly tabulated quantities are $g_f°(T_0)$, the standard molar Gibbs free energy of formation for the temperature T_0; $h_f°(T_0)$, the standard molar enthalpy of formation for the temperature T_0; and $s°(T_0)$, the standard molar entropy for the temperature T_0. For solids, liquids, and ideal gases $g_f°(T_0)$, $h_f°(T_0)$, and $s°(T_0)$ are equal to $g_f(T_0,p_0)$, $h_f(T_0,p_0)$, and $s(T_0,p_0)$, respectively. For real gases, if $g_f°(T_0)$, $h_f°(T_0)$, and $s°(T_0)$ are known, $g_f(T_0,p_0)$, $h_f(T_0,p_0)$, and $s(T_0,p_0)$ can be calculated by the methods discussed earlier. We shall, therefore, assume in all our discussions that we know $g_f(T_0,p_0)$, $h_f(T_0,p_0)$, and $s(T_0,p_0)$. In addition to these quantities, we shall have a need in later discussions to be able to calculate $g_f(T,p_0)$ and $h_f(T,p_0)$

at temperatures other than T_0. We shall therefore show how the tabulated data can be exploited to obtain these values.

Suppose we wish to find $h_f(T,p_0)$ for a certain compound. If we consider a constant pressure process from T_0, p_0 to T, p_0, we obtain

$$h_f(T,p_0) - h_f(T_0,p_0) = h(T,p_0) - h(T_0,p_0)$$

$$= \int_{T_0,p_0}^{T,p_0} dh = \int_{T_0,p_0}^{T,p_0} \left(\frac{\partial h}{\partial T}\right)_p dT$$

$$= \int_{T_0}^{T} c_p(T,p_0)dT \tag{25.10}$$

and therefore,

$$h_f(T,p_0) = h_f(T_0,p_0) + \int_{T_0}^{T} c_p(T,p_0)dT \tag{25.11}$$

Thus, if we know $h_f(T_0,p_0)$ and $c_p(T,p_0)$, we can calculate $h_f(T,p_0)$. To obtain an expression for $g_f(T,p_0)$ in terms of $g_f(T_0,p_0)$, we note that

$$g_f(T,p_0) - g_f(T_0,p_0) = g(T,p_0) - g(T_0,p_0)$$

$$= [h(T,p_0) - Ts(T,p_0)] - [h(T_0,p_0) - T_0s(T_0,p_0)]$$

$$= [h(T,p_0) - h(T_0,p_0)] - T[s(T,p_0) - s(T_0,p_0)]$$

$$- (T - T_0)s(T_0,p_0) \tag{25.12}$$

If we consider a constant pressure process from T_0, p_0 to T, p_0, we obtain, as shown in Equation (25.10),

$$h(T,p_0) - h(T_0,p_0) = \int_{T_0}^{T} c_p(T,p_0)dT \tag{25.13}$$

Similarly,

$$s(T,p_0) - s(T_0,p_0) = \int_{T_0,p_0}^{T,p_0} ds = \int_{T_0,p_0}^{T,p_0} \left(\frac{\partial s}{\partial T}\right)_p dT$$

$$= \int_{T_0}^{T} \frac{c_p(T,p_0)}{T} dT \tag{25.14}$$

If we substitute Equations (25.13) and (25.14) in (25.12), we obtain

$$g_f(T,p_0) = g_f(T_0,p_0) + \int_{T_0}^{T} c_p(T,p_0)dT$$

$$- T \int_{T_0}^{T} \frac{c_p(T,p_0)}{T} dT - (T - T_0)s(T_0,p_0) \tag{25.15}$$

From Equation (25.15) it follows that in order to obtain $g_f(T,p_0)$ for some temperature other than T_0, it is necessary to know $g_f(T_0,p_0)$, $c_p(T,p_0)$, and $s(T_0,p_0)$.

In Table 11 we have listed values of $g_f^\circ(298.15)$, $h_f^\circ(298.15)$, and $s^\circ(298.15)$ for a number of substances.

HEAT OF REACTION

If v_1 moles of species M_1 and v_2 moles of species M_2 combine to form v_3 moles of species M_3 and v_4 moles of species M_4, the amount of heat absorbed during the reaction is called the *heat of reaction*. The value of the heat of reaction for a particular reaction will, in general, depend on the respective initial states of the reactants, the final states of the products, and the path by which the system passes from the initial to the final state. However, if, as we shall assume, the only mechanism for the system doing work during the reaction is by expansion against a constant-pressure environment, the work done on the system is simply $-p\Delta V$, where p is the pressure of the environment and ΔV the change in volume of the system. Therefore, in this case it is sufficient to know the initial and final states of the system and the pressure of the environment in order to calculate the work done and, consequently, the heat transferred. The initial state of the system is uniquely determined by the respective temperatures and pressures, or temperatures and volumes, of the species M_1 and M_2 at the beginning of the reaction, together with the phase or condition of each (for example liquid, solid, gas, or aqueous). Similarly, the final state of the system is uniquely determined by the respective temperatures and pressures, or temperatures and volumes, of species M_3 and M_4 at the conclusion of the reaction together with the phase of each. The heat of reaction will be designated by Q and will be indicated for a particular reaction as follows:

$$v_1 M_1 + v_2 M_2 \xrightarrow{Q} v_3 M_3 + v_4 M_4 \qquad (25.16)$$

$$\begin{array}{cccc} \phi_1 & \phi_2 & \phi_3 & \phi_4 \\ T_1 & T_2 & T_3 & T_4 \\ p_1 & p_2 & p_3 & p_4 \end{array}$$

If Q is positive, heat is absorbed during the reaction, and the reaction is said to be endothermic. If Q is negative, heat is generated, and the reaction is said to be exothermic.

The heat of reaction for a particular reaction can be calculated from the relation

$$Q = E_f - E_i - W \qquad (25.17)$$

where E_i is the total internal energy of the reactants; E_f is the total internal energy of the products; and W is the work done on the system during the reaction.

If the total volume remains fixed, then

$$W = 0 \tag{25.18}$$

Substituting Equation (25.18) in (25.17), we obtain

$$Q = E_f - E_i = \Delta E \tag{25.19}$$

The heat of reaction at constant volume is thus equal to the increase in the internal energy of the system, which we designate ΔE.

If the reaction takes place in a constant pressure environment, then

$$W = -p(V_f - V_i) \tag{25.20}$$

It should be noted that for (25.20) to be true, it is necessary only for the system to be in equilibrium at pressure p at the beginning and end of the process. Substituting Equation (25.20) in (25.17), we obtain

$$Q = (E_f + p_f V_f) - (E_i + p_i V_i)$$
$$= H_f - H_i = \Delta H \tag{25.21}$$

where H_i is the total enthalpy of the reactants and H_f the total enthalpy of the products. The heat of reaction at constant pressure is thus equal to the increase in the enthalpy of the system, which we designate ΔH.

It is possible to measure the heat of reaction of some reactions by direct calorimetry. In contrast, many reactions cannot be satisfactorily carried out in a calorimeter, either because the reaction takes place too slowly or because it is impossible to carry out the reaction without forming considerable amounts of undesirable by-products. In these cases, however, it is usually possible to determine the heat of reaction indirectly. Suppose, for example, we know the heats of reaction for the following two reactions, both of which begin and end at temperature T and pressure p, and are such that wherever a particular species M_n occurs, it is in the same phase

$$\nu_1 M_1 + \nu_2 M_2 \rightarrow \nu_3 M_3 + \nu_4 M_4 \tag{25.22}$$

$$\nu_5 M_5 + \nu_6 M_6 \rightarrow \nu_3 M_3 + \nu_4 M_4 \tag{25.23}$$

The heat of reaction for the reaction

$$\nu_1 M_1 + \nu_2 M_2 \rightarrow \nu_5 M_5 + \nu_6 M_6 \tag{25.24}$$

can then be written in terms of the heats of reaction for the first two reactions. To illustrate, let us designate the system consisting of the reactants in reaction (25.22) by the letter a; the system consisting of the products in reaction (25.22) by the letter b; the system consisting of the reactants in reaction (25.23) by the letter c; and the three reactions by $a \rightarrow b$, $c \rightarrow b$, and $a \rightarrow c$, respectively. For the heat of reaction of the reaction $a \rightarrow c$, we can then write:

$$\Delta H(a \rightarrow c) = H_c - H_a = (H_b - H_a) - (H_b - H_c)$$

$$= \Delta H(a \rightarrow b) - \Delta H(c \rightarrow b) \qquad (25.25)$$

The heat of reaction for the reaction $a \rightarrow c$ is thus equal to the difference between the heat of reaction for the reaction $a \rightarrow b$ and the heat of reaction for the reaction $c \rightarrow b$.

The above technique can be used, as we shall now show, to reduce the determination of heats of reaction for arbitrary reactions to a systematic procedure.

If the enthalpies of the elements in their standard states are assumed to be zero, then the heat of reaction in the formation of one mole of a compound in its standard state at temperature T_0 from the component chemical elements in their respective standard states at temperature T_0 will be equal to the standard enthalpy of formation $h_f^\circ(T_0)$ of the compound for the temperature T_0. Thus if A and B are two elements, the value of $h_f^\circ(T_0)$ for the compound AB will be equal to the heat of reaction Q for the reaction $A + B \rightarrow AB$, in which one mole of A in its standard state at a temperature T_0 combines with one mole of B in its standard state at a temperature T_0 to form one mole of AB in its standard state at temperature T_0. Tables are available that provide a relatively extensive list of the standard molar enthalpies of formation $h_f^\circ(T_0)$. If we know $h_f^\circ(T_0)$ for all the compounds taking part in a reaction, we can usually find $h_f(T_0,p_0)$ without too much trouble, and if we know $h_f(T_0,p_0)$ for all the compounds taking part in a reaction that begins and ends at temperature T_0 and pressure p_0, we can readily calculate the heat of reaction for the reaction. Thus, if the general reaction given by Equation (25.16) is carried out at temperature T_0 and pressure p_0,

$$Q = H_f - H_i$$

$$= \nu_3 h_{f,3}(T_0,p_0) + \nu_4 h_{f,4}(T_0,p_0) - \nu_1 h_{f,1}(T_0,p_0) - \nu_2 h_{f,2}(T_0,p_0) \qquad (25.26)$$

where $h_{f,i}(T_0,p_0)$ is the value of $h_f(T_0,p_0)$ for species M_i.

To determine ΔH for a reaction carried out at a pressure other than p_0, and in which the reactants and products are at a temperature other than

T_0, we use the techniques of Part 2 of this text first to calculate ΔH for a process in which the reactants are brought from their respective actual states to states in which their temperatures are T_0 and pressures p_0, and then to calculate ΔH for a process in which the products are brought from the states in which their temperatures are T_0 and pressures are p_0 to their respective actual final states. The value of ΔH for the reaction will then be the sum of the ΔH for both of these processes and the ΔH for the reaction in which the reactants and products begin and end at temperature T_0 and pressure p_0. For an illustration of the evaluation of heats of reaction at constant pressure, see Example 2 at the end of this chapter.

THE EQUATION OF REACTION EQUILIBRIUM

In the preceding sections we have assumed that the reactants and products with which we were dealing were independent systems. In the present section we wish to consider what happens in the case of a homogeneous mixture of species that are capable of interacting chemically.

Let us suppose we have a simple system enclosed in a rigid adiabatic container and composed of arbitrary amounts of four chemical species M_1, M_2, M_3, and M_4 that are capable of undergoing the reaction

$$\nu_1 M_1 + \nu_2 M_2 \rightleftarrows \nu_3 M_3 + \nu_4 M_4 \tag{25.27}$$

The entropy of the system is given by

$$S = S(E,V,N_1,N_2,N_3,N_4) \tag{25.28}$$

The parameters N_1, N_2, N_3, and N_4, however, are not entirely independent. Suppose, for example, we prepare our system by mixing $N_1(0)$, $N_2(0)$, $N_3(0)$, and $N_4(0)$ moles, respectively, of species M_1, M_2, M_3, and M_4. If the reaction (25.27) takes place, the concentrations of the various species will change. The reaction (25.27) is said to have proceeded to an extent ξ if $\nu_1\xi$ moles of M_1 have combined with $\nu_2\xi$ moles of M_2 to form $\nu_3\xi$ moles of M_3 and $\nu_4\xi$ moles of M_4. If, after the initial mixing of the species M_1, M_2, M_3, and M_4, they react to an extent ξ, the resultant number of moles of each species will be given by

$$N_1(\xi) = N_1(0) - \nu_1\xi \tag{25.29}$$

$$N_2(\xi) = N_2(0) - \nu_2\xi \tag{25.30}$$

$$N_3(\xi) = N_3(0) + \nu_3\xi \tag{25.31}$$

$$N_4(\xi) = N_4(0) + \nu_4\xi \tag{25.32}$$

The range of allowed values of ξ is limited by the fact that $N_1(\xi)$, $N_2(\xi)$, $N_3(\xi)$, and $N_4(\xi)$ must each be greater than, or equal to, zero; thus, ξ must be less than, or equal to, both $N_1(0)/\nu_1$ and $N_2(0)/\nu_2$ and must also be greater than, or equal to, both $-N_3(0)/\nu_3$ and $-N_4(0)/\nu_4$. We shall designate the lower limit of ξ as ξ_- and the upper limit as ξ_+. When the reaction has proceeded to an extent ξ, the entropy is given by

$$S(E,V,\xi) = S[E,V,N_1(\xi),N_2(\xi),N_3(\xi),N_4(\xi)] \tag{25.33}$$

In equilibrium, the value assumed by ξ will be that value in the range ξ_- to ξ_+ which maximizes the entropy. Maximizing $S(E,V,\xi)$ with respect to ξ, we obtain

$$\frac{\partial S(E,V,N_1,N_2,N_3,N_4)}{\partial N_1}\frac{dN_1(\xi)}{d\xi}$$

$$+ \frac{\partial S(E,V,N_1,N_2,N_3,N_4)}{\partial N_2}\frac{dN_2(\xi)}{d\xi}$$

$$+ \frac{\partial S(E,V,N_1,N_2,N_3,N_4)}{\partial N_3}\frac{dN_3(\xi)}{d\xi}$$

$$+ \frac{\partial S(E,V,N_1,N_2,N_3,N_4)}{\partial N_4}\frac{dN_4(\xi)}{d\xi} = 0 \tag{25.34}$$

which becomes

$$\frac{\nu_1\mu_1}{T} + \frac{\nu_2\mu_2}{T} - \frac{\nu_3\mu_3}{T} - \frac{\nu_4\mu_4}{T} = 0 \tag{25.35}$$

or simply

$$\nu_1\mu_1 + \nu_2\mu_2 = \nu_3\mu_3 + \nu_4\mu_4 \tag{25.36}$$

Equation (25.36) is known as the equation of reaction equilibrium.

The equation of reaction equilibrium has been derived for a reaction taking place in an isolated system. Since it represents a relation between intensive variables of the system, however, it is, by arguments similar to those of page 114, quite generally valid for a chemical reaction that takes place under diverse conditions, such as conditions of constant temperature and constant pressure, or conditions of constant temperature and constant volume. We can also show this to be valid by noting that if the reaction is carried out in a rigid container immersed in a constant-temperature heat-bath, the equilibrium value of ξ will be the value that minimizes

$$F(T,V,\xi) = F[T,V,N_1(\xi),N_2(\xi),N_3(\xi),N_4(\xi)] \tag{25.37}$$

And if the reaction is carried out in a constant temperature and constant pressure environment, the equilibrium value of ξ will be the value that minimizes

$$G(T,p,\xi) = G[T,p,N_1(\xi),N_2(\xi),N_3(\xi),N_4(\xi)] \qquad (25.38)$$

If we minimize $F(T,V,\xi)$ or $G(T,p,\xi)$ with respect to ξ, we shall again obtain Equation (25.36).

DIRECTION OF CHEMICAL CHANGE

If a reaction

$$\nu_1 M_1 + \nu_2 M_2 \rightleftarrows \nu_3 M_3 + \nu_4 M_4 \qquad (25.39)$$

taking place in an isolated simple system is allowed to proceed by an infinitesimal amount $d\xi$, then the direction of the reaction must be such that the entropy increases or remains constant. Thus from Equation (25.33),

$$dS(\xi) = \frac{1}{T} (\nu_1\mu_1 + \nu_2\mu_2 - \nu_3\mu_3 - \nu_4\mu_4)d\xi \geq 0 \qquad (25.40)$$

It follows that if $\nu_1\mu_1 + \nu_2\mu_2 > \nu_3\mu_3 + \nu_4\mu_4$, then $d\xi \geq 0$, and reaction (25.39) will proceed from left to right, whereas if $\nu_1\mu_1 + \nu_2\mu_2 < \nu_3\mu_3 + \nu_4\mu_4$, then $d\xi \leq 0$, and reaction (25.39) will proceed from right to left.

We obtain the same condition for a reaction carried out in a constant-volume container in a constant-temperature environment, and also for a reaction carried out in a constant-temperature and constant-pressure environment.

THE ACTIVITY

In discussing chemical equilibrium, it is frequently convenient to introduce a quantity called the activity. The activity of species M_i in a multicomponent system is defined as

$$a_i \equiv \exp\left(\frac{\mu_i - \mu_i^\circ}{RT}\right) \qquad (25.41)$$

where μ_i°, called the standard chemical potential of species M_i, is some arbitrary reference value, or set of reference values, for the chemical potential of species M_i. Since the particular choice for μ_i° depends on the type of system and the type of problem considered, it may vary from one author to another. In one problem, for example, it may be convenient to let μ_i° be the value of the chemical potential of the pure species M_i at some fixed temperature and pressure, but in another problem, it may be convenient to have a different μ_i° for every temperature or every pressure of the system. Thus μ_i° may be a constant in one case, a function of the temperature in a second case, and so forth. In Chapter 26 we shall consider the usual choice of μ_i° for a component M_i in a gas mixture, and in Chapter 27 the usual choice of μ_i° for a component M_i in a solution.

If we solve Equation (25.41) for the chemical potential μ_i, we obtain

$$\mu_i = \mu_i^\circ + RT \ln a_i \tag{25.42}$$

THE LAW OF MASS ACTION

If Equation (25.42) is substituted in the equation of reaction equilibrium, Equation (25.36), we obtain

$$\frac{a_3{}^{\nu_3} a_4{}^{\nu_4}}{a_1{}^{\nu_1} a_2{}^{\nu_2}} = K \tag{25.43}$$

where

$$K \equiv \exp\left(-\frac{\Delta G^\circ}{RT}\right) \tag{25.44}$$

and

$$\Delta G^\circ \equiv \nu_3 \mu_3^\circ + \nu_4 \mu_4^\circ - \nu_1 \mu_1^\circ - \nu_2 \mu_2^\circ \tag{25.45}$$

Equation (25.43) is called the law of mass action; the quantity K is called the equilibrium constant; and the quantity ΔG° is called the standard free energy of reaction. Although K is called the equilibrium *constant*, it is really a *function*.

The law of mass action can assume a variety of forms, depending on the type of system under study and the choice of the standard chemical potentials μ_i°.

THE GIBBS PHASE RULE

An isolated n-component system that is in an equilibrium state is not necessarily a simple system, since it is possible to have states in which two or more phases are present. A multiphase system can be considered as a composite system in which the phases are the subsystems and in which the walls separating the subsystems are assumed to be moveable, diathermal, and completely permeable.

Let us consider a closed n-component system in which there are m phases present. For the m phases to be in equilibrium, their temperatures, pressures, and the chemical components of each species must be respectively equal; therefore, we obtain the following $(n + 2)(m - 1)$ equations

$$T_1 = T_2 = \cdots = T_m \equiv T$$

$$p_1 = p_2 = \cdots = p_m \equiv p$$

$$\mu_{11} = \mu_{12} = \cdots = \mu_{1m} \equiv \mu_1$$

$$\cdots$$

$$\mu_{n1} = \mu_{n2} = \cdots = \mu_{nm} \equiv \mu_n \tag{25.46}$$

In addition, from the Gibbs–Duhem relation, we can obtain m independent equations of the form

$$\phi_1(T_1, p_1, \mu_{11}, \cdots, \mu_{n1}) = 0$$

$$\cdots$$

$$\phi_m(T_1, p_1, \mu_{1m}, \cdots, \mu_{nm}) = 0 \tag{25.47}$$

Finally, if the components can react with one another by means of a series of c independent chemical reactions, we obtain c independent equations of reaction equilibrium,

$$\sum_r \nu_{r1} \mu_r = \sum_p \nu_{p1} \mu_p$$

$$\cdots$$

$$\sum_r \nu_{rc} \mu_r = \sum_p \nu_{pc} \mu_p \tag{25.48}$$

where ν_{rj} and ν_{pj} are the respective stoichiometric coefficients for the reactant r and product p in the jth chemical reaction. Thus, altogether we have $(n + 2)(m - 1) + m + c$ independent equations in the $m(n + 2)$ unknowns $T_1, p_1, \mu_{11}, \mu_{21}, \cdots, \mu_{n1}, \cdots, T_m, p_m, \mu_{1m}, \mu_{2m}, \cdots, \mu_{nm}$. It follows that the number of intensive parameters that can be independently varied, which we shall refer to as the number of degrees of freedom and designate as f, in an n-component m-phase system in which c independent chemical reactions are possible, will be equal to the difference between the number of unknowns and the number of equations which is simply

$$f = n - m - c + 2 \tag{25.49}$$

This relation is called the Gibbs phase rule. Since the number of degrees of freedom must be at least zero, an n-component system cannot have more than $n - c + 2$ phases present at the same time, and if $n - c + 2$ phases are present, the state is unique, since the number of degrees of freedom is then zero. Thus, a one-component system can have at most three phases present at the same time, a two-component system can have at most four phases present at the same time, and so forth.

EXAMPLES

Problem 1. Show that for a van der Waals gas at low densities the difference between $g(T_0,p_0)$, the molar Gibbs free energy in the reference state, and $g°(T_0)$, the standard molar Gibbs free energy for a temperature T_0, is approximately given by $p_0[b - (a/RT_0)]$, and that this difference is usually relatively small, compared to typical standard molar free energies of formation.

Solution. For a van der Waals gas

$$v = \frac{RT}{p + \left(\dfrac{a}{v^2}\right)} + b \approx \frac{RT}{p}\left(1 - \frac{a}{pv^2}\right) + b$$

$$\approx \frac{RT}{p}\left[1 - \frac{a}{p\left(\dfrac{RT}{p}\right)^2}\right] + b$$

$$= \frac{RT}{p} + b - \frac{a}{RT}$$

If we designate the molar volume and the molar Gibbs free energy of the corresponding ideal gas by $v^*(T,p)$ and $g^*(T,p)$, respectively, then, using Equation (25.7) and noting that $g°(T_0) = g^*(T_0,p_0)$, we obtain

$$g(T_0,p_0) - g°(T_0) = \int_0^{p_0} [v(T_0,p) - v^*(T_0,p)]dp$$

$$= \int_0^{p_0} \left[b - \left(\frac{a}{RT_0}\right)\right]dp = p_0\left[b - \left(\frac{a}{RT_0}\right)\right]$$

which is the desired result. Typically, a is of the order of 10^{-1} $Nm^4(mole)^{-1}$, and b is of the order of $10^{-5}m^3(mole)^{-1}$, therefore, $g(T_0,p_0) - g°(T_0)$ is of the order of 10 $J(mole)^{-1}$. Typical molar Gibbs free energies of formation are of the order of 10^5 $J(mole)^{-1}$.

Problem 2. Determine the heat of reaction when 1 mole of graphite at 298°K and at atmospheric pressure combines with 1 mole of water vapor at 298°K and at atmospheric pressure to form 1 mole of gaseous carbon monoxide at 400°K and at atmospheric pressure and 1 mole of gaseous hydrogen at 400°K and at atmospheric pressure.

Solution. The above reaction can be represented as follows

$$C \;\; + \;\; H_2O \;\; \rightarrow \;\; CO \;\; + \;\; H_2$$

graphite	gas	gas	gas
298°K	298°K	400°K	400°K
1 atm	1 atm	1 atm	1 atm

Since the reaction begins with the reactants at atmospheric pressure and ends with the products at atmospheric pressure, the heat of reaction will be equal to the change in enthalpy ΔH in the reaction, which is given by

$$\Delta H = h_{CO}(400°K, 1 \text{ atm}) + h_{H_2}(400°K, 1 \text{ atm})$$

$$- h_C(298°K, 1 \text{ atm}) - h_{H_2O}(298°K, 1 \text{ atm})$$

$$= h_{f,CO}(400°K, 1 \text{ atm}) + h_{f,H_2}(400°K, 1 \text{ atm})$$

$$- h_{f,C}(298°K, 1 \text{ atm}) - h_{f,H_2O}(298°K, 1 \text{ atm})$$

From Table 11 we have

$$h_{f,CO}(298°K, 1 \text{ atm}) \approx h^{\circ}_{f,CO}(298.15) = -26.4 \text{ kcal (mole)}^{-1}$$

$$h_{f,H_2}(298°K, 1 \text{ atm}) \approx h^{\circ}_{f,H_2}(298.15) = 0$$

$$h_{f,C}(298°K, 1 \text{ atm}) \approx h^{\circ}_{f,C}(298.15) = 0$$

$$h_{f,H_2O}(298°K, 1 \text{ atm}) \approx h^{\circ}_{f,H_2O}(298.15) = -57.8 \text{ kcal (mole)}^{-1}$$

The specific heats of carbon monoxide and hydrogen at atmospheric pressure from Table 4 are given approximately by

$$c_{p,CO} = 6.25 + 2.091 \times 10^{-3}T - 0.459 \times 10^{-6}T^2 \text{ cal/mole/°K}$$

$$c_{p,H_2} = 6.88 + 0.066 \times 10^{-3}T + 0.279 \times 10^{-6}T^2 \text{ cal/mole/°K}$$

Using Equation (25.11) and the above results, we obtain

$$h_{f,CO}(400°K, 1 \text{ atm}) = -26.4 + 0.7$$

$$= -25.7 \text{ kcal (mole)}^{-1}$$

$$h_{f,H_2}(400°K, 1 \text{ atm}) = 0 + 0.7 = 0.7 \text{ kcal (mole)}^{-1}$$

Gathering results, we obtain

$$\Delta H = (-25.7 + 0.7) - (0 - 57.8)$$

$$= 32.8 \text{ kcal (mole)}^{-1}$$

PROBLEMS

25.1 If 2 moles of hydrogen H_2 in its standard state react with 1 mole of oxygen O_2 in its standard state to form 2 moles of liquid water H_2O in its standard state, 136.64 kcal of heat are transferred from the system to the surroundings. What is the standard molar enthalpy of formation of liquid water?

25.2 What is the enthalpy change for the reaction $6C(gas) + 6H(gas) \rightarrow C_6H_6(gas)$? Assume that the reactants and products are in their standard states. Use the data in Table 11.

25.3 Determine the heat of reaction when 1 mole of hydrogen gas at 348°K and atmospheric pressure combines with $\frac{1}{2}$ mole of oxygen gas at 348°K and atmospheric pressure to form 1 mole of liquid water at the same temperature and pressure. Use the data in Tables 4 and 11.

25.4 The enthalpies of formation of PbO, SO_2, and PbS at 15°C and atmospheric pressure in kilocalories per mole are -50.30, -70.92, and $+19.30$, respectively. Calculate ΔH and ΔE for the reaction

$$PbS + 2\ PbO \rightarrow 3\ Pb + SO_2$$

in which the reactants and products are at 15°C and atmospheric pressure. Assume that the volumes of PbS, PbO, and Pb can be neglected in comparison with the volume of SO_2, and that SO_2 can be treated as an ideal gas.

25.5 Determine the heat of reaction of the following reaction at 25°C and atmospheric pressure:

$$CH_4 + Cl_2 \rightarrow CH_3Cl + HCl$$

$$\text{gas} \quad \text{gas} \quad \text{gas} \quad \text{gas}$$

25.6 At 25°C and 1 atm the heat of formation of HCl (gas) is -22.06 kcal (mole)$^{-1}$. Deduce an expression for the heat of formation as a function of temperature, using specific heats from Table 4.

25.7 Using specific heats from Table 4 and the heats of formation from

Table 11, derive an expression for the heat of reaction of the following reaction as a function of temperature

$$2CO + O_2 \rightarrow 2CO_2$$

gas   gas   gas

25.8   The adiabatic flame temperature is that temperature which would be attained if a compound were burned completely under adiabatic conditions so that all the heat evolved goes into heating the product gases. Find the adiabatic flame temperature for the burning of ethane C_2H_6 in an air mixture containing originally twice as much air as is necessary for complete combustion to $CO_2(gas)$ and $H_2O(gas)$. Assume that air is composed of 20 percent O_2 and 80 percent N_2 by volume. In using heat capacity equations, neglect all terms containing T^2 or higher powers of T. Assume also that the combustion occurs at constant pressure.

25.9   Two moles of liquid benzene C_6H_6 react with 15 moles of oxygen O_2 within an adiabatic constant-volume container of volume V to form 12 moles of gaseous carbon dioxide CO_2 and 6 moles of liquid water H_2O. The initial temperatures of the benzene and oxygen are 25°C. What rise in temperature will be observed in the container? Make any reasonable assumptions or approximations that may be necessary.

CHAPTER 26

Gas Mixtures

In the present chapter we wish to consider chemical reactions that are taking place in a mixture of gases.

PARTIAL PRESSURES

If a multicomponent gas, composed of species M_1, M_2, $\cdots$, M_i, $\cdots$, is placed in contact with a pure gas of species M_i, by means of a rigid membrane that is permeable to species M_i only, and if the pressure and temperature of the pure gas are adjusted so that the pure gas is in equilibrium with the mixture, then the pressure p_i of the pure gas is called the partial pressure of the species M_i in the mixture.

IDEAL MULTICOMPONENT GASES

From a microscopic point of view, an ideal multicomponent gas is one in which the molecules are separated by such large distances that the effects of the finite size of the molecules and the intermolecular forces can be neglected. Thus, except for the possibility of energy exchange among the component gases, each component in an ideal multicomponent gas behaves exactly as it would if it alone occupied the volume occupied by the whole gas. Since the component gases can freely exchange energy with one another, however, they have a common temperature. Rather than draw on the above microscopic picture, we shall attempt to arrive at the same result macroscopically.

From a macroscopic point of view, a mixture of gases contained in a volume V at a temperature T and total pressure p is an ideal multicomponent gas if, and only if

$$p_i = \frac{N_i RT}{V} \tag{26.1}$$

$$p = \sum_i p_i \tag{26.2}$$

where p_i is the partial pressure of species M_i and N_i the number of moles of species i. A mixture that satisfies these equations is said to obey Dalton's law.

Let us suppose we have a two-component gas, consisting of two species M_1 and M_2, that satisfies conditions (26.1) and (26.2). To determine the fundamental equation of the gas, consider a rigid adiabatic container, divided as shown in Figure 26.1, into three compartments by a rigid

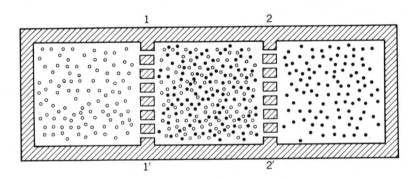

FIGURE 26.1

partition $11'$, permeable to species M_1 only, and a rigid partition $22'$, permeable to species M_2 only. Let us assume that the first compartment on the left contains only species M_1; the third compartment contains only species M_2; and the middle compartment is of volume V and contains N_1 moles of species M_1 and N_2 moles of species M_2.

In equilibrium, the values of T will be the same in all three compartments; the values of μ_1 will be the same in the first and second compartments; and the values of μ_2 will be the same in the second and third compartments. From the Gibbs–Duhem relation, the chemical potential μ_1 is a function of T and p_1 only where p_1 is the pressure in the first compartment, or the partial pressure of species M_1 in the second compartment. Similarly, μ_2 is a function of T and p_2 only where p_2 is the pressure in the third compartment, or the partial pressure of species M_2 in the second compartment. The Helmholtz free energy for the mixture in the middle compartment is thus given by

$$F_{12} = E_{12} - TS_{12} = -pV + \mu_1 N_1 + \mu_2 N_2$$

$$= -p_1 V - p_2 V + \mu_1(T,p_1)N_1 + \mu_2(T,p_2)N_2 \qquad (26.3)$$

Substituting (26.1) in (26.3) we obtain

$$F_{12}(T,V,N_1,N_2)$$

$$= -N_1 RT - N_2 RT + \mu_1(T,V,N_1)N_1 + \mu_2(T,V,N_2)N_2 \qquad (26.4)$$

Since $F_{12}\,(T,V,N_1,N_2)$ is a potential expressed in terms of its characteristic variables, it contains a complete thermodynamic description of the mixture. Noting that

$$F_{12}(T,V,N_1,0) = -N_1 RT + \mu_1(T,V,N_1)N_1 \qquad (26.5)$$

and

$$F_{12}(T,V,0,N_2) = -N_2 RT + \mu_2(T,V,N_2)N_2 \qquad (26.6)$$

we can rewrite (26.4)

$$F_{12}(T,V,N_1,N_2) = F_{12}(T,V,N_1,0) + F_{12}(T,V,0,N_2) \qquad (26.7)$$

The first term on the right-hand side of Equation (26.7) is the Helmholtz free energy for a gas consisting of N_1 moles of species M_1 occupying a volume V at a temperature T. The second term on the right-hand side of (26.7) is the Helmholtz free energy for a gas consisting of N_2 moles of species M_2 occupying a volume V at a temperature T. It follows that the Helmholtz free energy of the mixture at a temperature T and volume V is equal to the sum of the Helmholtz free energies that each component would have if it separately occupied a volume V at a temperature T; hence, each component gas acts as if it occupied the volume V alone, but at a common temperature T.

THE CHEMICAL POTENTIAL OF A COMPONENT IN AN IDEAL MULTICOMPONENT GAS

The chemical potential of a one-component system can be defined by the relation

$$\mu = \left(\frac{\partial F}{\partial N}\right)_{T,V} \tag{26.8}$$

If we use the expression for the Helmholtz free energy, $F(T,V,N)$, for an ideal gas as given by Equation (19.28) in Chapter 19, we obtain for an ideal gas

$$\mu^* = \text{fcn}\,(T) + RT \ln \left(\frac{N}{V}\right) \tag{26.9}$$

where the asterisk is used to indicate that the gas is ideal. Noting that for an ideal gas $N/V = p/RT$, Equation (26.9) can be written in the form

$$\mu^*(T,p) = \mu^*(T,p_0) + RT \ln \left(\frac{p}{p_0}\right) \tag{26.10}$$

where p_0 is some reference pressure.

Since the components in an ideal multicomponent gas at a temperature T and volume V behave as if each alone occupied the volume, the chemical potential of species M_i in an ideal multicomponent gas can, in analogy with Equation (26.10), be written

$$\mu_i^*(T,p_i) = \mu_i^*(T,p_0) + RT \ln \left(\frac{p_i}{p_0}\right) \tag{26.11}$$

where $\mu_i^*(T,p_0)$ is the chemical potential of an ideal gas consisting of species M_i at a temperature T and pressure p_0.

THE LAW OF MASS ACTION FOR A CHEMICAL REACTION TAKING PLACE IN AN IDEAL MULTICOMPONENT GAS

Let us assume that a reaction, such as that given by Equation (25.27) in Chapter 25, is taking place in an ideal multicomponent gas. To obtain the condition of equilibrium, we substitute Equation (26.11) in the equation of reaction equilibrium [Equation (25.36) in Chapter 25] and obtain

$$\frac{(p_3/p_0)^{\nu_3}(p_4/p_0)^{\nu_4}}{(p_1/p_0)^{\nu_1}(p_2/p_0)^{\nu_2}} = K(T) \tag{26.12}$$

where

$$K(T) \equiv \exp\left[\frac{\nu_1\mu_1^*(T,p_0) + \nu_2\mu_2^*(T,p_0) - \nu_3\mu_3^*(T,p_0) - \nu_4\mu_4^*(T,p_0)}{RT}\right]$$

(26.13)

Equation (26.12) is the law of mass action for a chemical reaction taking place in an ideal multicomponent gas.

Noting that

$$\frac{p_i}{p} = \frac{N_i}{N}$$

(26.14)

where $N = \Sigma\, N_i$ is the total number of moles, we can rewrite (26.12)

$$\frac{N_3^{\nu_3}N_4^{\nu_4}}{N_1^{\nu_1}N_2^{\nu_2}} = \left(\frac{Np_0}{p}\right)^{\nu_3+\nu_4-\nu_1-\nu_2}K(T)$$

(26.15)

Equation (26.15) is an alternate form of the law of mass action for a chemical reaction in an ideal multicomponent gas.

If we initially mix $N_1(0)$, $N_2(0)$, $N_3(0)$, and $N_4(0)$ moles of species M_1, M_2, M_3, and M_4, respectively, in a container and allow them to come to reaction equilibrium at a temperature T and pressure p, then if we know $K(T)$, we can use (26.15), together with Equations (25.29), (25.30), (25.31), and (25.32) in Chapter 25, to determine the respective values of N_1, N_2, N_3, and N_4 at equilibrium.

THE FUGACITY

In studying chemical reactions in a real gas mixture it is convenient to introduce a quantity called the fugacity. The fugacity f_i of species M_i in a real gas mixture is defined by the relation

$$f_i \equiv p_i \exp\left[\frac{\mu_i(T,p_i) - \mu_i^*(T,p_i)}{RT}\right]$$

(26.16)

where $\mu_i(T,p_i)$ is the chemical potential of species M_i in the mixture for a temperature T and partial pressure p_i, and $\mu_i^*(T,p_i)$ is the chemical potential of an ideal gas of species M_i at a temperature T and pressure p_i. For an ideal gas, $\mu_i(T,p_i)$ and $\mu_i^*(T,p_i)$ are identical, and the fugacity f_i

reduces to the partial pressure p_i. If we substitute Equation (26.11) in (26.16), we obtain as an alternate definition of the fugacity

$$f_i \equiv p_0 \exp\left[\frac{\mu_i(T,p_i) - \mu_i^*(T,p_0)}{RT}\right] \tag{26.17}$$

From Equation (26.17) it follows that the chemical potential of component M_i in a real gas mixture can be written

$$\mu_i(T,p_i) = \mu_i^*(T,p_0) + RT \ln\left(\frac{f_i}{p_0}\right) \tag{26.18}$$

Equation (26.18) is identical with the expression (26.11) for the chemical potential of species M_i in an ideal multicomponent gas, except that the partial pressure p_i has been replaced by the fugacity f_i.

The fugacity f_i is closely related to the activity a_i, which was defined in the preceding chapter. If we define the standard chemical potential μ_i° of species M_i in a real gas mixture as

$$\mu_i^\circ \equiv \mu_i^\circ(T) \equiv \mu_i^*(T,p_0) \tag{26.19}$$

then the activity is given by

$$a_i \equiv \exp\left[\frac{\mu_i(T,p_i) - \mu_i^*(T,p_0)}{RT}\right] \tag{26.20}$$

Comparing (26.20) and (26.17), we see that for this choice of the standard chemical potential of species M_i we obtain

$$f_i = a_i p_0 \tag{26.21}$$

If we had chosen some other definition for the standard chemical potential of species M_i in a gas mixture, we would have obtained a different relation.

The fugacity f (not to be confused with the molar Helmholtz free energy) of a one-component gas can be readily evaluated as a function of T and p by noting from Equation (25.7) in Chapter 25 that

$$\mu(T,p) - \mu^*(T,p) \equiv g(T,p) - g^*(T,p)$$

$$= -\int_0^p [v^*(T,p) - v(T,p)]dp \tag{26.22}$$

Substituting Equation (26.22) in (26.16) with p_i replaced by p, we obtain

$$f(T,p) = p \exp \left\{ -\frac{\displaystyle\int_0^p [v^*(T,p) - v(T,p)]dp}{RT} \right\} \qquad (26.23)$$

Since $v^*(T,p) = RT/p$, it follows that if we know $v(T,p)$ we can calculate $f(T,p)$.

THE LAW OF MASS ACTION FOR A CHEMICAL REACTION IN A REAL MULTICOMPONENT GAS

If we use Equation (26.18) in the equation of reaction equilibrium, Equation (25.36) in Chapter 25, we obtain

$$\frac{f_3^{\nu_3}f_4^{\nu_4}}{f_1^{\nu_1}f_2^{\nu_2}} = (p_0)^{\nu_3+\nu_4-\nu_1-\nu_2}K(T) \qquad (26.24)$$

where

$$K(T) \equiv \exp\left[-\frac{\Delta G^\circ(T)}{RT} \right] \qquad (26.25)$$

and

$$\Delta G^\circ(T) \equiv \nu_3\mu_3^*(T,p_0) + \nu_4\mu_4^*(T,p_0) - \nu_1\mu_1^*(T,p_0) - \nu_2\mu_2^*(T,p_0) \qquad (26.26)$$

Thus we obtain essentially the same equation as we obtained for the ideal multicomponent gas, except that the partial pressures p_i have been replaced by fugacities f_i.

This same result could have been obtained by substituting Equations (26.19) and (26.21) in the law of mass action, Equation (25.43) in Chapter 25.

THE EQUILIBRIUM CONSTANT

The equilibrium constant $K(T)$ for a reaction taking place in a multi-component gas is given by Equation (26.25). To determine $K(T)$ we must be able to evaluate the standard free energy of reaction $\Delta G^\circ(T)$ which is given by Equation (26.26).

Since $\mu_i^*(T,p_0)$ is the chemical potential for an ideal gas consisting of species M_i alone at a temperature T and pressure p_0, and since for a one-component gas $\mu = G/N = g$, expression (26.26) can be rewritten

$$\Delta G^\circ(T) \equiv \nu_3 g_3^*(T,p_0) + \nu_4 g_4^*(T,p_0) - \nu_1 g_1^*(T,p_0) - \nu_2 g_2^*(T,p_0) \qquad (26.27)$$

where $g_i^*(T,p_0)$ is the molar Gibbs free energy of an ideal gas consisting of species M_i at a temperature T and pressure p_0. But the standard molar Gibbs free energy of a gas for a temperature T is simply the molar Gibbs free energy of the corresponding ideal gas at the temperature T and standard pressure p_0. Thus

$$g_i^*(T,p_0) \equiv g_i^\circ(T) \tag{26.28}$$

And therefore,

$$\Delta G^\circ(T) = \nu_3 g_3^\circ(T) + \nu_4 g_4^\circ(T) - \nu_1 g_1^\circ(T) - \nu_2 g_2^\circ(T) \tag{26.29}$$

Furthermore, the value of expression (26.29) is independent of the values of $g^\circ(T_0)$ for the elements in their respective standard states for the temperature T_0; therefore, the values, $g_i^\circ(T)$ can be replaced by the values $g_{f,i}^\circ(T)$, where $g_{f,i}^\circ(T)$ is the standard molar Gibbs free energy of formation of species M_i for a temperature T. The value of $g_f^\circ(T)$ for a particular species can be determined by use of the tabulated values of $g_f^\circ(T_0)$, the tabulated values of the specific heat, and the techniques discussed in the preceding chapter.

Gathering results, we have

$$K(T) = \exp\left[-\frac{\Delta G^\circ(T)}{RT}\right] \tag{26.30}$$

where

$$\Delta G^\circ(T) = \nu_3 g_{f,3}^\circ(T) + \nu_4 g_{f,4}^\circ(T) - \nu_1 g_{f,1}^\circ(T) - \nu_2 g_{f,2}^\circ(T) \tag{26.31}$$

THE VARIATION OF THE EQUILIBRIUM CONSTANT WITH TEMPERATURE

From the results of the preceding section, we can write

$$\ln K(T) = \frac{\nu_1 g_1^*(T,p_0) + \nu_2 g_2^*(T,p_0) - \nu_3 g_3^*(T,p_0) - \nu_4 g_4^*(T,p_0)}{RT} \tag{26.32}$$

If we take the derivative of Equation (26.32) with respect to temperature, noting that

$$\left[\frac{\partial}{\partial T}\left(\frac{g}{T}\right)\right]_p = \frac{T\left(\frac{\partial g}{\partial T}\right)_p - g}{T^2} = \frac{-Ts - g}{T^2} = -\frac{h}{T^2} \tag{26.33}$$

we obtain

$$\frac{d}{dT}[\ln K(T)] = \frac{\Delta H^\circ(T)}{RT} \tag{26.34}$$

where

$$\Delta H°(T) = \nu_3 h_3^*(T,p_0) + \nu_4 h_4^*(T,p_0) - \nu_1 h_1^*(T,p_0) - \nu_2 h_2^*(T,p_0)$$

$$= \nu_3 h_3°(T) + \nu_4 h_4°(T) - \nu_1 h_1°(T) - \nu_2 h_2°(T)$$

$$= \nu_3 h_{f,3}°(T) + \nu_4 h_{f,4}°(T) - \nu_1 h_{f,1}°(T) - \nu_2 h_{f,2}°(T) \qquad (26.35)$$

The quantity $\Delta H°(T)$ is the heat of reaction for a reaction in which ν_1 moles of species M_i, in its standard state at a temperature T, combine with ν_2 moles of species M_2, in its standard state at a temperature T, to form ν_3 moles of species M_3, in its standard state at a temperature T, and ν_4 moles of species M_4, in its standard state at a temperature T. Equation (26.34), which is called the van't Hoff equation, can be used to calculate the heat of reaction from knowledge of the temperature variation of the equilibrium constant, or, conversely, it can be used to determine how the equilibrium constant changes with temperature, from knowledge of the heat of reaction.

EXAMPLE

Problem. Eight moles of nitrogen are mixed with two moles of oxygen to form a sample of air. The resultant gas is then heated to 2000°K at atmospheric pressure. How many moles of nitric oxide are present in the sample at this temperature and pressure? Assume the gases are ideal.

Solution. We wish to study the reaction $N_2 + O_2 \rightarrow 2NO$.

We shall let $T_0 = 298.15°K$; $p_0 = 1$ atm; species $1 \equiv N_2$; species $2 \equiv O_2$; and species $3 \equiv NO$. To determine $K(T)$ for the above reaction, we can either calculate $\Delta G°(T)$ and use Equation (26.26), or we can calculate $\Delta H°(T)$ and use the van't Hoff equation, Equation (26.34). We shall use the latter approach.

If we integrate the van't Hoff equation between T_0 and T, we obtain

$$K(T) = K(T_0) \exp \left\{ \int_{T_0}^{T} \left[\frac{\Delta H°(T)}{RT^2} \right] dT \right\}$$

$$= \exp \left\{ -\left[\frac{\Delta G°(T_0)}{RT_0} \right] + \int_{T_0}^{T} \left[\frac{\Delta H°(T)}{RT^2} \right] dT \right\}$$

Using Table 11, we obtain

$$\Delta G°(T_0) = 41,438 \text{ cal (mole)}^{-1}$$

From Equation (25.11) in Chapter 25,

$$\Delta H°(T) = \Delta H°(T_0) + \int_{T_0}^{T} \Delta C_p(T,p_0)dT$$

where

$$\Delta C_p(T,p_0) = 2c_{p,3}(T,p_0) - c_{p,2}(T,p_0) - c_{p,1}(T,p_0)$$

Using Table 11, we obtain

$$\Delta H°(T_0) = 43,200 \text{ cal (mole)}^{-1}$$

Using Table 4, we obtain

$$\Delta C_p(T,p_0) = (0.14 + 0.307 \times 10^{-3}T - 0.109 \times 10^{-6}T^2) \text{ cal (°K)}^{-1}$$

Combining results we obtain

$$K(T) = \exp\left\{\frac{-43,146 + 4.886T + 0.14T \ln T + 0.1535 \times 10^{-3}T^2 - 0.01816 \times 10^{-6}T^3}{RT}\right\}$$

For $T = 2000°K$, we obtain

$$K(2000) = 4.35 \times 10^{-4}$$

Using this value of the equilibrium constant in the law of mass action, Equation (26.15), we obtain

$$\frac{N_3^2}{N_1 N_2} = 4.35 \times 10^{-4}$$

Expressing N_1, N_2, and N_3 in terms of the extent of reaction ξ, we obtain

$$\frac{(2\xi)^2}{(8 - \xi)(2 - \xi)} = 4.35 \times 10^{-4}$$

Solving for ξ, we obtain

$$\xi = 4.12 \times 10^{-2}$$

and therefore,

$$N_3 = 8.24 \times 10^{-2} \text{ moles}$$

PROBLEMS

26.1   Derive an expression for K as a function of T for the reaction

$$2 \text{ HCl} + \tfrac{1}{2}O_2 \rightarrow H_2O + Cl_2$$

gas   gas   gas   gas

26.2 Determine the mole percentage of H_2 which is dissociated at 2000°K and 1 atm pressure. At what pressure is half the original H_2 dissociated at 2000°K?

26.3 One-half mole of an ideal gas A is mixed with $\frac{1}{2}$ mole of an ideal gas B. The two species are subject to the reaction $A \rightarrow B$, with an equilibrium constant K. Show that the heat capacity at constant pressure for the system is given by

$$C_p = \frac{C_{p,A}}{(K+1)} + \frac{KC_{p,B}}{(K+1)} + \frac{\Delta H^2 K}{RT^2(K+1)^2}$$

26.4 The values of ΔH for a reaction $A + B \rightarrow C + D$ (in which the chemical species are all gases) carried out at atmospheric pressure at various temperatures are given below:

$T°K$	300	400	500	600	700	800	900
ΔH kcal	41	20	7	1.8	-2.0	-7.0	-19

Under what circumstances would you expect to obtain the maximum yield of C and D?

CHAPTER 27

Solutions

In the present chapter we wish to investigate a few simple properties of solutions. A solution is a homogeneous liquid or solid mixture. The term solution sometimes includes gas mixtures, but we shall use the term in the restricted sense given above.

VAPOR PRESSURE

In our earlier discussions of the vapor pressure of a pure liquid, we considered situations in which the only pressure exerted on the liquid was the pressure due to the vapor. In such cases the vapor pressure is a function of temperature only. It is possible, however, that the pressure on the liquid, which we shall designate as $\bar{p}$, may be different from the vapor pressure, which we shall designate as $\hat{p}$. This could occur, for example, if the liquid and vapor were separated by a porous wall, or if the liquid and vapor were confined in a vessel that also contained an inert gas insoluble in the liquid. In the present section, we wish to consider the dependence of $\hat{p}$ on $\bar{p}$.

The chemical potential of the liquid, which we shall designate as $\bar{\mu}$, will be a function of T and $\bar{p}$; and the chemical potential of the vapor, which we shall designate as $\hat{\mu}$, will be a function of T and $\hat{p}$. In equilibrium,

$$\hat{\mu}(T,\hat{p}) = \bar{\mu}(T,\bar{p}) \tag{27.1}$$

Taking the differential of Equation (27.1), we obtain

$$\hat{s}(T,\hat{p})dT + \hat{v}(T,\hat{p})d\hat{p} = \bar{s}(T,\bar{p})dT + \bar{v}(T,\bar{p})d\bar{p} \tag{27.2}$$

where $\hat{s}$ and $\hat{v}$ are the molar entropy and molar volume, respectively, of the vapor, and $\bar{s}$ and $\bar{v}$ are the molar entropy and molar volume of the liquid, respectively. From (27.2), it follows that

$$\left(\frac{\partial \hat{p}}{\partial \bar{p}}\right)_T = \frac{\bar{v}(T,\bar{p})}{\hat{v}(T,\hat{p})} \tag{27.3}$$

From Equation (27.3), known as Poynting's relation, it follows that the vapor pressure $\hat{p}$ is a function of the pressure $\bar{p}$. However, since $\bar{v}(T,\bar{p})$ will, in general, be small compared to $\hat{v}(T,\hat{p})$, the dependence is slight.

DILUTE SOLUTIONS

Let us consider a solution at a temperature T and pressure $\bar{p}$ that is in equilibrium with its vapor. For simplicity we shall assume the solution is made up of only two species M_1 and M_2, and that the number of moles of species M_1 in the solution is larger than the number of moles of species M_2. We shall refer to M_1 as the solvent and to M_2 as the solute. We will *not* assume that the vapor is ideal. If the vapor were ideal, the fugacities f_i that occur in the following arguments could be simply replaced by partial pressures p_i. Quantities associated with the solution will be designated with a tilde ($\sim$), and quantities associated with the vapor will be designated with a caret (^). Thus, $\tilde{N}_i$ is the number of moles of species M_i in the solution; $\tilde{n}_i$ is the mole fraction of species M_i in the solution, that is, $\tilde{n}_i = \tilde{N}_i / \tilde{N}$, where $\tilde{N} = \Sigma\, \tilde{N}_i$; $\hat{f}_i$ is the fugacity of species M_i in the vapor; and so forth. We shall designate any quantity associated with a pure substance with a large dot. Thus, $\hat{f}_i^{\bullet}$ is the fugacity of the vapor of the pure liquid M_i, or equivalently, it is the fugacity of species M_i in the vapor in the limit as $\tilde{n}_i$ approaches unity.

It is found experimentally that if T and $\bar{p}$ are held constant, then, in the limit as the mole fraction of the solvent M_1 approaches unity, the fugacity of the solvent in the vapor is proportional to the mole fraction of the solvent in solution, that is,

$$\hat{f}_1 = k_1(T,\bar{p})\tilde{n}_1 \tag{27.4}$$

where $k_1(T,\bar{p})$ is a proportionality factor. In the limit as $\tilde{n}_1 \to 1, \hat{f}_1 \to f_1^{\bullet}$, and therefore,

$$k_1(T,\bar{p}) = f_1^{\bullet}(T,\bar{p}) \tag{27.5}$$

Combining Equations (27.4) and (27.5), we obtain

$$\hat{f}_1 = f_1^{\bullet}(T,\bar{p})\tilde{n}_1 \tag{27.6}$$

Equation (27.6) is known as Raoult's law. A solution is said to be dilute over the range of values of $\tilde{n}_1$ for which Raoult's law is valid.

We shall now show that when a solvent obeys Raoult's law, $\hat{f}_2$, the fugacity of the solute in the vapor, will be proportional to $\tilde{n}_2$, the mole fraction of the solute in solution. However, the proportionality factor will not, in general, be equal to $f_2^{\bullet}$ as in Raoult's law. To show that this is true, we first note from the Gibbs–Duhem relation, Equation (23.7) of Chapter 23, that

$$\tilde{s}dT - \bar{v}d\bar{p} + \tilde{n}_1 d\bar{\mu}_1 + \tilde{n}_2 d\bar{\mu}_2 = 0 \tag{27.7}$$

From (27.7), it follows that

$$\tilde{n}_1\left(\frac{\partial\bar{\mu}_1}{\partial\tilde{n}_1}\right)_{T,\bar{p}} + \tilde{n}_2\left(\frac{\partial\bar{\mu}_2}{\partial\tilde{n}_1}\right)_{T,\bar{p}} = 0 \tag{27.8}$$

But $\tilde{n}_1 + \tilde{n}_2 = 1$, therefore, $\partial/\partial\tilde{n}_1 = -\partial/\partial\tilde{n}_2$, and thus Equation (27.8) can be written

$$\tilde{n}_1\left(\frac{\partial\bar{\mu}_1}{\partial\tilde{n}_1}\right)_{T,\bar{p}} = \tilde{n}_2\left(\frac{\partial\bar{\mu}_2}{\partial\tilde{n}_2}\right)_{T,\bar{p}} \tag{27.9}$$

In equilibrium,

$$\bar{\mu}_i = \hat{\mu}_i \tag{27.10}$$

From Equation (26.18) in Chapter 26

$$\hat{\mu}_i = \hat{\mu}^*(T,p_0) + RT\ln\left(\frac{\hat{f}_i}{p_0}\right) \tag{27.11}$$

Combining Equations (27.10) and (27.11), we obtain

$$\bar{\mu}_i = \hat{\mu}_i = \hat{\mu}_i^*(T,p_0) - RT\ln p_0 + RT\ln\hat{f}_i$$
$$= \text{fcn}\,(T) + RT\ln\hat{f}_i \tag{27.12}$$

From (27.12), it follows that

$$\left(\frac{\partial \bar{\mu}_i}{\partial \bar{n}_i}\right)_{T,\bar{p}} = RT\left[\frac{\partial(\ln f_i)}{\partial \bar{n}_i}\right]_{T,\bar{p}}$$

$$= \frac{RT}{\bar{n}_i}\left[\frac{\partial(\ln f_i)}{\partial(\ln \bar{n}_i)}\right]_{T,\bar{p}} \tag{27.13}$$

Substituting (27.13) in (27.9), we obtain

$$\left[\frac{\partial(\ln f_1)}{\partial(\ln \bar{n}_1)}\right]_{T,\bar{p}} = \left[\frac{\partial(\ln f_2)}{\partial(\ln \bar{n}_2)}\right]_{T,\bar{p}} \tag{27.14}$$

If Raoult's law is valid, then

$$\left[\frac{\partial(\ln f_1)}{\partial(\ln \bar{n}_1)}\right]_{T,\bar{p}} = \frac{\bar{n}_1}{f_1}\left(\frac{\partial f_1}{\partial \bar{n}_1}\right)_{T,\bar{p}} = 1 \tag{25.15}$$

Substituting (27.15) in (27.14), we obtain

$$\left[\frac{\partial(\ln f_2)}{\partial(\ln \bar{n}_2)}\right]_{T,\bar{p}} = 1 \tag{27.16}$$

From Equation (27.16), it follows that

$$f_2 = k_2(T,\bar{p})\bar{n}_2 \tag{27.17}$$

where $k_2(T,\bar{p})$ is a proportionality factor that must be determined by experiment. Equation (27.17) is known as Henry's law.

From the above results, it follows that in a dilute solution

$$f_i = k_i(T,\bar{p})\bar{n}_i \tag{27.18}$$

where $k_i(T,\bar{p})$ for the solvent is equal simply to the fugacity of the vapor of the pure solvent at temperature T and pressure $\bar{p}$, and $k_i(T,\bar{p})$ for the solute is an experimentally determined proportionality factor.

THE CHEMICAL POTENTIAL OF A COMPONENT IN A DILUTE SOLUTION

If we substitute Equation (27.18) in (27.12), we obtain

$$\bar{\mu}_i = \bar{\mu}_i^*(T,p_0) + RT\ln\left[\frac{k_i(T,\bar{p})}{p_0}\right] + RT\ln \bar{n}_i$$

$$= \text{fcn}(T,\bar{p}) + RT\ln \bar{n}_i \tag{27.19}$$

which can be rewritten in the form

$$\bar{\mu}_i = \bar{\mu}_i(T,\bar{p},\tilde{n}_1^\circ) + RT \ln \left(\frac{\tilde{n}_i}{\tilde{n}_1^\circ}\right) \tag{27.20}$$

where $\bar{\mu}_i(T,\bar{p},\tilde{n}_i^\circ)$ is the chemical potential of the species M_i in a dilute solution at a temperature T and pressure $\bar{p}$, and in which the mole fraction of species M_i in solution is $\tilde{n}_i^\circ$. The reference mole fraction $\tilde{n}_i^\circ$ may be chosen in any way desired.

Since the chemical potential of species M_i in solution is equal to the chemical potential of species M_i in the vapor, we could also have written

$$\bar{\mu}_i = \hat{\mu}_i(T,\hat{p}_i) \tag{27.21}$$

where $\hat{\mu}_i(T,\hat{p}_i)$ is the chemical potential of species M_i in the vapor at a temperature T and partial pressure $\hat{p}_i$.

THE BOILING POINT OF A DILUTE SOLUTION

The boiling point of a pure liquid is defined as the temperature at which the vapor pressure $\hat{p}$ is equal to the applied pressure $\bar{p}$. In the present section, we wish to consider how the boiling point of a solvent M_1 is affected by the addition of a small amount of a nonvolatile solute M_2. A nonvolatile substance is a substance whose vapor pressure under the conditions existing is too small to be significant.

The chemical potential of the solvent M_1 in a dilute solution is given by Equation (27.20), that is.

$$\bar{\mu}_1 = \bar{\mu}_1(T,\bar{p},\tilde{n}_1^\circ) + RT \ln \left(\frac{\tilde{n}_1}{\tilde{n}_1^\circ}\right) \tag{27.22}$$

If we choose $\tilde{n}_1^\circ = 1$, then Equation (27.22) can be written

$$\bar{\mu}_1 = \bar{\mu}_1^\bullet(T,\bar{p}) + RT \ln \tilde{n}_1 \tag{27.23}$$

where $\bar{\mu}_1^\bullet(T,\bar{p})$ is the chemical potential of the pure solvent at a temperature T and pressure $\bar{p}$.

We can also express the chemical potential of the solvent in terms of the chemical potential of the species M_1 in the vapor. Thus, from Equation (27.21),

$$\bar{\mu}_1 = \hat{\mu}_1(T,\hat{p}_1) \tag{27.24}$$

where $\hat{\mu}_1(T,\hat{p}_1)$ is the chemical potential of the solvent in the vapor phase at a temperature T and partial pressure $\hat{p}_1$. But the chemical potential of species M_i in the vapor at temperature T and partial pressure $\hat{p}_i$ is, from the definition of partial pressure, equal to the chemical potential of a pure vapor of species M_i at a temperature T and pressure $\hat{p}_i$. Thus,

$$\hat{\mu}_1(T,\hat{p}_1) \equiv \hat{\mu}_1^{\bullet}(T,\hat{p}_1) \tag{27.25}$$

And, therefore, we can write Equation (27.24) in the alternate form:

$$\bar{\mu}_1 = \hat{\mu}_1^{\bullet}(T,\hat{p}_1) \tag{27.26}$$

Combining Equations (27.23) and (27.26) and rearranging, we obtain

$$\ln \tilde{n}_1 = \frac{\hat{\mu}_1^{\bullet}(T,\hat{p}_1) - \bar{\mu}_1^{\bullet}(T,\tilde{p})}{RT} \tag{27.27}$$

Boiling occurs when the vapor pressure $\hat{p}$, which is approximately $\hat{p}_1$, is equal to the applied pressure $\bar{p}$. Setting $\hat{p}_1 = \bar{p} = p$ in (27.27), we obtain

$$\ln \tilde{n}_1 = \frac{\hat{\mu}_1^{\bullet}(T,p) - \bar{\mu}_1^{\bullet}(T,p)}{RT} \tag{27.28}$$

We have shown in Equation (26.33), Chapter 26, that for a pure substance

$$\left[\frac{\partial}{\partial T} \left(\frac{\mu}{T} \right) \right]_p = \left[\frac{\partial}{\partial T} \left(\frac{g}{T} \right) \right]_p = -\frac{h}{T^2} \tag{27.29}$$

Using Equation (27.29), we can rewrite (27.28)

$$\ln \tilde{n}_1 = -\int_{T_0}^{T} \left[\frac{\hat{h}_1^{\bullet}(T,p) - \tilde{h}_1^{\bullet}(T,p)}{RT^2} \right] dT \tag{27.30}$$

where T_0 is the boiling point of the pure solvent, that is, the boiling point when $\tilde{n}_1 = 1$, and where $\hat{h}_1^{\bullet}(T,p)$ and $\tilde{h}_1^{\bullet}(T,p)$ are the molar enthalpies of the species M_1 as a pure gas and a pure liquid, respectively, at the temperature T and pressure p.

Since $\tilde{n}_1 = 1 - \tilde{n}_2$, and $\tilde{n}_2$ is small, the left-hand side of (27.30) can be approximated as

$$\ln \tilde{n}_1 = \ln (1 - \tilde{n}_2) \approx -\tilde{n}_2 \tag{27.31}$$

Furthermore, for small values of $\tilde{n}_2$, $|T - T_0| \ll T_0$, and the integral on the right-hand side of (27.30) can be approximated as

$$\int_{T_0}^{T} \left[\frac{\hat{h}_1^{\bullet}(T,p) - \tilde{h}_1^{\bullet}(T,p)}{RT^2} \right] dT \approx \left[\frac{\hat{h}_1^{\bullet}(T_0,p) - \tilde{h}_1^{\bullet}(T_0,p)}{RT_0^2} \right](T - T_0) \tag{27.32}$$

If we substitute (27.31) and (27.32) in (27.30) and note that

$$\hat{h}_1^{\bullet}(T_0,p) - \bar{h}_1^{\bullet}(T_0,p) = \ell \tag{27.33}$$

where ℓ is the latent heat of vaporization for the pure solvent at temperature T_0 and pressure p, we obtain

$$T = T_0 + \frac{RT_0^2 \tilde{n}_2}{\ell} \tag{27.34}$$

From (27.34) it follows that the boiling point of a liquid is raised by the addition of a nonvolatile solute. Equation (27.34) can be used in calculating the change in the boiling point of a solvent resulting from the addition of a small amount of a nonvolatile solute. Alternatively, if the change in the boiling point, produced by the addition of a known number of moles of a nonvolatile solute to a solvent, is known, Equation (27.34) can then be used to calculate the latent heat of vaporization of the solvent. Or, if the latent heat of the solvent is known, and if the change in the boiling point, occurring upon the addition of a known mass of an unknown solute, is measured, Equation (27.34) can be used to calculate the molecular weight of the solute.

THE FREEZING POINT OF A DILUTE SOLUTION

We can use the same techniques employed in the preceding section in studying the effect of the addition of a small amount of solute on the freezing point of a solution.   Let us consider a dilute solution, consisting of a solute of species M_2, dissolved in a solvent of species M_1. Let us further assume that the solute is such that, when the temperature of the solution is lowered to the freezing point, only the solvent will pass into the solid phase. Therefore, at the freezing point a pure solid phase of species M_1 will be in equilibrium with a solution consisting of species M_1 and M_2. We shall designate quantities associated with the solid by a bar (—), and quantities associated with the liquid by a tilde ($\sim$).

The chemical potential of species M_1 in the solid phase will be equal to the chemical potential of a pure solid of species M_1 at a temperature T and pressure p, that is,

$$\bar{\mu}_1 = \bar{\mu}_1^{\bullet}(T,p) \tag{27.35}$$

The chemical potential of species M_1 in the liquid phase is, from (27.23), given by

$$\tilde{\mu}_1 = \tilde{\mu}_1^{\bullet}(T,p) + RT \ln \tilde{n}_1 \tag{27.36}$$

In equilibrium $\bar{\mu}_1$ and $\tilde{\mu}_1$ will be equal. Equating (27.35) and (27.36) and rearranging, we obtain

$$\ln \tilde{n}_1 = \frac{\bar{\mu}_1^{\bullet}(T,p) - \tilde{\mu}_1^{\bullet}(T,p)}{RT} \tag{27.37}$$

Proceeding from this point exactly as in the preceding section, we obtain

$$T = T_0' - \frac{RT^2 \tilde{n}_2}{\ell'} \tag{27.38}$$

where T_0' is the freezing point of the pure solvent and ℓ' is the latent heat of fusion, that is,

$$\ell'(T_0',p) = \tilde{h}_1^{\bullet}(T_0',p) - \bar{h}_1^{\bullet}(T_0',p) \tag{27.39}$$

From Equation (27.38), it follows that the freezing point of a liquid is lowered by the addition of a solute that dissoves only in the liquid phase.

IDEAL SOLUTIONS

An ideal solution is one in which every component obeys Raoult's law for all values of $\tilde{n}_i$, that is, for which

$$\hat{f}_i = f_i^{\bullet}(T,\tilde{p}) \tilde{n}_i \tag{27.40}$$

Starting with Equation (27.40), it is possible to show, as in the derivation of Equation (27.19), that the chemical potential of species M_i in such a solution is given by

$$\bar{\mu}_i = \hat{\mu}_i^*(T,p_0) + RT \ln \left[\frac{f_i^{\bullet}(T,\tilde{p}) \tilde{n}_i}{p_0} \right] \tag{27.41}$$

Conversely, starting with Equation (27.41), we can derive Equation (27.40). It follows that an ideal solution can be equivalently defined as one in which the chemical potentials of the components satisfy Equation (27.41) throughout all ranges of $\tilde{n}_i$. Since only a few solutions approximate the behavior of an ideal solution, it is of limited interest.

An ideal dilute solution is a completely hypothetical solution, in which one component, called the solvent, which we choose to be M_1, obeys Raoult's law for all values of $\tilde{n}_1$, and all other components, called solutes, obey Henry's law for all values of $\tilde{n}_i$. Thus, an ideal dilute solution is one for which

$$f_1 = f^{\bullet}_1(T,\bar{p})\tilde{n}_1 \tag{27.42}$$

and for $i > 1$,

$$f_i = k_i(T,\bar{p})\tilde{n}_i \tag{27.43}$$

Starting with Equations (27.42) and (27.43), we can show

$$\bar{\mu}_1 = \hat{\mu}^*_1(T,p_0) + RT \ln\left[\frac{f^{\bullet}_1(T,\bar{p})\tilde{n}_1}{p_0}\right] \tag{27.44}$$

and for $i > 1$,

$$\bar{\mu}_i = \hat{\mu}^*_i(T,p_0) + RT \ln\left[\frac{k_i(T,\bar{p})\tilde{n}_i}{p_0}\right] \tag{27.45}$$

Conversely, starting with Equations (27.44) and (27.45), we can derive Equations (27.42) and (27.43). It follows that an ideal dilute solution can be equivalently defined as one in which the chemical potentials are given by Equations (27.44) and (27.45) throughout all ranges of $\tilde{n}_i$. An ideal dilute solution, except for those cases in which it reduces to an ideal solution, is a hypothetical solution, since, in the limit, as $\tilde{n}_i$ approaches one, the fugacity f_i in a real solution must approach the fugacity of the pure substance and not $k_i(T,\bar{p})$, as would be the case in an ideal dilute solution. Despite this fact, the concept of an ideal dilute solution will be found to be a helpful construct in defining standard free energies in solutions. An ideal dilute solution is sometimes referred to as an infinitely dilute solution.

THE ACTIVITY OF A COMPONENT IN A SOLUTION

In studying chemical equilibrium in a solution, we shall make use of the law of mass action, Equation (25.43) in Chapter 25. Before we can apply this equation, it is necessary to choose standard chemical potentials. We shall define the *standard chemical potential of species M_i in a solution* as the chemical potential that species M_i would have in an ideal dilute solution at a temperature T, pressure $\bar{p}$, and mole fraction $\tilde{n}_i^{\circ}$, and we shall designate it as $\hat{\mu}^*_i(T,\bar{p},\tilde{n}_i^{\circ})$. Thus,

$$\bar{\mu}_i^{\circ} \equiv \bar{\mu}_i^{\circ}(T,\bar{p}) \equiv \hat{\mu}^*_i(T,\bar{p},\tilde{n}_i^{\circ}) \tag{27.46}$$

where

$$\hat{\mu}^*_1(T,\bar{p},\tilde{n}_1) = \hat{\mu}^*_1(T,p_0) + RT \ln\left[\frac{f^{\bullet}_1(T,\bar{p})\tilde{n}_1}{p_0}\right] \tag{27.47}$$

and for $i > 1$,

$$\hat{\mu}^*_i(T,\bar{p},\tilde{n}_i) = \hat{\mu}^*_i(T,p_0) + RT \ln\left[\frac{k_i(T,\bar{p})\tilde{n}_i}{p_0}\right] \tag{27.48}$$

For the above choice of standard chemical potentials, the activities a_i, defined by Equation (25.41) in Chapter 25, are given by

$$\bar{a}_i = \exp\left[\frac{\bar{\mu}_i(T,\bar{p},\bar{n}_2,\bar{n}_3,\bar{n}_4) - \bar{\mu}_i^*(T,\bar{p},\bar{n}_i^\circ)}{RT}\right]$$

$$\equiv \frac{\bar{n}_i}{\bar{n}_i^\circ} \exp\left[\frac{\bar{\mu}_i(T,\bar{p},\bar{n}_2,\bar{n}_3,\bar{n}_4) - \bar{\mu}_i^*(T,\bar{p},\bar{n}_i)}{RT}\right] \qquad (27.49)$$

We are still free to choose $\bar{n}_i^\circ$. Experience shows that it is most convenient to choose $\bar{n}_i^\circ$ to be unity for the solvent, and for a solute to be either unity, or the mole fraction corresponding to one mole of solute per thousand grams of solvent (that is, unit molality) or the mole fraction corresponding to one mole of solute per liter of solution (that is, unit molarity). It should be noted that if we choose $\bar{n}_i^\circ$ equal to unity for the solvent, then $\bar{\mu}_i^\circ$ is just equal to the chemical potential of the pure solvent M_1 at temperature T and pressure $\bar{p}$, but if we choose $\bar{n}_i^\circ$ equal to unity for the solute, $\bar{\mu}_i^\circ$ is *not* equal to the chemical potential of the pure solute M_i at temperature T and pressure $\bar{p}$. It should also be noted that the activity $\bar{a}_i$ of a dilute solution, which is not necessarily ideal, is equal to $\bar{n}_i/\bar{n}_i^\circ$, and if we choose $\bar{n}_i^\circ$ equal to unity, the activity $\bar{a}_i$ of a dilute solution is equal to the mole fraction $\bar{n}_i$.

The above choice of standard chemical potentials for components in solution is not the only possible choice and not even the only practical choice. If the solution is of the type in which two liquids are completely miscible, so that there is no essential difference between solvent and solute, then the standard chemical potential of both solute and solvent are usually chosen to be the chemical potential associated with the pure substance at temperature T and pressure $\bar{p}$. It is also common to find the standard chemical potential of species M_i defined as the chemical potential that species M_i would have in an ideal dilute solution at a temperature T, and mole fraction $\bar{n}_i^\circ$, but at a fixed pressure $\bar{p}_0$, rather than at the pressure $\bar{p}$ of the solution. In this case $\bar{p}_0$ is practically always chosen to be one atmosphere. Since the values of $f_1^\bullet(T,\bar{p})$ and $k_i(T,\bar{p})$ depend only slightly on $\bar{p}$, the latter choice is not significantly different in most cases from the choice we made.

THE LAW OF MASS ACTION FOR A CHEMICAL REACTION IN A SOLUTION

Let us assume that four chemical species M_1, M_2, M_3, and M_4, which react according to the reaction represented by Equation (25.27) in Chapter 25, are in equilibrium in a solution, and let us assume that M_1 is the solvent.

If we apply the law of mass action, Equation (25.43) in Chapter 25, using the definition of standard chemical potential given in the preceding section, we obtain as the condition of equilibrium

$$\frac{\tilde{a}_3{}^{\nu_3}\tilde{a}_4{}^{\nu_4}}{\tilde{a}_1{}^{\nu_1}\tilde{a}_2{}^{\nu_2}} = K(T,\tilde{p}) \tag{27.50}$$

where

$$K(T,\tilde{p}) = \exp\left[-\frac{\Delta G^\circ(T,\tilde{p})}{RT}\right] \tag{27.51}$$

and

$$\Delta G^\circ \equiv \nu_3\tilde{\mu}_3^*(T,\tilde{p},\tilde{n}_3^\circ) + \nu_4\tilde{\mu}_4^*(T,\tilde{p},\tilde{n}_4^\circ)$$

$$-\nu_1\tilde{\mu}_1^*(T,\tilde{p},\tilde{n}_1^\circ) - \nu_2\tilde{\mu}_2^*(T,\tilde{p},\tilde{n}_2^\circ) \tag{27.52}$$

Note that $\tilde{a}_i$ and $\tilde{\mu}_i^*(T,\tilde{p},\tilde{n}_i^\circ)$ have been defined in the preceding section.

PROBLEMS

27.1 Consider a dilute solution of a nonvolatile solute B in a volatile solvent A. Assume that Trouton's rule holds, that is, the ratio of the molar latent heat of vaporization ℓ_{vap} to the normal boiling point T_0 is a constant, approximately 21 cal $(mole)^{-1}(°K)^{-1}$. Show that the boiling point T_s of the solution is related to the mole fraction n of the solvent by the equation $-\ln n = 10.5[1 - (T_0/T_s)]$. Show further that if n is small, $T_s n^{0.095} = T_0$.

27.2 Calculate the vapor pressure of water at 100°C and 10 atm external pressure. The density of water at 100°C and 1 atm is 0.9588 g$(cm)^{-3}$.

27.3 Calculate the vapor pressure of liquid bromine at 20°C under a pressure of 1000 atm of the inert gas argon. The vapor pressure of bromine at 1 atm is 175 torr, and its density is 3.12 g$(cm)^{-3}$. Bromine exists as Br_2 molecules in the vapor phase. Neglect the solubility of argon in liquid bromine.

27.4 When 1 mole of a nonvolatile solute is dissolved in 1000 g of ethyl alcohol (C_2H_5OH), the boiling point is raised by 1.20°C. The boiling point of pure alcohol is 78°C. From this information calculate the latent heat of vaporization of ethyl alcohol.

27.5 A solution of 4.00 g of sulphur in 100 g of carbon disulfide is observed to boil 0.381°C higher than pure carbon disulfide. It is known that if a small amount of a nonvolatile solute is added to 1 kg of carbon disulfide, the boiling point elevation is 2.40°C per mole of solute. What is the molecular weight of sulfur in carbon disulfide solution? How many atoms are there in the sulfur molecule in this solution?

27.6   How many grams of methyl alcohol (CH_3OH) must be added to 10 kg of water to lower the freezing point of the solution to $-10°C$?

PART SIX

Thermodynamics of General Systems

In the preceding sections, we have restricted our attention to systems for which the macroscopic equilibrium properties are determined by the energy, the volume, and the number of moles of each species present. In the present section, we wish to extend our analysis to systems in which the equilibrium properties are not determined only by the above parameters.

CHAPTER 28

In the earlier sections of the text we assumed that we were dealing with homogeneous isotropic systems on which the only force acting was the uniform surface force of the container. The thermodynamic state of such systems was found to depend on the energy, volume, and the mole numbers of the various species.

If we allow the presence of electric and magnetic fields, or if we consider anisotropic systems acted upon by nonuniform forces, then the thermodynamic state of a system is no longer determined only by the above parameters. In the present chapter, we wish to consider the modifications necessary in the basic postulates in order to include these new situations.

In order to avoid excessive circumlocution, it will be convenient to redefine a simple system to include the above possibilities. Thus a simple system will in this section be defined as a system (1) that is macroscopically homogeneous and (2) whose local properties are unaffected by partitioning the system into independent subsystems.

THE BASIC POSTULATES

The generalization of the earlier results is straightforward. In place of our previous postulates we now have the following postulates.

239

Postulate I. For every system there exists a quantity E, called the internal energy, that has the following properties:

(a) A unique value of the internal energy is associated with each state of the system.

(b) The internal energy of a closed system has a lower bound but no upper bound.

(c) The difference between the internal energy in one state and the internal energy in another state of a closed system is equal to the work required to bring the system, while adiabatically enclosed, from the one state to the other.

Postulate II. There exist particular states of a system, called equilibrium states, that are uniquely determined by the internal energy E, and a set of extensive parameters $X_1, X_2, \cdots, X_n$. The specific extensive parameters necessary to determine the state depend on the nature of the system.

Postulate III. For every system there exists a state function S, called the entropy, that has the following properties.

(a) For a simple system, S is a single-valued function of $E, X_1, X_2, \cdots, X_n$.

(b) The entropy of a composite system is equal to the sum of the entropies of its component systems.

(c) If an internal constraint is removed from a composite system, consisting of m simple systems 1, 2, $\cdots$, m, and if $\sum_{j=1}^{m} E_j$ and $\sum_{j=1}^{m} X_{ij}$ are held fixed, and the system is allowed to come to an equilibrium state, then the values assumed by the extensive variables $E_1, X_{11}, \cdots, X_{n1}, \cdots, E_m, X_{1m}, \cdots, X_{nm}$, will be those values consistent with the remaining internal and external constraints that maximize the entropy of the composite system.

(d) During a quasistatic adiabatic change in state of a simple system, the entropy of the system remains constant.

Postulate IV. The temperature $(\partial E / \partial S)_{X_1, X_2, \cdots, X_n}$ and entropy S of a system, in which $X_1, X_2, \cdots$, and X_n are held fixed, vanish in the state of minimum energy and are greater than zero in all other states.

THE INTENSIVE VARIABLES

Given $S(E, X_1, \cdots, X_n)$, we define the intensive parameters

$$T = \left(\frac{\partial E}{\partial S}\right)_{X_1, \cdots, X_n} \tag{28.1}$$

$$P_j = \left(\frac{\partial E}{\partial X_j}\right)_{S, X_1, \cdots, X_{j-1}, X_{j+1}, \cdots, X_n} \tag{28.2}$$

For a quasistatic change, we have

$$dE = TdS + \sum_{j=1}^{n} P_j dX_j \qquad (28.3)$$

If we let

$$P_0 \equiv T \quad \text{and} \quad X_0 \equiv S \qquad (28.4)$$

then Equation (28.3) can be written

$$dE = \sum_{j=0}^{n} P_j dX_j \qquad (28.5)$$

The labeling of the variables is arbitrary, and we could, if desired, rearrange the variables in any desired order. When we do not wish to single out the variables T and S, we shall simply write (28.5) as

$$dE = \sum_{j=1}^{m} P_j dX_j \qquad (28.6)$$

where $m = n + 1$.

LEGENDRE TRANSFORMATIONS

If we know $S(E,X_1, \cdots, X_n)$, we have a complete thermodynamic description of a system. It will, however, be more convenient to work with the function $E(S,X_1, \cdots, X_n) \equiv E(X_0,X_1, \cdots, X_n) \equiv E(X_1, \cdots, X_m)$. If we know $E(X_1, \cdots, X_m)$, or any one of the Legendre transformations of $E(X_1, \cdots, X_m)$, as a function of its characteristic variables, then we also have a complete thermodynamic description of that system. Let us designate the Legendre transformation of $E(X_1, \cdots, X_m)$ with respect to the variables $X_1, \cdots, X_r$ as $L_{1,\ldots,r}$. Thus,

$$L_{1,\ldots,r} = E - \sum_{j=1}^{r} P_j X_j \qquad (28.7)$$

and if we know $L_{1, \ldots, r}(P_1, \cdots, P_r, X_{r+1}, \cdots, X_m)$, then we have a complete thermodynamic description of a system.

MAXWELL RELATIONS

If we equate the mixed partial derivatives of each of the Legendre transformations of $E(X_1, \cdots, X_m)$, we shall obtain the general results

$$\frac{\partial P_i}{\partial X_j} = \frac{\partial P_j}{\partial X_i} \qquad (28.8)$$

$$\frac{\partial P_i}{\partial P_j} = -\frac{\partial X_j}{\partial X_i} \qquad (28.9)$$

$$\frac{\partial X_i}{\partial P_j} = \frac{\partial X_j}{\partial P_i} \qquad (29.10)$$

where the P_i and P_j in (28.8) are considered as functions of X_i, X_j, and either member of each of the remaining pairs of variables (P_s, X_s); the P_i and X_j in (28.9) are considered as functions of X_i, P_j, and either member of each of the remaining pairs of variables (P_s, X_s); and the X_i and X_j in Equation (28.10) are considered as functions of P_i, P_j, and either member of each of the remaining pairs of variables (P_s, X_s), provided that in at least one case the member chosen is the extensive variable. Note that in Equations (28.8), (28.9), and (28.10) the terms diagonally opposed to one another each contain one member of a pair (P_s, X_s), and if the denominators both contain extensive variables or both contain intensive variables, the sign is positive, while if one denominator contains an intensive variable and the other an extensive variable, the sign is negative. It should also be noted in applying these results that frequently a particular intensive variable may implicitly contain a minus sign. For example, the intensive variable corresponding to the extensive variable V is $-p$, *not* $+p$.

EQUILIBRIUM CONDITIONS

It can be shown from the basic postulates that if an internal constraint is removed in a composite system in which: (a) the values of $P_1, \cdots, P_r$ are each held constant and have the same value in each subsystem, and (b) the total values of $X_{r+1}, \cdots, X_m$ for the composite system are held constant, then the equilibrium values of the parameters $X_{r+1}, \cdots, X_m$ for the individual subsystems will be the values which minimize $L_{1,\ldots,r}(P_1, \cdots, P_r, X_{r+1}, \cdots, X_m)$ subject to the external constraints (a) and (b) noted above and also to the remaining internal constraints.

In particular, if we consider a composite system, consisting of two subsystems that we shall designate by a prime and a double prime, respectively, in which: (a) $P'_1 = P''_1 \equiv P_1 = $ const, $\cdots$, $P'_r = P''_r \equiv P_r = $ const, and (b) $X'_{r+1} + X''_{r+1} = C_{r+1} = $ const, $\cdots$, $X'_m + X''_m = C_m = $ const, then the equilibrium values of the parameters $X'_{r+1}, \cdots, X'_m, X''_{r+1}, \cdots, X''_m$ will be the values that minimize the function

$$\psi(X'_{r+1}, \cdots, X'_m) = L'_{1,\ldots,r}(P_1, \cdots, P_r, X'_{r+1}, \cdots, X'_m)$$
$$+ L''_{1,\ldots,r}(P_1, \cdots, P_r, C_{r+1} - X'_{r+1}, \cdots, C_m - X'_m) \quad (28.11)$$

From Appendix 3, we find that the following two conditions are necessary for equilibrium:

$$\frac{\partial \psi(X'_{r+1}, \cdots, X'_m)}{\partial X_m} = 0 \quad (28.12)$$

$$\frac{\partial^2 \psi(X'_{r+1}, \cdots, X'_m)}{\partial^2 X_m} \geq 0 \quad (28.13)$$

These are not the only necessary conditions, but they will suffice for our purposes. From condition (28.12), we obtain the result

$$P'_m = P''_m \tag{28.14}$$

and from condition (28.13), we obtain the result

$$\frac{\partial P_m(P'_1,..., P'_r, X'_{r+1},..., X'_m)}{\partial X'_m} + \frac{\partial P''_m(P''_1,..., P''_r, X''_{r+1},..., X''_m)}{\partial X''_m} \geq 0 \tag{28.15}$$

If we consider the two subsystems simply as two identical halves of the same system, then the two terms in (28.15) are equal, and we obtain, as a condition of intrinsic stability, the result:

$$\frac{\partial P_m(P_1, \cdots, P_r, X_{r+1}, \cdots, X_m)}{\partial X_m} \geq 0 \tag{28.16}$$

Since the value of r can range from 1 to $m - 1$, and since X_m can be any arbitrary extensive parameter, we arrive at the general result:

$$\frac{\partial P_m}{\partial X_m} \geq 0 \tag{28.17}$$

where the P_m in (28.17) is considered to be a function of X_m and of either member of each of the remaining pairs of variables (P_i, X_i).

ZERO TEMPERATURE

We can show exactly as we did for the simple one-component chemical systems in Chapter 15 that Postulate IV leads to the facts that, at $T = 0$,

$$T \frac{\partial S}{\partial T} = 0 \tag{28.18}$$

$$\frac{\partial S}{\partial X_i} = -\frac{\partial P_i}{\partial T} = 0 \tag{28.19}$$

$$\frac{\partial S}{\partial P_i} = \frac{\partial X_i}{\partial T} = 0 \tag{28.20}$$

where in (28.18) S is considered to be a function of T and of one member of each of the remaining pairs of variables (P_j, X_j); in (28.19) S and P_i are considered to be functions of T, X_i, and of one member of each of the remaining pairs of variables (P_j, X_j); and in (28.20) S and X_i are considered to be functions of T, P_i, and of one member of each of the remaining pairs of variables (P_j, X_j).

CHAPTER 29

Elastic Filaments

INTRODUCTION

If an elastic system is subjected to a stress, it will undergo a deformation or strain. The strain will depend on the temperature as well as on the stress; hence, an elastic system constitutes a thermodynamic system. In order to describe the stresses and resultant strains of such a system, it is ordinarily necessary to resort to the use of tensors. Since we are interested in the thermodynamic behavior of an elastic system, primarily as an illustration of the application of thermodynamics to general systems, we shall restrict our attention to elastic systems that are subjected to a uniform force per unit area in one direction, and consequently undergo a uniform deformation in this direction only. A filament of wire or rubber subjected to tension are examples of systems that approximately satisfy the stated conditions. Actually, these systems have a finite cross-sectional extension that can be altered by longitudinal stresses; thus, their properties depend to some extent on their respective cross-sectional dimensions, but we shall assume that such effects can be neglected.

244

FUNDAMENTAL EQUATIONS

Let us assume an elastic filament of fixed cross-sectional area A is subjected to a tensile force τ. The thermodynamic state of the filament is determined by the internal energy E, the length L, and the number of moles N. It follows that if we know $S(E,L,N)$ or $E(S,L,N)$, we have a complete thermodynamic description of the filament.

By making Legendre transformations of $E(S,L,N)$ or $S(E,L,N)$, we can obtain other thermodynamic potentials, that when expressed in terms of their respective characteristic variables, also contain a complete thermodynamic description of the filament. In particular, if we know $E - TS$ as a function of T, L, and N; or $E - \tau L$ as a function of S, τ, and N; or $E - TS - \tau L$ as a function of T, τ, and N; we then know everything that can be known thermodynamically about the filament.

FIRST DERIVATIVES

If a fixed mass of an elastic filament undergoes a quasistatic change in length, then

$$dE = \left(\frac{\partial E}{\partial S}\right)_{L,N} dS + \left(\frac{\partial E}{\partial L}\right)_{S,N} dL \qquad (29.1)$$

From the definition of temperature,

$$\left(\frac{\partial E}{\partial S}\right)_{L,N} = T \qquad (29.2)$$

For an adiabatic quasistatic change Equation (29.1) becomes

$$dE = \left(\frac{\partial E}{\partial L}\right)_{S,N} dL \qquad (29.3)$$

while, from the first postulate, for such a process,

$$dE = dW = \tau dL \qquad (29.4)$$

From (29.3) and (29.4), it follows that

$$\left(\frac{\partial E}{\partial L}\right)_{S,N} = \tau \qquad (29.5)$$

Combining Equations (29.1), (29.2), and (29.5), we obtain for a quasistatic change in length

$$dE = TdS + \tau dL \qquad (29.6)$$

This result is identical with that obtained for a simple, closed, one-component system in Part 1, except that V is replaced by L and p by $-\tau$. It follows that all the results derived for such a system can be applied to elastic filaments, if we simply replace V by L and p by $-\tau$.

From (29.6) we can also obtain the first derivatives of the three Legendre transformations introduced in the preceding section. Thus, for a filament of fixed mass, we find

$$d(E - TS) = -SdT + \tau dL \tag{29.7}$$

$$d(E - \tau L) = TdS - Ld\tau \tag{29.8}$$

$$d(E - TS - \tau L) = -SdT - Ld\tau \tag{29.9}$$

From Equations (29.6), (29.7), (29.8), and (29.9), we obtain the Maxwell relations:

$$\left(\frac{\partial T}{\partial L}\right)_{S,N} = \left(\frac{\partial \tau}{\partial S}\right)_{L,N} \tag{29.10}$$

$$-\left(\frac{\partial S}{\partial L}\right)_{T,N} = \left(\frac{\partial \tau}{\partial T}\right)_{L,N} \tag{29.11}$$

$$\left(\frac{\partial T}{\partial \tau}\right)_{S,N} = -\left(\frac{\partial L}{\partial S}\right)_{\tau,N} \tag{29.12}$$

$$-\left(\frac{\partial S}{\partial \tau}\right)_{T,N} = -\left(\frac{\partial L}{\partial T}\right)_{\tau,N} \tag{29.13}$$

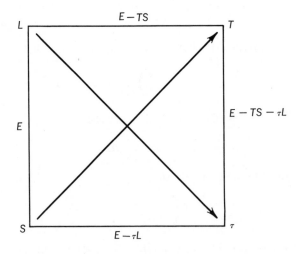

FIGURE 29.1

The same results could have been obtained directly from Equations (28.8), (28.9), and (28.10) in Chapter 28. All the above results are summarized in the mnemonic diagram shown in Figure 29.1.

SECOND DERIVATIVES

In place of the coefficients α, β, c_p, and c_V, which were introduced earlier, we make use of the following coefficients in our study of elastic filaments.

$$\alpha_L \equiv \frac{1}{L}\left(\frac{\partial L}{\partial T}\right)_{\tau,N} \equiv \frac{1}{L}\left(\frac{\partial S}{\partial \tau}\right)_{T,N} \tag{29.14}$$

$$\beta_L \equiv \frac{1}{L}\left(\frac{\partial L}{\partial \tau}\right)_{T,N} \tag{29.15}$$

$$c_\tau \equiv \frac{T}{N}\left(\frac{\partial S}{\partial T}\right)_{\tau,N} \tag{29.16}$$

$$c_L \equiv \frac{T}{N}\left(\frac{\partial S}{\partial T}\right)_{L,N} \tag{29.17}$$

where α_L is called the linear coefficient of thermal expansion; β_L the linear isothermal compressibility; c_τ the specific heat at constant tension; and c_L the specific heat at constant length.

Rather than β_L, it is usually more convenient to use

$$Y_T \equiv \frac{L}{A}\left(\frac{\partial \tau}{\partial L}\right)_{T,N} = \frac{1}{A\beta_L} \tag{29.18}$$

where Y_T is called the isothermal modulus of elasticity, or the isothermal Young's modulus. The isothermal modulus of elasticity Y_T is a characteristic of the material out of which the filament is made and does not depend on the cross-sectional area of the filament, as is the case with β_L.

Any derivative encountered in the study of elastic filaments can be reduced to an expression containing only the quantities S, L, N, T, τ, c_τ, α_L, and β_L. For example,

$$c_L = \frac{T}{N}\left(\frac{\partial S}{\partial T}\right)_{L,N} = \frac{TJ\left(\dfrac{S,L,N}{T,\tau,N}\right)}{NJ\left(\dfrac{T,L,N}{T,\tau,N}\right)}$$

$$= \frac{T\left[\left(\dfrac{\partial S}{\partial T}\right)_{\tau,N}\left(\dfrac{\partial L}{\partial \tau}\right)_{T,N} - \left(\dfrac{\partial S}{\partial \tau}\right)_{T,N}\left(\dfrac{\partial L}{\partial T}\right)_{\tau,N}\right]}{N\left(\dfrac{\partial L}{\partial \tau}\right)_{T,N}}$$

$$= c_\tau - \frac{\alpha_L^2 LT}{N\beta_L} \tag{29.19}$$

THE EQUATION OF STATE

At a given temperature, the fractional increase in the lengths of many filaments will be proportional to the tension in the respective filaments. This law is called Hooke's law and can be written

$$\tau = K(T)\left[\frac{L - L_0(T)}{L_0(T)}\right] \tag{29.20}$$

where the constant of proportionality K and the length at zero tension are functions of temperature.

EXAMPLE

Problem. When the length of a stretched rubber band is rapidly decreased, the temperature of the rubber band also decreases. To demonstrate this property, hold a stretched rubber band against your forehead; allow it to come to thermal equilibrium; and then suddenly release the tension, while maintaining the rubber band in contact with your forehead. Use the above property to show theoretically that when the tension on a rubber band is maintained constant and the rubber band heated, the rubber band will shrink. To demonstrate the latter fact, hang a weight on the rubber band, hold a match close to the rubber band, playing the flame up and down to avoid burning the rubber band, and observe the rise of the weight.

Solution. If the length of a stretched rubber band is rapidly decreased, the process can be considered as a quasistatic adiabatic process. The observed decrease in temperature in this process can be expressed mathematically by writing $(\partial T/\partial L)_{S,N} > 0$. We shall use this fact to show that $(\partial L/\partial T)_{\tau,N} < 0$, that is, if the temperature of the rubber band is increased and the tension held constant, the length will decrease. To show this, we note that if we reduce the above two derivatives to expressions in terms of S, L, N, T, τ, c_τ, c_L, α_L, and β_L, we obtain

$$\left(\frac{\partial T}{\partial L}\right)_{S,N} = -\frac{\alpha_L T}{N c_L \beta_L}$$

$$\left(\frac{\partial L}{\partial T}\right)_{\tau,N} = \alpha_L L$$

In order that the system be intrinsically stable, it is necessary that $c_L > 0$ and $\beta_L > 0$. Thus, if the first expression above is positive, $\alpha_L < 0$; therefore, the second expression must be negative.

PROBLEMS

29.1 Show that the ratio of the adiabatic modulus of elasticity $Y_S = (1/A)$ $(\partial \tau/\partial L)_{S,N}$ to the isothermal modulus of elasticity $Y_T = (1/A)$ $(\partial \tau/\partial L)_{T,N}$ is given by $Y_S/Y_T = c_\tau/c_L$.

29.2 The linear coefficient of thermal expansion of copper is positive. If a piece of copper wire is stretched elastically, does its temperature rise or fall?

29.3 The tension in a steel wire of length 1 m, diameter 1 mm, and temperature 300°K is increased reversibly and isothermally from 0 to 10^8 dyn.
(a) How much heat in joules is transferred to the wire?
(b) How much work in joules is done on the wire?
(c) What is the change in internal energy of the wire?
(d) What would the temperature change be if the process were carried out isentropically?
Assume: $\alpha_L = 12.0 \times 10^{-6}$ (°K)$^{-1}$; $Y_T = 2.00 \times 10^{12}$ dyn (cm)$^{-2}$; $\rho = 7.86$ g (cm)$^{-3}$; and $c_\tau' = 0.115$ cal (g)$^{-1}$(°K)$^{-1}$, where ρ is the density and c_τ' the specific heat at constant tension per gram.

29.4 An elastic filament is such that when stretched by a force τ, the extension x is given by the equation $a[1 + b(T - T_0)]x = c(T - T_0) + \tau$, where a, b, c, and T_0 are positive constants. When the filament is maintained at a constant length and heated, its heat capacity is given by $C = AT$. Show that:
(a) A is independent of x.

(b) The entropy is given by $S = S_0 + cx - (abx^2/2) + A(T - T_0)$, where S_0 is the value of S when $x = 0$ and $T = T_0$.

(c) If the filament is heated under no tension, the heat capacity is given by $C = \{A + a^{-1}c^2[1 + b(T - T_0)]^{-3}\}T$.

(d) For small extensions under adiabatic condition the filament cools.

(e) When the adiabatic extension is increased so that $x > c/ab$, the filament starts to get warmer.

CHAPTER 30

Magnetic Systems

INTRODUCTION

If a magnetizable substance is placed in a static magnetic field, the randomly distributed atomic currents and magnetic moments within the sample will become partially aligned and will produce a net macroscopic magnetic moment per unit volume $\mathfrak{M}$ which we call the magnetization.

The value of the magnetization will depend not only on the strength of the applied magnetic field and the nature of the substance, but on the temperature; hence, magnetization is a subject for thermodynamic analysis.

WORK

The work required to increase infinitesimally the magnetic field within a volume V that contains a magnetizable substance is given by

$$dW' = \int \mathfrak{IC} \cdot d\mathfrak{B} dV \tag{30.1}$$

where $\mathfrak{IC}$ is the magnetic intensity, and

$$\mathfrak{B} \equiv \mu_0 \mathfrak{IC} + \mu_0 \mathfrak{M} \tag{30.2}$$

is the magnetic induction. The constant μ_0, which should not be confused with the chemical potential, has the value

$$\mu_0 = 4\pi \times 10^{-7} \text{ Wb(A)}^{-1}\text{(m)}^{-1} \tag{30.3}$$

tute (30.2) in (30.1), we obtain

$$dW' = \mu_0 \int (\mathfrak{IC} \cdot d\mathfrak{IC}) dV + \mu_0 \int (\mathfrak{IC} \cdot d\mathfrak{M}) dV \tag{30.4}$$

The first term on the right-hand side of Equation (30.4), present even when there is no matter in the volume V, is the work required to increase the magnetic intensity in empty space. The second term on the right-hand side of Equation (30.4) is the work done in increasing the magnetization

251

of the material; we shall interpret this term as the work done on the magnetic system. Thus

$$dW = \mu_0 \int (\mathfrak{IC} \cdot d\mathfrak{M}) dV \tag{30.5}$$

If $\mathfrak{IC}$ and $\mathfrak{M}$ are constant and parallel throughout the volume V, then

$$dW = \mu_0 \mathfrak{IC} d(\mathfrak{M}V) \tag{30.6}$$

The quantity $\mathfrak{M}V$ is the total magnetic moment of the sample, which we shall designate by the letter M, that is,

$$M \equiv \mathfrak{M}V \tag{30.7}$$

If we substitute (30.7) in (30.6), we obtain

$$dW = \mu_0 \mathfrak{IC} dM \tag{30.8}$$

FUNDAMENTAL EQUATION

The equilibrium state of a homogeneous substance in the presence of a homogeneous field $\mathfrak{IC}$ is uniquely determined by the extensive variables E, V, N, and M. The thermodynamic properties of such a system are known if the entropy S of the system is known as a function of E, V, N, and M. Alternatively, if $E(S,V,N,M)$ or any of the Legendre transformations of E, as a function of its characteristic variables, is known, then we have a complete thermodynamic description of the system. There are fourteen nonvanishing Legendre transformations of $E(S,V,N,M)$.

THE FIRST DERIVATIVES

If the system discussed in the preceding section undergoes a quasistatic change, then

$$dE = \left(\frac{\partial E}{\partial S}\right)_{V,N,M} dS + \left(\frac{\partial E}{\partial V}\right)_{S,N,M} dV + \left(\frac{\partial E}{\partial N}\right)_{S,V,M} dN + \left(\frac{\partial E}{\partial M}\right)_{S,V,N} dM \tag{30.9}$$

From our discussions of simple systems in Part 1, we can identify

$$\left(\frac{\partial E}{\partial S}\right)_{V,N,M} = T \tag{30.10}$$

$$\left(\frac{\partial E}{\partial V}\right)_{S,N,M} = -p \tag{30.11}$$

$$\left(\frac{\partial E}{\partial N}\right)_{S,V,M} = \mu \tag{30.12}$$

To identify the remaining intensive variable, we note that if the volume and mole number are held constant and if the system undergoes a quasistatic adiabatic change in the field, then from Equation (30.9),

$$dE = \left(\frac{\partial E}{\partial M}\right)_{S,V,N} dM \tag{30.13}$$

and from (30.8)

$$dE = dW = \mu_0 \mathfrak{IC} dM \tag{30.14}$$

Comparing (30.13) and (30.14), we obtain

$$\left(\frac{\partial E}{\partial M}\right)_{S,V,N} = \mu_0 \mathfrak{IC} \tag{30.15}$$

Substituting Equations (30.10), (30.11), (30.12), and (30.15) in (30.9), we obtain

$$dE = TdS - pdV + \mu dN + \mu_0 \mathfrak{IC} dM \tag{30.16}$$

THE EQUATION OF STATE

From a microscopic point of view, the magnetization of many paramagnetic and ferromagnetic materials can be shown to be given approximately by Brillouin's equation,

$$\mathfrak{M} = \frac{NAm_0}{V}\left\{\left(\frac{2J+1}{2J}\right) \coth\left[\left(\frac{2J+1}{2J}\right)\frac{m_0\mu_0(\mathfrak{IC}+\gamma\mathfrak{M})}{kT}\right] \right.$$
$$\left. - \left(\frac{1}{2J}\right) \coth\left[\left(\frac{1}{2J}\right)\frac{m_0\mu_0(\mathfrak{IC}+\gamma\mathfrak{M})}{kT}\right]\right\} \tag{30.17}$$

where A is Avogadro's number; m_0 is the magnetic moment of one of the molecules (or ions); J is the intrinsic angular momentum of one of the molecules (or ions) in units of $h/2\pi$, where h is Planck's constant; γ is a constant that is different for different materials; and $k \equiv R/A$ is Boltzmann's constant. For paramagnetic substances $\gamma \approx 0$. Numerous approximations to Equation (30.17) are frequently employed; they are obtained by noting that coth $x \approx (1/x) + (x/3)$ for small x. Thus, if J is large, then Equation (30.17) can be approximated by the equation

$$\mathfrak{M} = \frac{NAm_0}{V}\left\{\coth\left[\frac{m_0\mu_0(\mathfrak{K} + \gamma\mathfrak{M})}{kT}\right] - \frac{kT}{m_0\mu_0(\mathfrak{K} + \gamma\mathfrak{M})}\right\} \quad (30.18)$$

which is known as the Langevin–Weiss equation. And if $kT \gg m_0\mu_0(\mathfrak{K} + \gamma\mathfrak{M})$, Equation (30.17) can be approximated by the equation

$$\mathfrak{M} = \frac{C(\mathfrak{K} + \gamma\mathfrak{M})}{T} \quad (30.19)$$

where C, Curie's constant, is given by

$$C = \left(\frac{J+1}{J}\right)\left(\frac{NAm_0^2\mu_0}{3\,kV}\right) \quad (30.20)$$

Solving for $\mathfrak{M}$, we obtain the Curie–Weiss equation,

$$\mathfrak{M} = \frac{C\mathfrak{K}}{T - \theta} \quad (30.21)$$

where $\theta = C\gamma$. This equation can be shown to be generally valid as long as $T > |\theta|$ and the fields are not extremely high. For ferromagnetic materials, θ is usually fairly large. For example, for iron $\theta = 1093°\text{K}$. For paramagnetic materials $\theta \approx 0$. If we set $\theta = 0$ in Equation (30.21), we obtain Curie's equation

$$\mathfrak{M} = \frac{C\mathfrak{K}}{T} \quad (30.22)$$

SPECIFIC HEAT

To determine the dependence of the specific heat of a magnetic system on the magnetic field $\mathfrak{K}$, we note first that

$$d(E - TS - \mu_0\mathfrak{K}M) = -S\,dT - p\,dV + \mu\,dN - \mu_0M\,d\mathfrak{K} \quad (30.23)$$

from which we obtain the Maxwell relation,

$$\frac{\partial S(T,V,N,\mathcal{H})}{\partial \mathcal{H}} = \mu_0 \frac{\partial M(T,V,N,\mathcal{H})}{\partial T} \qquad (30.24)$$

This same result could also have been obtained by using Equation (28.10) in Chapter 28. Taking the derivative of Equation (30.24) with respect to T, and interchanging the order of differentiation on the left-hand side, we obtain

$$\frac{\partial^2 S(T,V,N,\mathcal{H})}{\partial \mathcal{H} \partial T} = \mu_0 \frac{\partial^2 M(T,V,N,\mathcal{H})}{\partial T^2} \qquad (30.25)$$

If we define the specific heat

$$c_{V,\mathcal{H}} \equiv \frac{T}{N}\left(\frac{\partial S}{\partial T}\right)_{V,\mathcal{H},N} \qquad (30.26)$$

then Equation (30.25) becomes

$$\frac{\partial c_{V\mathcal{H}}(T,V,N,\mathcal{H})}{\partial \mathcal{H}} = \left(\frac{\mu_0 T}{N}\right)\frac{\partial^2 M(T,V,N,\mathcal{H})}{\partial T^2} \qquad (30.27)$$

Integrating over $d\mathcal{H}$ from 0 to $\mathcal{H}$, while holding T, V, and N constant, we obtain

$$c_{V,\mathcal{H}}(T,V,N,\mathcal{H}) = c_{V,\mathcal{H}}(T,V,N,0) + \frac{\mu_0 T}{N}\int_0^{\mathcal{H}} \frac{\partial^2 M(T,V,N,\mathcal{H})}{\partial T^2} \, d\mathcal{H} \qquad (30.28)$$

It follows that if we know the specific heat at zero field and the total magnetic moment as a function of T, V, N, and $\mathcal{H}$, we can obtain the dependence of the specific heat on the field $\mathcal{H}$.

For a substance obeying the Curie–Weiss law, Equation (30.21), we obtain

$$c_{V,\mathcal{H}}(T,V,N,\mathcal{H}) = c_{V,\mathcal{H}}(T,V,N,0) + \frac{CTV\mu_0\mathcal{H}^2}{N(T-\theta)^3} \qquad (30.29)$$

THE MAGNETOCALORIC EFFECT

If a magnetic substance in an applied field $\mathcal{H}$ is insulated from its surroundings, maintained at a constant volume V, and the field $\mathcal{H}$ is changed by an infinitesimal amount $d\mathcal{H}$, the temperature of the substance will also change by an amount

$$dT = \left(\frac{\partial T}{\partial \mathcal{H}}\right)_{S,V,N} d\mathcal{H} \qquad (30.30)$$

The derivative in (30.30) can be written

$$\left(\frac{\partial T}{\partial \mathcal{H}}\right)_{S,V,N} = -\frac{(\partial S/\partial \mathcal{H})_{T,V,N}}{(\partial S/\partial T)_{\mathcal{H},V,N}} \tag{30.31}$$

Making use of Equations (30.24) and (30.26), we obtain

$$\left(\frac{\partial T}{\partial \mathcal{H}}\right)_{S,V,N} = -\frac{\mu_0 T(\partial M/\partial T)_{\mathcal{H},V,N}}{N c_{V,\mathcal{H}}} \tag{30.32}$$

For a magnetic substance obeying the Curie–Weiss law,

$$\left(\frac{\partial M}{\partial T}\right)_{\mathcal{H},V,N} = -\frac{CV\mathcal{H}}{(T-\theta)^2} \tag{30.33}$$

and the specific heat $c_{V,\mathcal{H}}$ is given by Equation (30.29). Substituting (30.33) and (30.29) in (30.32), and the result in (30.30), we obtain

$$dT = \frac{\dfrac{CTV\mu_0\mathcal{H}d\mathcal{H}}{N(T-\theta)^2}}{C_{V,\mathcal{H}}(T,V,N,0) + \dfrac{CTV\mu_0\mathcal{H}^2}{N(T-\theta)^3}} \tag{30.34}$$

For paramagnetic salts, $\theta \approx 0$, and at low temperatures for many such salts

$$C_{V,\mathcal{H}} \approx \frac{\alpha}{T^2} \tag{30.35}$$

where α is a constant. In such cases

$$\frac{dT}{T} = \frac{\beta\mathcal{H}d\mathcal{H}}{\alpha + \beta\mathcal{H}^2} \tag{30.36}$$

where

$$\beta = \frac{CV\mu_0}{N} \tag{30.37}$$

Integrating (30.36), we obtain

$$\frac{T_f}{T_i} = \left[\frac{\alpha + \beta\mathcal{H}_f^2}{\alpha + \beta\mathcal{H}_i^2}\right]^{1/2} \tag{30.38}$$

where the subscripts i and f indicate initial and final values. At sufficiently strong fields, α will be small compared to $\beta\mathcal{H}^2$. Thus a decrease in the field can result in a significant decrease in temperature. This effect is used to obtain very low temperatures. Certain paramagnetic salts are first cooled by means of liquid helium to about 1°K in a strong magnetic field. The salt is then insulated from its surroundings, and the field is switched off, resulting in a decrease in the temperature to a final value of the order of 0.001°K.

PROBLEMS

30.1   Obtain an expression for the entropy S of a paramagnetic substance as a function of T, V, N, and $\mathcal{H}$, using Brillouin's equation with $\gamma = 0$. Assume that the zero-field entropy is known.

30.2   Assuming that the zero-field thermodynamic properties of a paramagnetic substance, satisfying Brillouin's equation with $\gamma = 0$, are completely known, obtain a thermodynamic potential that, when expressed as a function of T, V, N, and $\mathcal{H}$, contains a complete thermodynamic description of the substance.

30.3   One mole of gadolinium sulphate $Gd_2(SO_4)_3 \cdot 8\ H_2O$ is initially at a temperature of 1.5°K in a magnetic field of 10,000 Oe. The gadolinium sulphate then undergoes a constant-volume adiabatic demagnitization to zero field. What is the change in temperature? Assume that: (1) the gadolinium ions satisfy Curie's law; (2) J for each ion $= \frac{7}{2}$; (3) the magnetic moment per ion $= 7\ m_B$ where $m_B = $ a Bohr magneton $= 9.27 \times 10^{-24}$ A m²; and (4) $c_{\mathcal{H},V}(T,V,N,0) = (2.66/T^2)$ J (mole of ions)$^{-1}$(°K)$^{-1}$.

30.4   One mole of nickel is initially at a temperature of 427°C in a magnetic field of 10,000 Oe. The nickel is then adiabatically demagnetized. What is the change in temperature? Data for nickel are: $\theta = 358°C$; $(CV\mu_0/N) = 6.316 \times 10^{-12}$ (MKS units); and $c_{V,\mathcal{H}}\ (T,V,N,0) = 32$ J (mole)$^{-1}$(°K)$^{-1}$.

30.5   Show that the specific heat at constant volume and constant magnetic moment, that is, $c_{V,M}$ of a substance that obeys the Curie–Weiss law, is not a function of $\mathcal{H}$.

30.6   A magnetic substance that obeys the Curie–Weiss law is in contact with a reservoir at a temperature T. How much heat does the system exchange with the reservoir when a small applied field is imposed? Assume that the volume remains constant.

30.7   Show that if the magnetization of a magnetic substance can be expressed as a function of V, N, and $\mathcal{H}/T$, the magnetization will be constant if a change in the magnetic field occurs under constant-volume adiabatic conditions.

CHAPTER 31

INTRODUCTION

If a dielectric material is placed in a static electric field, it will become polarized. The net electric dipole moment per unit volume $\mathcal{P}$ is called the polarization.

The value of the polarization will depend not only on the strength of the applied field and the nature of the material, but also on the temperature; hence, polarization is a subject for thermodynamic analysis.

WORK

The work required to increase infinitesimally the electric field within a volume V that contains a dielectric is given by

$$dW' = \int \mathcal{E} \cdot d\mathcal{D}\, dV \tag{31.1}$$

where $\mathcal{E}$ is the electric field intensity, and

$$\mathcal{D} \equiv \epsilon_0 \mathcal{E} + \mathcal{P} \tag{31.2}$$

is the electric displacement. The constant ϵ_0 has the value

$$\epsilon_0 = 8.854 \times 10^{-12} \text{ F(m)}^{-1} \tag{31.3}$$

If we substitute Equation (31.2) in (31.1), we obtain

$$dW' = \epsilon_0 \int \mathcal{E} \cdot d\mathcal{E} dV + \int \mathcal{E} \cdot d\mathcal{P} dV \tag{31.4}$$

The first term on the right-hand side of Equation (31.4), which will be present even when there is no matter in the volume V, is the work required to increase the electric field in empty space. The second term on the right-hand side of Equation (31.4) is the work done in increasing the polarization of the material; we shall interpret this term as the work done on the dielectric. Thus

$$dW = \int \mathcal{E} \cdot d\mathcal{P} dV \tag{31.5}$$

If $\mathcal{E}$ and $\mathcal{P}$ are constant and parallel throughout the volume V, then

$$dW = \mathcal{E}d(\mathcal{P}V) \tag{31.6}$$

The quantity $\mathcal{P}V$ is the total electric dipole moment of the sample, which we shall designate by the letter P, that is,

$$P = \mathcal{P}V \tag{31.7}$$

If we substitute (31.7) in (31.6), we obtain

$$dW = \mathcal{E}dP \tag{31.8}$$

FUNDAMENTAL EQUATION

The equilibrium state of a homogeneous substance in the presence of a homogeneous electric field $\mathcal{E}$ is uniquely determined by the extensive variables E, V, N, and P. The thermodynamic properties of such a system are

known when $S(E,V,N,P)$, $E(S,V,N,P)$, or any one of the Legendre transformations of $E(S,V,N,P)$ is known as a function of its characteristic
variables.

THE FIRST DERIVATIVES

In analogy with the magnetic system discussed in the preceding chapter,
we obtain

$$dE = TdS - pdV + \mu dN + \mathcal{E}dP \qquad (31.9)$$

THE EQUATION OF STATE

From a microscopic point of view, the polarization of many dilute gases
can be shown to be given approximately by

$$\mathcal{P} = \frac{NA}{V}\left\{\alpha_e\mathcal{E} + \alpha_a\mathcal{E} + p_0\left[\coth\left(\frac{p_0\mathcal{E}}{kT}\right) - \frac{kT}{p_0\mathcal{E}}\right]\right\} \qquad (31.10)$$

where A is avogadros number; p_0 is the permanent electric dipole moment of
one of the molecules; α_e, the electronic polarizability, is a constant and a
measure of the distortion of the electronic charge distribution in a molecule
produced by the electric field; and α_a, the atomic polarizability, is a constant
and a measure of the distortion of the molecular structure produced by the
electric field.

For small x, the function $\coth x - (1/x)$ is approximately equal to $x/3$.
It follows that if $p_0\mathcal{E} \ll kT$, then Equation (31.10) becomes

$$\mathcal{P} = \frac{NA}{V}\left\{\alpha_e + \alpha_a + \frac{p_0^2}{3\,kT}\right\}\mathcal{E} \qquad (31.11)$$

Equations (31.10) and (31.11) can be extended to dense gases if we replace
$\mathcal{E}$ by $\mathcal{E}'$, where

$$\mathcal{E}' = \mathcal{E} + \left(\frac{\mathcal{P}}{3\epsilon_0}\right) \qquad (31.12)$$

Since the extension of Equations (31.10) and (31.11) to liquids and solids
is more complicated, we shall not go into those subjects.

PROBLEMS

31.1   Assuming that $P = NA\chi(T)\mathcal{E}$, where A is Avogadro's number,
and $\chi(T)$, the susceptibility, is a function of temperature only, show
that $E(T,V,N,\mathcal{E}) = E(T,V,N,0) + (NA\mathcal{E}^2/2)[\chi + T(d\chi/dT)]$.

31.2 Given $P(T,V,N,\mathcal{E})$, obtain an expression for the specific heat $c_{V,\mathcal{E}}(T,V,N,\mathcal{E})$,   where $c_{V,\mathcal{E}} \equiv (T/N)(\partial S/\partial T)_{V,\mathcal{E},N}$.   Assume   that $c_{V,\mathcal{E}}(T,V,N,0)$ is known.

31.3 Show that

$$c_{V,\mathcal{E}} - c_{V,P} = \left(\frac{T}{N}\right) \frac{[(\partial P/\partial T)_{\mathcal{E},V,N}]^2}{(\partial P/\partial \mathcal{E})_{T,V,N}}$$

31.4 Assuming that the zero-field thermodynamic properties of a dilute dielectric gas are known, obtain a thermodynamic potential that, when expressed as a function of T, V, N, and $\mathcal{E}$, will contain a complete thermodynamic description of the gas. Assume that $p_0\mathcal{E} \ll kT$.

PART SEVEN

Thermodynamics of Steady States

In the preceding sections, we have restricted our attention to systems in equilibrium states. In the present section, we wish to consider systems whose properties are constant in time but that are not in equilibrium states.

CHAPTER 32

The Basic Principles of the Thermodynamics of Steady States

STEADY STATE

If one end of a metal rod is placed in contact with a heat reservoir at a temperature T_1, and the other in contact with a heat reservoir at a temperature $T_2 \neq T_1$, the rod will eventually reach a state in which its properties remain constant in time. In addition, there will be a steady flow of energy from the high-temperature to the low-temperature reservoir. Although the properties of the rod in this state remain constant in time, the rod is not in thermodynamic equilibrium. The rod cannot be isolated from its surroundings without destruction of the state in which it is; and even though the state of the rod is constant in time, the states of the reservoirs with which it is in contact are changing; as a result the entropy of the universe is steadily increasing. A state of a system that remains constant in time but requires the production of entropy to maintain it is called a steady state.

ENTROPY PRODUCTION

Let us suppose we have a system in a steady state. For the sake of simplicity, let us assume the system is in the shape of a cylinder of cross-sectional area A and that the local properties of the system vary only along

265

the axial direction of the cylinder, which we choose to be the x direction. If we divide the system into segments of thickness Δx that are parallel to the y-z plane, then, as long as the properties of the segments do not change appreciably in a distance Δx, we can treat each of these segments as if it were a homogeneous system whose state is describable in terms of the thermodynamic variables associated with equilibrium states. For the sake of simplicity, let us initially assume the system we are dealing with is a one-component system of the type discussed in Part 1, and let us concentrate on the segment that falls between x and $x + \Delta x$. The segment in question is schematically illustrated by the shaded region in Figure 32.1.

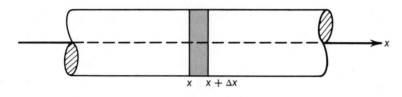

$$x \quad x + \Delta x$$

FIGURE 32.1

If we are interested only in this portion of the system, we can replace the remainder of the system by two heat and particle reservoirs, which have temperatures of $T(x)$ and $T(x + \Delta x)$, respectively, and chemical potentials of $\mu(x)$ and $\mu(x + \Delta x)$, respectively. This situation is schematically illustrated in Figure 32.2. We shall designate the reservoirs by the numbers 1

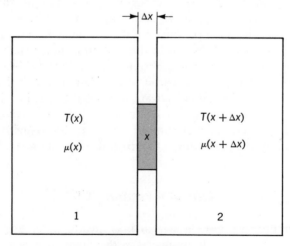

FIGURE 32.2

and 2, respectively, and the segment by the letter x. The total entropy of the three systems is given by

$$S = S_1(E_1,V_1,N_1) + S_2(E_2,V_2,N_2) + S_x(E_x,V_x,N_x) \tag{32.1}$$

The total rate of entropy production is given by

$$\frac{dS}{dt} = \frac{dS_1}{dt} + \frac{dS_2}{dt} + \frac{dS_x}{dt} \tag{32.2}$$

The first term on the right-hand side of Equation (32.2) can be written

$$\frac{dS_1}{dt} = \left(\frac{\partial S_1}{\partial E_1}\right)_{V_1,N_1} \frac{dE_1}{dt} + \left(\frac{\partial S_1}{\partial V_1}\right)_{E_1,N_1} \frac{dV_1}{dt} + \left(\frac{\partial S_1}{\partial N_1}\right)_{E_1,V_1} \frac{dN_1}{dt} \tag{32.3}$$

Assuming the volume of the reservoir is not changing, and replacing the partial derivatives by their definitions in terms of μ and T, we obtain

$$\frac{dS_1}{dt} = \frac{1}{T(x)} \frac{dE_1}{dt} - \frac{\mu(x)}{T(x)} \frac{dN_1}{dt} \tag{32.4}$$

Similarly, for the second term on the right-hand side of Equation (32.2), we obtain

$$\frac{dS_2}{dt} = \frac{1}{T(x + \Delta x)} \frac{dE_2}{dt} - \frac{\mu(x + \Delta x)}{T(x + \Delta x)} \frac{dN_2}{dt} \tag{32.5}$$

And since the properties of the system x are not changing with time,

$$\frac{dS_x}{dt} = 0 \tag{32.6}$$

Since the total number of molecules and the total internal energy of the composite system, made up of reservoir 1, reservoir 2, and system x, remain constant, we have

$$N_1 + N_x + N_2 = \text{const} \tag{32.7}$$

$$E_1 + E_x + E_2 = \text{const} \tag{32.8}$$

But the properties of system x are not changing with time, and therefore N_x and E_x are constant. It follows that

$$N_1 + N_2 = \text{const} \tag{32.9}$$

$$E_1 + E_2 = \text{const} \tag{32.10}$$

From (32.9) and (32.10), it follows that

$$\frac{dN_1}{dt} = -\frac{dN_2}{dt} \tag{32.11}$$

and

$$\frac{dE_1}{dt} = -\frac{dE_2}{dt} \tag{32.12}$$

Combining Equations (32.2), (32.4), (32.5), (32.6), (32.11), and (32.12), we obtain

$$\frac{dS}{dt} = \left[\frac{1}{T(x + \Delta x)} - \frac{1}{T(x)}\right]\frac{dE_2}{dt} - \left[\frac{\mu(x + \Delta x)}{T(x + \Delta x)} - \frac{\mu(x)}{T(x)}\right]\frac{dN_2}{dt} \tag{32.13}$$

Letting Δx approach zero, we obtain

$$\lim_{\Delta x \to 0}\left[\frac{1}{T(x + \Delta x)} - \frac{1}{T(x)}\right] = \frac{d}{dx}\left[\frac{1}{T(x)}\right]\Delta x \tag{32.14}$$

$$\lim_{\Delta x \to 0}\left[\frac{\mu(x + \Delta x)}{T(x + \Delta x)} - \frac{\mu(x)}{T(x)}\right] = \frac{d}{dx}\left[\frac{\mu(x)}{T(x)}\right]\Delta x \tag{32.15}$$

Substituting (32.14) and (32.15) in (32.13), we obtain

$$\frac{dS}{dt} = \frac{d}{dx}\left[\frac{1}{T(x)}\right]\Delta x\,\frac{dE_2}{dt} + \frac{d}{dx}\left[-\frac{\mu(x)}{T(x)}\right]\Delta x\,\frac{dN_2}{dt} \tag{32.16}$$

If we divide Equation (32.16) by the volume of system x,

$$V_x = A\,\Delta x \tag{32.17}$$

then we obtain

$$\frac{d}{dt}\left[\frac{S}{V_x}\right] = \frac{d}{dx}\left[\frac{1}{T(x)}\right]\frac{1}{A}\frac{dE_2}{dt} + \frac{d}{dx}\left[-\frac{\mu(x)}{T(x)}\right]\frac{1}{A}\frac{dN_2}{dt} \tag{32.18}$$

The quantities $(1/A)dE_2/dt$ and $(1/A)dN_2/dt$ are the respective rates of energy and mole flow per unit area in the x direction and will be designated by the symbols J_E and J_N, respectively. Thus

$$J_E = \frac{1}{A}\frac{dE_2}{dt} \tag{32.19}$$

$$J_N = \frac{1}{A}\frac{dN_2}{dt} \tag{32.20}$$

The quantities J_E and J_N are called flux densities, or in those cases where no confusion is likely to arise, simply fluxes. The term on the left-hand side of (32.18) will be designated as θ, that is,

$$\theta \equiv \frac{d}{dt}\left(\frac{S}{V_x}\right) \tag{32.21}$$

and will be called the entropy production per unit volume per unit time, or in cases where no confusion is likely to arise, simply the entropy production. The name arises from the fact that if we choose to view entropy as a fluid, then, since more entropy is flowing into the low-temperature reservoir than is flowing out of the high-temperature reservoir, entropy must be being produced within the system x to compensate for the difference. Since the net rate of increase of the entropy of the reservoirs is equal to dS/dt, then the rate at which entropy is being produced within the system x will also be equal to dS/dt; and the rate of entropy production per unit volume per unit time in the system x will be equal to dS/dt divided by the volume of the system x. Substituting Equations (32.19), (32.20), and (32.21) in Equation (32.18), we obtain

$$\theta = \frac{d}{dx}\left(\frac{1}{T}\right)J_E + \frac{d}{dx}\left(-\frac{\mu}{T}\right)J_N \tag{32.22}$$

If we had considered a situation in which the properties varied in more than one direction, the entropy production would be given by

$$\theta = \nabla\left(\frac{1}{T}\right)\cdot \mathbf{J}_E + \nabla\left(-\frac{\mu}{T}\right)\cdot \mathbf{J}_N \tag{32.23}$$

where $\mathbf{J}_E$ and $\mathbf{J}_N$ are vector flux densities. Letting the three spatial directions be x_1, x_2, and x_3, we could alternatively have written Equation (32.23) as

$$\theta = \sum_{j=1}^{3}\frac{\partial}{\partial x_j}\left[\frac{1}{T}\right]J_{Ej} + \sum_{j=1}^{3}\frac{\partial}{\partial x_j}\left[-\frac{\mu}{T}\right]J_{Nj} \tag{32.24}$$

where J_{Ej} and J_{Nj} are the jth components of the fluxes $\mathbf{J}_E$ and $\mathbf{J}_N$.

If we had considered general systems in which the characteristic variables for the entropy were the extensive variables V, Y_1, Y_2, $\cdots$, Y_n, then the entropy production would be given by

$$\theta = \sum_{i=1}^{n}\nabla\left[\frac{\partial S(V,Y_1,Y_2,\cdots,Y_n)}{\partial Y_i}\right]\cdot \mathbf{J}_i \tag{32.25}$$

where $\mathbf{J}_i$ is the vector flux density of the quantity Y_i. Letting the three spatial directions be x_1, x_2, and x_3, we could alternatively have written Equation (32.25) as

$$\theta = \sum_{i=1}^{n} \sum_{j=1}^{3} \frac{\partial}{\partial x_j} \left[\frac{\partial S(V, Y_1, Y_2, \cdots, Y_n)}{\partial Y_i} \right] J_{ij} \tag{32.26}$$

where J_{ij} is the jth component of the flux of the quantity Y_i.

EXTERNAL POTENTIALS

In the analysis at the beginning of the preceding section, we assumed that the total internal energy of the composite system, consisting of the two reservoirs 1 and 2 and the system x, remained constant. However, if the system x is in an external electric or gravitational field that is capable of exerting a significant force on the particles, then the work done by this force as a particle moves from one point to another must be taken into account, and the total internal energy is no longer conserved.

To find the change that such a field makes necessary in our analysis, let us reconsider the one-dimensional situation discussed at the beginning of the preceding section. However, let us assume that, in addition to the thermodynamic forces produced by the gradients of the chemical potential and temperature, the particles are also in an external force field that is describable by a potential $\psi(x)$, where $\psi(x)$ represents the potential energy per mole at the point x due to the external field. The reservoir 1 will be assumed to be at a potential $\psi(x)$, and the reservoir 2 at a potential $\psi(x + \Delta x)$. The total entropy production will still be given by Equation (32.3), with dS_1/dt, dS_2/dt, and dS_x/dt given by Equations (32.4), (32.5), and (32.6), respectively. Furthermore, since the total number of molecules of the composite system, consisting of the reservoirs 1 and 2 and the system x, remain constant, Equations (32.9) and (32.11) also are still valid. However, Equations (32.10) and (32.12) are *not* valid since the total internal energy is not conserved. In place of Equation (32.10), we now have the conservation equation

$$E_1 + N_1 \psi(x) + E_2 + N_2 \psi(x + \Delta x) = \text{const} \tag{32.27}$$

From (32.27), it follows that

$$\frac{dE_1}{dt} = -\frac{dE_2}{dt} - \psi(x) \frac{dN_1}{dt} - \psi(x + \Delta x) \frac{dN_2}{dt} \tag{32.28}$$

Combining (32.2), (32.4), (32.5), (32.6), (32.11), and (32.28), we now obtain

$$\frac{dS}{dt} = \left[\frac{1}{T(x + \Delta x)} - \frac{1}{T(x)}\right]\frac{dE_2}{dt}$$

$$- \left\{\left[\frac{\mu(x + \Delta x)}{T(x + \Delta x)} - \frac{\mu(x)}{T(x)}\right] + \frac{1}{T(x)}[\psi(x + \Delta x) - \psi(x)]\right\}\frac{dN_2}{dt} \quad (32.29)$$

In the limit as Δx approaches zero, we obtain

$$\frac{dS}{dt} = \frac{d}{dx}\left[\frac{1}{T(x)}\right]\Delta x \frac{dE_2}{dt} - \left\{\frac{d}{dx}\left[\frac{\mu(x)}{T(x)}\right] + \frac{1}{T(x)}\frac{d}{dx}[\psi(x)]\right\}\Delta x \frac{dN_2}{dt} \quad (32.30)$$

Dividing by $A\Delta x$, where A is the cross-sectional area of the system x, and proceeding as before, we obtain

$$\theta = \frac{d}{dx}\left(\frac{1}{T}\right)J_E - \left[\frac{d}{dx}\left(\frac{\mu}{T}\right) + \frac{1}{T}\frac{d\psi}{dx}\right]J_N \quad (32.31)$$

For the three-dimensional situation, we obtain

$$\theta = \nabla\left(\frac{1}{T}\right)\cdot\mathbf{J}_E - \left[\nabla\left(\frac{\mu}{T}\right) + \frac{1}{T}\nabla\psi\right]\cdot\mathbf{J}_N \quad (32.32)$$

THE HEAT FLUX DENSITY

It is frequently more convenient to express the entropy production θ in terms of the heat flux density than in terms of the energy flux density. If we consider the simple one-dimensional situation studied earlier, we can define the heat flux density as

$$J_Q \equiv \frac{T}{A}\frac{dS_2}{dt} = \frac{1}{A}\left(\frac{dE_2}{dt} - \mu\frac{dN_2}{dt}\right) = J_E - \mu J_N \quad (32.33)$$

If we solve Equation (32.33) for J_E and substitute the result in Equation (32.31), we obtain

$$\theta = \frac{d}{dx}\left(\frac{1}{T}\right)(J_Q + \mu J_N) - \left[\frac{d}{dx}\left(\frac{\mu}{T}\right) + \frac{1}{T}\frac{d\psi}{dx}\right]J_N \quad (32.34)$$

which can be simplified to

$$\theta = \frac{d}{dx}\left(\frac{1}{T}\right)J_Q - \frac{1}{T}\left[\frac{d}{dx}(\mu + \psi)\right]J_N \quad (32.35)$$

For the three-dimensional situation, we have

$$\theta = \nabla\left(\frac{1}{T}\right)\cdot \mathbf{J}_Q - \frac{1}{T}[\nabla(\mu + \psi)]\cdot \mathbf{J}_N \tag{32.36}$$

If more than one species is present, Equation (32.36) becomes

$$\theta = \nabla\left(\frac{1}{T}\right)\cdot \mathbf{J}_Q - \sum_{i=1}^{n}\frac{1}{T}[\nabla(\mu_i + \psi_i)]\cdot \mathbf{J}_i \tag{32.37}$$

where $\mathbf{J}_i$ is the mole flux density associated with species i and n is the number of species present.

TOTAL ENERGY

Instead of the internal energy E, it is sometimes more convenient to deal with the total energy $\bar{E}$, defined as

$$\bar{E} \equiv E + N\psi \tag{32.38}$$

The total energy $\bar{E}$ is merely the sum of the internal energy E and of the potential energy $N\psi$ due to the presence of the external field. The corresponding flux density $J_{\bar{E}}$ is defined as

$$J_{\bar{E}} = J_E + \psi J_N \tag{32.39}$$

If we replace J_E in Equation (32.31) by $J_{\bar{E}} - \psi J_N$, we obtain

$$\theta = \frac{d}{dx}\left(\frac{1}{T}\right)J_{\bar{E}} - \frac{d}{dx}\left(\frac{\mu + \psi}{T}\right)J_N \tag{32.40}$$

THE ELECTROCHEMICAL POTENTIAL

The potential ψ is frequently combined with the chemical potential μ to form a new potential $\bar{\mu}$, that is,

$$\bar{\mu} \equiv \mu + \psi \tag{32.41}$$

If the potential ψ is due to an external electric field, then $\bar{\mu}$ is called the electrochemical potential. For convenience, we shall use the term electrochemical potential for $\bar{\mu}$ quite generally. In terms of the electrochemical potential, Equations (32.40) and (32.35) become

$$\theta = \frac{d}{dx}\left(\frac{1}{T}\right)J_{\bar{E}} - \frac{d}{dx}\left(\frac{\bar{\mu}}{T}\right)J_N \tag{32.42}$$

and

$$\theta = \frac{d}{dx}\left(\frac{1}{T}\right)J_Q - \frac{1}{T}\frac{d\bar{\mu}}{dx} J_N \tag{32.43}$$

respectively.

THERMODYNAMIC FORCES

When we examine the results of the preceding sections, we see that we are always able to write the entropy production in the form

$$\theta = \sum_i F_i J_i \tag{32.44}$$

where J_i is the flux density associated with the transport of some quantity in a particular direction. The quantities F_i that multiply the fluxes in the expression for entropy production are called *thermodynamic forces* or *affinities*. The name force arises from the fact that these quantities are generally the gradients of intensive variables, and it is these gradients that drive the various fluxes and cause the production of entropy. The particular values that the forces assume depend on the choice of the fluxes. For example, if we consider the simple one-dimensional situation resulting in the entropy production given by Equation (32.31), we have

$$\theta = F_E J_E + F_N J_N \tag{32.45}$$

where

$$F_E = \frac{d}{dx}\left(\frac{1}{T}\right) \tag{32.46}$$

and

$$F_N = -\left[\frac{d}{dx}\left(\frac{\mu}{T}\right) + \frac{1}{T}\frac{d\psi}{dx}\right] \tag{32.47}$$

But if we choose to work with J_Q and J_N, rather than with J_E and J_N, the entropy production is given by Equation (32.35), rather than Equation (32.31), and we have

$$\theta = F_Q J_Q + F_N J_N \tag{32.48}$$

where

$$F_Q = \frac{d}{dx}\left(\frac{1}{T}\right) \tag{32.49}$$

$$F_N = -\frac{1}{T}\left[\frac{d}{dx}(\mu + \psi)\right] \tag{32.50}$$

The value of F_N is different in the two cases. Hence, the value of a particular force F_i is not determined by the corresponding flux J_i alone, but by the whole set $\{J_i\}$.

THE PHENOMENOLOGICAL EQUATIONS

The fluxes J_i are functions of the local equilibrium thermodynamic properties of the system and the thermodynamic forces F_i. If we consider the dependence of the flux J_i on all the thermodynamic forces, that is, $F_1, F_2, \cdots, F_m$, and expand in a Taylor series, we obtain

$$J_i(F_1, F_2, \cdots, F_m) = \left[\sum_{n=0}^{\infty}\frac{1}{n!}\left(\sum_{j=1}^{m}F_j\frac{\partial}{\partial u_j}\right)^n J_i(y_1, u_2, \cdots, u_m)\right]_{u_1, u_2, \cdots, u_m = 0}$$

$$\equiv L_i + \sum_j L_{ij}F_j + \sum_j\sum_k L_{ijk}F_jF_k + \cdots \tag{32.51}$$

where the u_i are simply dummy variables. The coefficients in the expansion, that is, L_i, L_{ij}, L_{ijk}, $\cdots$ are called kinetic coefficients and are functions of the local equilibrium thermodynamic properties of the system. When all the thermodynamic forces are zero, the flux J_i will vanish. It follows that

$$L_i = 0 \tag{32.52}$$

Furthermore, if the thermodynamic forces are small enough, the quadratic and higher-order terms in Equation (32.51) can be neglected; we then obtain

$$J_i = \sum_j L_{ij}F_j \tag{32.53}$$

These equations are called the phenomenological equations. From a thermodynamic point of view, the coefficients L_{ij} must be determined experimentally.

THE ONSAGER THEOREM

Although the phenomenological equations derived in the preceding section are useful in organizing a large amount of experimental data, they are not particularly fruitful by themselves in predicting quantitatively new results. However, L. Onsager in 1931 proposed a new theorem that can be stated as follows:

Onsager's Theorem. If the kinetic coefficients L_{ij} are functions of the local thermodynamic variables $y_1, y_2, \cdots, y_n$ and possibly also of the magnetic field intensity $\mathcal{3C}_e$, which would be produced by the sources in the absence of the material we are investigating, then

$$L_{ij}(y_1, y_2, \cdots, y_n, \mathcal{3C}_e) = L_{ji}(y_1, y_2, \cdots, y_n, - \mathcal{3C}_e) \qquad (32.54)$$

From a macroscopic point of view, Onsager's theorem is a postulate that is verifiable by experiment. However, it can be justified from a more fundamental view, using the principles of nonequilibrium statistical mechanics.

The Onsager theorem provides us with a powerful analytical tool for predicting the results of an experiment on the basis of results obtained from an apparently independent experiment. To illustrate this association, we note that from Onsager's theorem and the phenomenological equations, (32.53), excluding the situation in which a magnetic field is present, we obtain

$$\frac{\partial J_i(F_1, F_2, \cdots, F_n)}{\partial F_j} = \frac{\partial J_j(F_1, F_2, \cdots, F_n)}{\partial F_i} \qquad (32.55)$$

Thus, if we know how J_i varies when F_j is changed, we can predict how J_j will vary when F_i is changed. This is analogous to the situation involved when we use Maxwell's relations to connect apparently unrelated quasistatic processes. The similarity between Equation (32.55) and the general expressions for Maxwell's relations obtained in Chapter 28 should be noted.

PROBLEMS

32.1 We are given a set of fluxes J_i, thermodynamic forces F_i, and kinetic coefficients L_{ij} that satisfy the equations $\theta = \sum_i F_i J_i$ and $J_i = \sum_j L_{ij} F_j$.
A new set of fluxes J_i' is defined by the relations $J_i' = \sum_j a_{ij} J_j$, where

a_{ij} are constants, resulting in a new set of thermodynamic forces F_i' and kinetic coefficients L_{ij}'. Show that if coefficients L_{ij} satisfy Onsager's theorem, coefficients L_{ij}' also satisfy Onsager's theorem.

32.2 A gas occupies two regions, 1 and 2, on either side of a barrier M of thickness ℓ, through which the gas may flow. The gas in region 1 is maintained at a constant temperature T by a heat reservoir A and at a constant pressure p by a weighted piston. The gas in region 2 is maintained at a constant temperature $T + dT$ by a heat reservoir B and at a constant pressure $p + dp$ by a weighted piston.

(a) Show that the entropy production per unit length of M is given by

$$\theta = d\left(\frac{1}{T}\right)\frac{dQ_{A1}}{dt} - \frac{v}{T}dp\frac{dN_2}{dt}$$

where dQ_{A1}/dt is the rate at which heat is transferred from the reservoir A to system 1, v is the molar volume of system 1, and dN_2/dt is the rate of increase of the number of moles in system 2.

(b) What thermodynamic forces F_1 and F_2 correspond to the fluxes $J_1 \equiv dQ_{A1}/dt$ and $J_2 \equiv dN_2/dt$?

(c) Find the relationship between $(J_1/J_2)_{dT=0}$ and $(F_1/F_2)_{J_2=0}$.

(d) If the barrier M consists of pores that are small when compared to the mean free path of the gas, then from kinetic theory $(J_1/J_2)_{dT=0} = -RT/2$ for an ideal gas. Show that in this case when $J_2 = 0$, the quantity $pT^{-1/2}$ is a constant as one traverses the barrier.

32.3 Assume an ideal gas with molecules of mass m to be in equilibrium in a uniform gravitational field. The force on a molecule in this field is given by $-\mathbf{k}mg$, where $\mathbf{k}$ is a unit vector in the $+z$ direction and g the acceleration due to gravity. Show that the pressure is given by $p = p_0 \exp(-mgz/kT)$, where p_0 is the value of the pressure at $z = 0$ and $k \equiv R/A$ is Boltzmann's constant. Note that in equilibrium there will be no flux of energy or molecules.

32.4 A two-component ideal gas made up of molecules of masses m_1 and m_2, respectively, is in equilibrium in a uniform gravitational field that is directed in the $-z$ direction. Let $n_1(z)$ and $n_2(z)$ be the respective densities of the two gases, and let $R(z) \equiv n_1(z)/n_2(z)$. Given $R(0)$, find $R(z)$.

CHAPTER 33

Thermoelectric Effects

BASIC EQUATIONS

Let us assume that we have a conducting rod in which an electric current and a heat current are flowing in the axial direction, which we shall designate the x direction. Let us furthermore assume that there is a single type of charge and heat carrier, and that the total charge per mole of the carrier is e. For example, if the charge carriers are electrons, then $e = -(1.6021 \times 10^{-19}) \times (6.025 \times 10^{23})$ C mole^{-1}. Alternatively, if we let N be the number of carriers, rather than the number of moles of carriers, then e will simply be the charge of a carrier. In this case, all molar quantities must be replaced by the corresponding quantity per particle rather than per mole. The equations that we will derive will be consistent with either interpretation. From Equation (32.35) in Chapter 32, the entropy production can be written

$$\theta = \frac{d}{dx}\left(\frac{1}{T}\right)J_Q - \frac{1}{T}\frac{d}{dx}(\mu + \psi)J_N \qquad (33.1)$$

If we choose as fluxes the electric current density, which we designate I, that is,

$$I \equiv eJ_N \qquad (33.2)$$

277

and the heat flux density, which we designate J, that is,

$$J \equiv J_Q \tag{33.3}$$

and if we define the electric potential energy per unit charge by the letter ϕ, that is,

$$\phi = \frac{\psi}{e} \tag{33.4}$$

then the entropy production can be written

$$\theta = -\frac{1}{eT}\frac{d}{dx}(\mu + e\phi)I + \frac{d}{dx}\left(\frac{1}{T}\right)J \tag{33.5}$$

It follows that the thermodynamic forces corresponding to the fluxes I and J are

$$F_I = -\frac{1}{eT}\frac{d}{dx}(\mu + e\phi) \tag{33.6}$$

and

$$F_J = \frac{d}{dx}\left(\frac{1}{T}\right) \tag{33.7}$$

Thus the phenomenological equations are

$$I = -L_{11}\frac{1}{eT}\left[\frac{d}{dx}(\mu + e\phi)\right] + L_{12}\frac{d}{dx}\left(\frac{1}{T}\right) \tag{33.8}$$

$$J = -L_{12}\frac{1}{eT}\left[\frac{d}{dx}(\mu + e\phi)\right] + L_{22}\frac{d}{dx}\left(\frac{1}{T}\right) \tag{33.9}$$

Note that, by virtue of the Onsager theorem, we have set $L_{21} = L_{12}$.

THE ELECTRICAL CONDUCTIVITY

If the conducting rod discussed in the preceding section is homogeneous and is maintained at a constant temperature, then

$$\frac{d\mu}{dx} = 0 \quad \text{and} \quad \frac{d}{dx}\left(\frac{1}{T}\right) = 0 \tag{33.10}$$

Substituting (33.10) in (33.8), we obtain

$$I = -\sigma\frac{d\phi}{dx} \tag{33.11}$$

where

$$\sigma \equiv \frac{L_{11}}{T} \tag{33.12}$$

From (33.12) it follows that the electric current density is proportional to the electric field, $-d\phi/dx$. The constant of proportionality σ is called the electrical conductivity. Equation (33.11) is called Ohm's law.

THE HEAT CONDUCTIVITY

If there is a temperature gradient but no electrical current, that is,

$$I = 0 \tag{33.13}$$

then Equations (33.8) and (33.9) become

$$0 = -L_{11}\frac{1}{eT}\left[\frac{d}{dx}(\mu + e\phi)\right] + L_{12}\frac{d}{dx}\left(\frac{1}{T}\right) \tag{33.14}$$

$$J = -L_{12}\frac{1}{eT}\left[\frac{d}{dx}(\mu + e\phi)\right] + L_{22}\frac{d}{dx}\left(\frac{1}{T}\right) \tag{33.15}$$

Eliminating $d(\mu + e\phi)/dx$, we obtain

$$J = -\kappa\frac{dT}{dx} \tag{33.16}$$

where

$$\kappa \equiv \frac{L_{11}L_{22} - L_{12}^2}{L_{11}T^2} \tag{33.17}$$

From Equation (33.16) it follows that the heat flux is proportional to the negative of the temperature gradient $-dT/dx$. The constant of proportionality κ is called the heat conductivity. Equation (33.16) is called Fourier's law.

THE SEEBECK EFFECT

Let us consider further the situation described by Equations (33.14) and (33.15), which are valid when there is no current flowing. Rearranging (33.14), and introducing the electrochemical potential,

$$\tilde{\mu} = \mu + e\phi \tag{33.18}$$

we obtain

$$\frac{d}{dx}\left(\frac{\tilde{\mu}}{e}\right) = \epsilon\frac{dT}{dx} \tag{33.19}$$

where

$$\epsilon \equiv -\frac{L_{12}}{L_{11}T} \tag{33.20}$$

From Equation (33.19), it follows that if a temperature gradient is maintained in a metal rod through which no current is flowing, a gradient will be produced in the electrochemical potential; and the gradient in the electrochemical potential will be proportional to the temperature gradient. The constant of proportionality ϵ is called the absolute thermoelectric power of the medium.

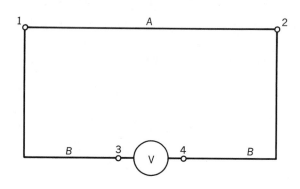

FIGURE 33.1

The effect represented by Equation (33.19) has a very practical application in the thermocouple. Let us suppose we have two dissimilar metal wires A and B and a voltmeter V, which are joined as shown in Figure 33.1 to form a circuit. We assume that the voltmeter will allow a heat flow along the wire B but will not allow a current flow. If junctions 1 and 2 are maintained at different temperatures, and if junctions 3 and 4 are maintained at the same temperature, then it follows from Equation (33.19) that a voltage difference will be generated between the points 3 and 4. This effect is called the Seebeck effect. To demonstrate the existence of this effect, let us integrate Equation (33.19) along the path 3124. Doing this we obtain

$$\frac{1}{e}(\bar{\mu}_4 - \bar{\mu}_3) = \int_{T_3}^{T_1} \epsilon_B dT + \int_{T_1}^{T_2} \epsilon_A dT + \int_{T_2}^{T_4} \epsilon_B dT \qquad (33.21)$$

where ϵ_A snd ϵ_B are the absolute thermoelectric powers of the metals A and B, respectively. Since junctions 3 and 4 are maintained at the same temperature, $T_3 = T_4$; therefore,

$$\int_{T_3}^{T_1} \epsilon_B dT + \int_{T_2}^{T_4} \epsilon_B dT = \int_{T_3}^{T_1} \epsilon_B dT + \int_{T_2}^{T_3} \epsilon_B dT$$

$$= \int_{T_2}^{T_1} \epsilon_B dT = -\int_{T_1}^{T_2} \epsilon_B dT \qquad (33.22)$$

Substituting (33.22) in (33.21), we obtain

$$\frac{1}{e}(\bar{\mu}_4 - \bar{\mu}_3) = \int_{T_1}^{T_2} (\epsilon_A - \epsilon_B)dT \qquad (33.23)$$

Furthermore, since junctions 3 and 4 are at the same temperature, we also have

$$\mu_3 = \mu_4 \qquad (33.24)$$

and therefore,

$$\frac{1}{e}(\bar{\mu}_4 - \bar{\mu}_3) = \phi_4 - \phi_3 \qquad (33.25)$$

Substituting (33.25) in (33.23), we obtain

$$\phi_4 - \phi_3 = \int_{T_1}^{T_2} (\epsilon_A - \epsilon_B)dT \qquad (33.26)$$

The quantity $\phi_4 - \phi_3$ is the voltage difference between the points 3 and 4. The quantity $\epsilon_A - \epsilon_B$ is called the thermoelectric power of the thermocouple. From (33.26), it follows that the voltage difference between points 3 and 4 is a function of the temperature difference between points 1 and 2. If junction 2 is maintained at a constant known temperature, the readings on the voltmeter can then be calibrated in terms of the temperature of junction 1. Once the voltmeter has been calibrated, we can determine the temperature of an unknown substance by simply bringing junction 1 into thermal equilibrium with the substance, maintaining junction 2 at the known temperature, and noting any deflection on the voltmeter.

THE PELTIER EFFECT

If two dissimilar conducting rods are joined together, and a current is then passed across the junction while the junction is maintained at a constant temperature, heat will be evolved at the junction. This effect is known as the Peltier effect.

The Peltier effect also follows from phenomenological Equations (33.8) and (33.9). To show this, let us suppose we have a material in which there is no temperature gradient. From (33.8) and (33.9), it then follows that

$$I = -\frac{L_{11}}{eT}\left[\frac{d}{dx}(\mu + e\phi)\right] \qquad (33.27)$$

$$J = -\frac{L_{12}}{eT}\left[\frac{d}{dx}(\mu + e\phi)\right] \qquad (33.28)$$

Dividing Equation (33.27) by Equation (33.28), we obtain

$$J = \pi I \qquad (33.29)$$

where

$$\pi \equiv \frac{L_{12}}{L_{11}} \qquad (33.30)$$

From (33.30), it follows that when there is no temperature gradient in a conductor, the heat flux will be directly proportional to the current. We shall refer to the constant of proportionality π as the absolute Peltier coefficient.

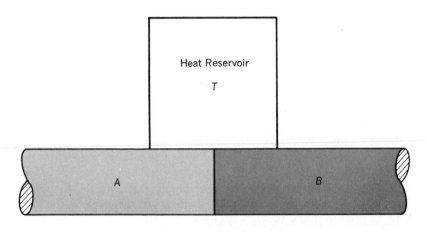

FIGURE 33.2

Let us now suppose two dissimilar conducting rods A and B of unit cross-sectional area are joined at one end, and the junction is kept in contact with a heat reservoir at temperature T, as shown in Figure 33.2. If a current is passed through the junction, the current in A must be equal to the current in B, that is,

$$I_A = I_B \equiv I \qquad (33.31)$$

But in the region of constant temperature, the heat fluxes in A and B are given respectively by

$$J_A = \pi_A I_A \qquad (33.32)$$

$$J_B = \pi_B I_B \qquad (33.33)$$

and therefore, since the current flux density in the two rods is the same, the heat flux densities must be different; hence, heat must be being evolved or absorbed at the junction. If the current is taken to be positive when it moves from A to B, the rate of heat flow from the reservoir is equal to $J_B - J_A$. Combining (33.31), (33.32), and (33.33), we obtain

$$J_B - J_A = (\pi_B - \pi_A)I \qquad (33.34)$$

The quantity $\pi_A - \pi_B$ is called the Peltier coefficient; it is equal to the heat that passes from the junction to the reservoir when a unit electric current passes from conductor A to conductor B.

THE THOMSON EFFECT

If there are no sources of charge along a conductor such as we have been discussing, then in the steady state the electric current will be constant along the length of the conductor, that is,

$$\frac{dI}{dx} = 0 \qquad (33.35)$$

However, if heat sources are present along the length of the wire, and if electric forces act on the charges, the total energy flux in the steady state will not necessarily be a constant throughout the length of the wire.

If we assume the conductor has a unit cross-sectional area, the rate at which energy is supplied per unit length of wire by the external heat sources and the electric field will together be equal to the change in the total energy flux per unit length, that is,

$$\frac{dJ_{\bar{E}}}{dx} \equiv \frac{d}{dx}\,[J_E + \psi J_N]$$

$$= \frac{d}{dx}\,[(J_Q + \mu J_N) + \psi J_N]$$

$$= \frac{d}{dx}\left[J + \left(\frac{\mu + e\phi}{e}\right)I\right] \qquad (33.36)$$

Using (33.35) in (33.36), we obtain

$$\frac{dJ_{\bar{E}}}{dx} = \frac{dJ}{dx} + I\frac{d}{dx}\left(\frac{\mu + e\phi}{e}\right) \qquad (33.37)$$

From the phenomenological equations (33.8) and (33.9), we obtain

$$J = \frac{L_{12}}{L_{11}} I_1 + \left(\frac{L_{11}L_{22} - L_{12}^2}{L_{11}}\right) \frac{d}{dx}\left(\frac{1}{T}\right) \qquad (33.38)$$

$$\frac{d}{dx}\left(\frac{\mu + e\phi}{e}\right) = -\left(\frac{T}{L_{11}}\right)I + \frac{TL_{12}}{L_{11}} \frac{d}{dx}\left(\frac{1}{T}\right) \qquad (33.39)$$

Substituting (33.38) and (33.39) in (33.37), and making use of Equation (33.35), we obtain

$$\frac{dJ_{\bar{E}}}{dx} = \frac{d}{dx}\left(\frac{L_{12}}{L_{11}}\right)I - \frac{d}{dx}\left[\left(\frac{L_{11}L_{22} - L_{12}^2}{L_{11}T^2}\right)\frac{dT}{dx}\right] - \frac{TI^2}{L_{11}} - \frac{L_{12}I}{L_{11}T}\frac{dT}{dx} \qquad (33.40)$$

Substituting

$$\frac{d}{dx}\left(\frac{L_{12}}{L_{11}}\right) = \frac{d}{dT}\left(\frac{L_{12}}{L_{11}}\right)\frac{dT}{dx} \qquad (33.41)$$

in (33.40), and rearranging, we obtain

$$\frac{dJ_{\bar{E}}}{dx} = \left[T\frac{d}{dT}\left(\frac{L_{12}}{L_{11}T}\right)\right]\frac{dT}{dx}I - \frac{d}{dx}\left[\left(\frac{L_{11}L_{22} - L_{12}^2}{L_{11}T^2}\right)\frac{dT}{dx}\right] - \frac{TI^2}{L_{11}} \qquad (33.42)$$

If there is no temperature gradient, then

$$\frac{dJ_{\bar{E}}}{dx} = -\frac{TI^2}{L_{11}} \equiv -\frac{I^2}{\sigma} \qquad (33.43)$$

where σ is the electrical conductivity. Expression (33.43) represents the familiar Joule heat loss.

If there is no electric current, then

$$\frac{dJ_{\bar{E}}}{dx} = -\frac{d}{dx}\left[\left(\frac{L_{11}L_{22} - L_{12}^2}{L_{11}T^2}\right)\frac{dT}{dx}\right] \equiv -\frac{d}{dx}\left[\kappa\frac{dT}{dx}\right] \qquad (33.44)$$

where κ is the heat conductivity. Expression (33.44) represents the heat that would be necessary to maintain a nonlinear thermal gradient in a rod.

The remaining term on the right-hand side of (33.42) represents heat absorbed from the reservoirs when an electric current flows through a conductor in which there is a temperature gradient. Called the Thomson heat, this heat is directly proportional to both the temperature gradient and the electric current. The constant of proportionality is called the Thomson coefficient and will be designated by the letter τ, that is,

$$\tau \equiv T \frac{d}{dT}\left(\frac{L_{12}}{L_{11}T}\right) \tag{33.45}$$

The evolution of heat as an electric current traverses a temperature gradient in a material is called the Thomson effect.

THE THOMSON RELATIONS

In the preceding sections we have discussed five effects; they are: Ohm's law, Fourier's law, the Seebeck effect, the Peltier effect, and the Thomson effect. We have also defined five coefficients; they are: the electrical conductivity σ, the thermal conductivity κ, the absolute thermoelectric power ϵ, the absolute Peltier coefficient π, and the Thomson coefficient τ. However, only three of these coefficients are independent, since all can be expressed in terms of the three kinetic coefficients L_{11}, L_{22}, and L_{12}. It is, therefore, possible to derive two independent equations connecting the five coefficients σ, κ, ϵ, π, and τ. If we choose σ, κ, and ϵ as the fundamental coefficients, then π and τ can be written

$$\pi = -\epsilon T \tag{33.46}$$

$$\tau = -T\frac{d\epsilon}{dT} \tag{33.47}$$

Equation (33.46) is called Thomson's (or Kelvin's) second relation, and Equation (33.47) is called Thomson's (or Kelvin's) first relation. Thomson's first relation is frequently written as

$$\tau = \epsilon + \frac{d\pi}{dT} \tag{33.48}$$

which can be obtained by combining (33.46) and (33.47).

In applications, we are usually not interested in the absolute Peltier coefficient of a material, but rather in the relative Peltier coefficient, or simply Peltier coefficient, defined for a pair of conductors A and B by

$$\pi_{AB} = \pi_A - \pi_B \tag{33.49}$$

Similarly, we are usually interested in the relative thermoelectric power, or simply the thermoelectric power, defined for a pair of conductors A and B by

$$\epsilon_{AB} = \epsilon_A - \epsilon_B \tag{33.50}$$

In terms of these coefficients, the Thomson relations become

$$\pi_{AB} = -\epsilon_{AB}T \tag{33.51}$$

and

$$\tau_A - \tau_B = -T\frac{d\epsilon_{AB}}{dT} \tag{33.52}$$

PROBLEMS

33.1 (a) Obtain an expression, in terms of the temperature gradient dT/dx and the heat conductivity κ, for the entropy production in a conductor in which there is a temperature gradient but no electric current.

(b) Obtain an expression, in terms of the electric current I and the electrical conductivity σ, for the entropy production in an isothermal conductor through which an electric current is flowing.

(c) Obtain an expression, in terms of I, dT/dx, and the coefficients L_{ij}, for the entropy production in a conductor in which there is a temperature gradient and an electrical current.

(d) Show that the expression arrived at in (c) is the sum of those arrived at in (a) and (b).

33.2 A metallic ring consists of three metallic conductors connected in series. The conductors are made of copper, constantan, and iron, respectively. The copper-constantan interface is held at 300°C, the constantan-iron interface is held at 200°C, and the iron-copper interface is held at 100°C. The thermoelectric powers ϵ_{AB} of the copper-constantan, and iron-constantan thermocouples are 3.9 $\times$ 10^{-5}V(°K)$^{-1}$ and 5.0 $\times$ 10^{-5}V(°K)$^{-1}$. If the total electric resistance of the ring is 3 ohms, find the value and direction for the electron current that flows in the ring.

33.3 Show that the electrical conductivity σ and the heat conductivity κ must be positive.

33.4 When one junction of a copper-iron thermocouple is at 273.15°K and the other at a temperature T, the Seebeck emf of the couple is given in volts by $\Delta\phi = a(T - 273.15) + b(T - 273.15)^2 + c(T - 273.15)^3$, where $a = -13.403 \times 10^{-6}$; $b = 13.75 \times 10^{-9}$; and $c = 86.67 \times 10^{-12}$.

(a) Find the Seebeck emf when $T = 373.15$°K.

(b) Find the Peltier coefficient at each junction.

(c) Find the net Thomson coefficient.

33.5 A thermocouple is made of two metals whose respective Thomson coefficients are proportional to the absolute temperature. Show that if one junction is kept at a temperature of 273.15°K and the other at a temperature T, the Seebeck emf $\Delta\phi$ is given by $\Delta\phi = a(T - 273.15) + b(T - 273.15)^2$, where a and b are constants. For a copper-lead couple $a = 2.8 \times 10^{-6} V(°K)^{-2}$ and $b = 6 \times 10^{-9} V(°K)^{-1}$; for a constantan-lead thermocouple $a = 38.1 \times 10^{-6} V(°K)^{-2}$ and $b = 45 \times 10^{-9} V(°K)^{-1}$. Calculate both the Peltier coefficient of a copper-constantan junction and the difference between the Thomson coefficients of copper and constantan at 373.15°K. At what temperature does $\Delta\phi$ for a copper-constantan thermocouple have its maximum value?

CHAPTER 34

BASIC EQUATIONS

Let us assume we have a conducting solid that is in a constant external magnetic field $\mathcal{H}_e$, which is parallel to the z axis. For simplicity, we shall consider the case in which all fluxes and forces are parallel to the x-y plane.

In analogy with Equation (33.5) in Chapter 33, the entropy production is given by

$$\theta = -\frac{1}{eT}\frac{\partial \bar{\mu}}{\partial x} I_x - \frac{1}{eT}\frac{\partial \bar{\mu}}{\partial y} I_y - \frac{1}{T^2}\frac{\partial T}{\partial x} J_x - \frac{1}{T^2}\frac{\partial T}{\partial y} J_y \qquad (34.1)$$

where

$$\bar{\mu} = \mu + e\phi \qquad (34.2)$$

and where I_x and I_y are the x and y components, respectively, of the charge flux density and J_x and J_y are the x and y components, respectively, of the heat flux density. It follows that the forces corresponding to the fluxes I_x, I_y, J_x, and J_y are $-(1/eT)(\partial \bar{\mu}/\partial x)$, $-(1/eT)(\partial \bar{\mu}/\partial y)$, $-(1/T^2)(\partial T/\partial x)$, and $-(1/T^2)(\partial T/\partial y)$, respectively; hence, the phenomenological equations are

$$
\begin{bmatrix} I_x \\ I_y \\ J_x \\ J_y \end{bmatrix} = \begin{bmatrix} L_{11} & L_{12} & L_{13} & L_{14} \\ L_{21} & L_{22} & L_{23} & L_{24} \\ L_{31} & L_{32} & L_{33} & L_{34} \\ L_{41} & L_{42} & L_{43} & L_{44} \end{bmatrix} \begin{bmatrix} -\left(\dfrac{1}{eT}\right)\left(\dfrac{\partial \bar{\mu}}{\partial x}\right) \\ -\left(\dfrac{1}{eT}\right)\left(\dfrac{\partial \bar{\mu}}{\partial y}\right) \\ -\left(\dfrac{1}{T^2}\right)\left(\dfrac{\partial T}{\partial x}\right) \\ -\left(\dfrac{1}{T^2}\right)\left(\dfrac{\partial T}{\partial y}\right) \end{bmatrix}
$$

(34.3)

If we assume that the solid is isotropic in the x-y plane, then not all the kinetic coefficients will be independent. To show this, let us suppose there are no thermal gradients; then from (34.3) we obtain,

$$
\begin{bmatrix} I_x \\ I_y \end{bmatrix} = \begin{bmatrix} L_{11} & L_{12} \\ L_{21} & L_{22} \end{bmatrix} \begin{bmatrix} -\left(\dfrac{1}{eT}\right)\left(\dfrac{\partial \bar{\mu}}{\partial x}\right) \\ -\left(\dfrac{1}{eT}\right)\left(\dfrac{\partial \bar{\mu}}{\partial y}\right) \end{bmatrix}
$$

(34.4)

Since the solid is isotropic in the x-y plane, we do not expect the matrix $[L_{ij}]$ in (34.4) to change if we rotate our reference frame through an angle of $\pi/2$ about the z axis; thus, we expect

$$
\begin{bmatrix} L_{11} & L_{12} \\ L_{21} & L_{22} \end{bmatrix} = \begin{bmatrix} 0 & 1 \\ -1 & 0 \end{bmatrix}\begin{bmatrix} L_{11} & L_{12} \\ L_{21} & L_{22} \end{bmatrix}\begin{bmatrix} 0 & -1 \\ 1 & 0 \end{bmatrix} = \begin{bmatrix} L_{22} & -L_{21} \\ -L_{12} & L_{11} \end{bmatrix}
$$

(34.5)

From (34.5) we obtain $L_{11} = L_{22}$ and $L_{21} = -L_{12}$. In a similar fashion, we can show $L_{13} = L_{24}$, $L_{23} = -L_{14}$, $L_{31} = L_{42}$, $L_{41} = -L_{32}$, $L_{33} = L_{44}$, and $L_{43} = -L_{34}$. Substituting these results in (34.3), we obtain

$$
\begin{bmatrix} I_x \\ I_y \\ J_x \\ J_y \end{bmatrix} = \begin{bmatrix} L_{11} & L_{12} & L_{13} & L_{14} \\ -L_{12} & L_{11} & -L_{14} & L_{13} \\ L_{31} & L_{32} & L_{33} & L_{34} \\ -L_{32} & L_{31} & -L_{34} & L_{33} \end{bmatrix} \begin{bmatrix} -\left(\dfrac{1}{eT}\right)\left(\dfrac{\partial \bar{\mu}}{\partial x}\right) \\ -\left(\dfrac{1}{eT}\right)\left(\dfrac{\partial \bar{\mu}}{\partial y}\right) \\ -\left(\dfrac{1}{T^2}\right)\left(\dfrac{\partial T}{\partial x}\right) \\ -\left(\dfrac{1}{T^2}\right)\left(\dfrac{\partial T}{\partial y}\right) \end{bmatrix}
$$

(34.6)

The Onsager theorem can be used to further reduce, by two, the number of independent coefficients. If we designate a kinetic coefficient in which $\mathfrak{K}_e$ has been replaced by $-\mathfrak{K}_e$ by an asterisk, that is,

$$L_{ij}^{*}(\mathfrak{K}_e) \equiv L_{ij}(-\mathfrak{K}_e) \tag{34.7}$$

Then, from Onsager's theorem,

$$L_{ji} = L_{ij}^{*} \tag{34.8}$$

and thus Equation (34.6) can be further simplified, by noting that $L_{31} = L_{13}^{*}$ and $-L_{32} = L_{41} = L_{14}^{*}$. Substituting these results in (34.6), we obtain

$$
\begin{bmatrix} I_x \\ I_y \\ J_x \\ J_y \end{bmatrix} =
\begin{bmatrix}
L_{11} & L_{12} & L_{13} & L_{14} \\
-L_{12} & L_{11} & -L_{14} & L_{13} \\
L_{13}^{*} & -L_{14}^{*} & L_{33} & L_{34} \\
L_{14}^{*} & L_{13}^{*} & -L_{34} & L_{44}
\end{bmatrix}
\begin{bmatrix}
-\left(\dfrac{1}{eT}\right)\left(\dfrac{\partial\bar{\mu}}{\partial x}\right) \\
-\left(\dfrac{1}{eT}\right)\left(\dfrac{\partial\bar{\mu}}{\partial y}\right) \\
-\left(\dfrac{1}{T^2}\right)\left(\dfrac{\partial T}{\partial x}\right) \\
-\left(\dfrac{1}{T^2}\right)\left(\dfrac{\partial T}{\partial y}\right)
\end{bmatrix}
\tag{34.9}
$$

We can still further simplify Equation (34.9). Consider Equation (34.4). We do not expect the matrix $[L_{ij}]$ in Equation (34.4) to change when we rotate our reference frame through an angle of π about the x axis and also change the sign of $\mathfrak{K}_e$. Thus, we expect

$$
\begin{bmatrix} L_{11} & L_{12} \\ L_{21} & L_{22} \end{bmatrix} =
\begin{bmatrix} 1 & 0 \\ 0 & -1 \end{bmatrix}
\begin{bmatrix} L_{11}^{*} & L_{12}^{*} \\ L_{21}^{*} & L_{22}^{*} \end{bmatrix}
\begin{bmatrix} 1 & 0 \\ 0 & -1 \end{bmatrix}
$$

$$
= \begin{bmatrix} L_{11}^{*} & -L_{12}^{*} \\ -L_{21}^{*} & L_{22}^{*} \end{bmatrix}
\tag{34.10}
$$

From Equation (34.10), it follows that $L_{11} = L_{11}^{*}$ and $L_{12} = -L_{12}^{*}$. In a similar fashion, we can show that $L_{33} = L_{33}^{*}$, $L_{34} = -L_{34}^{*}$, $L_{13} = L_{13}^{*}$, and $L_{14} = -L_{14}^{*}$. Substituting the latter two results in (34.9), we obtain

$$
\begin{bmatrix} I_x \\ I_y \\ J_x \\ J_y \end{bmatrix} =
\begin{bmatrix}
L_{11} & L_{12} & L_{13} & L_{14} \\
-L_{12} & L_{11} & -L_{14} & L_{13} \\
L_{13} & L_{14} & L_{33} & L_{34} \\
-L_{14} & L_{13} & -L_{34} & L_{33}
\end{bmatrix}
\begin{bmatrix}
-\left(\dfrac{1}{eT}\right)\left(\dfrac{\partial\bar{\mu}}{\partial x}\right) \\
-\left(\dfrac{1}{eT}\right)\left(\dfrac{\partial\bar{\mu}}{\partial y}\right) \\
-\left(\dfrac{1}{T^2}\right)\left(\dfrac{\partial T}{\partial x}\right) \\
-\left(\dfrac{1}{T^2}\right)\left(\dfrac{\partial T}{\partial y}\right)
\end{bmatrix}
\tag{34.11}
$$

Equations (34.11) are the basic phenomenological equations that describe thermomagnetic phenomena. We shall, however, find it convenient to recast them in an alternate form in which the coefficients are more directly connected with the commonly encountered experimental coefficients.

We note first that Equation (34.11) can be written as two matrix equations:

$$I = AX + BY \qquad (34.12)$$

$$J = BX + CY \qquad (34.13)$$

where

$$I \equiv \begin{bmatrix} I_x \\ I_y \end{bmatrix} \qquad J \equiv \begin{bmatrix} J_x \\ J_y \end{bmatrix} \qquad (34.14)$$

$$A \equiv \begin{bmatrix} L_{11} & L_{12} \\ -L_{12} & L_{11} \end{bmatrix} \quad B \equiv \begin{bmatrix} L_{13} & L_{14} \\ -L_{14} & L_{13} \end{bmatrix} \quad C \equiv \begin{bmatrix} L_{33} & L_{34} \\ -L_{34} & L_{33} \end{bmatrix} \qquad (34.15)$$

$$X \equiv \begin{bmatrix} -\left(\frac{1}{eT}\right)\left(\frac{\partial \bar{\mu}}{\partial x}\right) \\ -\left(\frac{1}{eT}\right)\left(\frac{\partial \bar{\mu}}{\partial y}\right) \end{bmatrix} \qquad Y = \begin{bmatrix} -\left(\frac{1}{T^2}\right)\left(\frac{\partial T}{\partial x}\right) \\ -\left(\frac{1}{T^2}\right)\left(\frac{\partial T}{\partial y}\right) \end{bmatrix} \qquad (34.16)$$

Solving (34.12) and (34.13) for X and J in terms of I and Y, we obtain

$$X = A^{-1}I - A^{-1}BY \qquad (34.17)$$

$$J = BA^{-1}I + (C - BA^{-1}B)Y \qquad (34.18)$$

From the symmetry of the matrices A, B, and C, it can be shown that the matrices A^{-1}, $A^{-1}B$, and $(C - BA^{-1}B)$ have the same type of symmetry as A, B, and C, and also that $A^{-1}B = BA^{-1}$. It follows that (34.17) and (34.18) can be written in the form

$$X = LI + MY \qquad (34.19)$$

$$J = -MI + NY \qquad (34.20)$$

where L, M, and N are matrices having the same type of symmetry as A, B, and C. Thus Equation (34.11) can be written in the alternate form:

$$
\begin{bmatrix}
-\left(\dfrac{1}{eT}\right)\left(\dfrac{\partial\bar{\mu}}{\partial x}\right) \\[2ex]
-\left(\dfrac{1}{eT}\right)\left(\dfrac{\partial\bar{\mu}}{\partial y}\right) \\[2ex]
J_x \\[2ex]
J_y
\end{bmatrix}
=
\begin{bmatrix}
M_{11} & M_{12} & M_{13} & M_{14} \\[1.5ex]
-M_{12} & M_{11} & -M_{14} & M_{13} \\[1.5ex]
-M_{13} & -M_{14} & M_{33} & M_{34} \\[1.5ex]
M_{14} & -M_{13} & -M_{34} & M_{33}
\end{bmatrix}
\begin{bmatrix}
I_x \\[2ex]
I_y \\[2ex]
-\left(\dfrac{1}{T^2}\right)\left(\dfrac{\partial T}{\partial x}\right) \\[2ex]
-\left(\dfrac{1}{T^2}\right)\left(\dfrac{\partial T}{\partial y}\right)
\end{bmatrix}
$$

$$(34.21)$$

where the M_{ij} are a new set of coefficients and are functions of the L_{ij}.

It can also be shown by examining the expressions for the matrices L, M, and N, in terms of the matrices A, B, and C, that the M_{ij} retain the same symmetry properties with respect to the magnetic field as do the L_{ij}, that is,

$$M_{ij}(\mathfrak{IC}_e) = M_{ij}(-\mathfrak{IC}_e) \qquad i+j = 2,\,4,\,6 \qquad (34.22)$$

$$M_{ij}(\mathfrak{IC}_e) = -M_{ij}(-\mathfrak{IC}_e) \qquad i+j = 3,\,5,\,7 \qquad (34.23)$$

In order to bring out more explicitly the dependence of the coefficients M_{ij} on the field $\mathfrak{IC}_e$, we shall introduce a new set of coefficients: $a_1 \equiv M_{11}$, $a_2 \equiv M_{12}/\mathfrak{IC}_e$, $a_3 \equiv M_{13}$, $a_4 \equiv M_{14}/\mathfrak{IC}_e$, $a_5 \equiv M_{33}$, $a_6 \equiv M_{34}/\mathfrak{IC}_e$. In terms of these coefficients, Equation (34.21) becomes

$$
\begin{bmatrix}
-\left(\dfrac{1}{eT}\right)\left(\dfrac{\partial\bar{\mu}}{\partial x}\right) \\[2ex]
-\left(\dfrac{1}{eT}\right)\left(\dfrac{\partial\bar{\mu}}{\partial y}\right) \\[2ex]
J_x \\[2ex]
J_y
\end{bmatrix}
=
\begin{bmatrix}
a_1 & a_2\mathfrak{IC}_e & a_3 & a_4\mathfrak{IC}_e \\[1.5ex]
-a_2\mathfrak{IC}_e & a_1 & -a_4\mathfrak{IC}_e & a_3 \\[1.5ex]
-a_3 & -a_4\mathfrak{IC}_e & a_5 & a_6\mathfrak{IC}_e \\[1.5ex]
a_4\mathfrak{IC}_e & -a_3 & -a_6\mathfrak{IC}_e & a_5
\end{bmatrix}
\begin{bmatrix}
I_x \\[2ex]
I_y \\[2ex]
-\left(\dfrac{1}{T^2}\right)\left(\dfrac{\partial T}{\partial x}\right) \\[2ex]
-\left(\dfrac{1}{T^2}\right)\left(\dfrac{\partial T}{\partial y}\right)
\end{bmatrix}
$$

$$(34.24)$$

The coefficients a_i are all even functions in the magnetic field, that is,

$$a_i(\mathfrak{IC}_e) = a_i(-\mathfrak{IC}_e) \qquad (34.25)$$

It follows that we can expand the a_i in even powers of $\mathfrak{K}_e$, that is,

$$a_i = \alpha_i + \alpha_i'\mathfrak{K}_e^2 + \alpha_i''\mathfrak{K}_e^4 + \cdots \qquad (34.26)$$

where the expansion coefficients α_i, α_i', α_i'', $\cdots$ are functions of the temperature, but not of the magnetic field. If the strength of the field is small enough to permit the neglect of terms that depend quadratically on the field, then

$$a_i \approx \alpha_i(T) \qquad (34.27)$$

In these cases the dependence of the various thermomagnetic phenomena on the field $\mathfrak{K}_e$ is explicitly displayed in the Equations (34.24).

The form (34.24) is a little more convenient than the form (34.11) in the discussion of thermomagnetic phenomena, and we shall use it as the starting point for our analysis.

OHM'S LAW

If a potential gradient is maintained in the x direction in the sample discussed in the previous section, and if the sample is homogeneous and maintained at a constant temperature, then

$$\frac{\partial T}{\partial x} = \frac{\partial T}{\partial y} = \frac{\partial \mu}{\partial x} = I_y = 0 \qquad (34.28)$$

Substituting these conditions in (34.24), and making use of (34.2), we obtain

$$I_x = -\sigma_i \frac{\partial \phi}{\partial x} \qquad (34.29)$$

where

$$\sigma_i = (a_1 T)^{-1} \qquad (34.30)$$

It follows that, under the above conditions, a negative gradient of the electric potential in the x direction will produce a current in the x direction, and the magnitude of that current will be proportional to the magnitude of the electric potential gradient. The constant of proportionality is called the isothermal electrical conductivity. As long as terms quadratic in $\mathfrak{K}_e$ can be neglected, the isothermal electrical conductivity is independent of the magnetic field.

If the same potential gradient is maintained in the sample, but rather than the sample being maintained at a constant temperature, it is insulated in such manner as to prevent any steady flow of heat or current in the y direction, and, in addition, if we do not allow a temperature gradient to be established in the x direction, then

$$\frac{\partial T}{\partial x} = J_y = I_y = \frac{\partial \mu}{\partial x} = 0 \tag{34.31}$$

Substituting these conditions in (34.24), we obtain

$$I_x = -\sigma_a \frac{\partial \phi}{\partial x} \tag{34.32}$$

where

$$\sigma_a = \frac{a_5}{T[a_1 a_5 - a_4{}^2 \mathfrak{K}_e{}^2]} \tag{34.33}$$

The current is again proportional to the electric field, but the proportionality constant is different from that obtained previously. The proportionality constant σ_a is called the adiabatic electrical conductivity. If the magnetic field is small enough to allow neglect of terms quadratic in $\mathfrak{K}_e$, then σ_a reduces to σ_i.

FOURIER'S LAW

If no electrical currents are allowed to flow, and the conductor is kept in contact with heat reservoirs that maintain a temperature gradient in the x direction and zero temperature gradient in the y direction, then

$$I_x = I_y = \frac{\partial T}{\partial y} = 0 \tag{34.34}$$

and from (34.24)

$$J_x = -\kappa_i \frac{\partial T}{\partial x} \tag{34.35}$$

where

$$\kappa_i \equiv \frac{a_5}{T^2} \tag{34.36}$$

It follows that, under the above conditions, a negative gradient of the temperature in the x direction will produce a heat flux in the x direction, and the magnitude of that heat flux will be proportional to the magnitude of the temperature gradient. The constant of proportionality κ_i is called the isothermal heat conductivity. As long as terms quadratic in $\mathfrak{K}_e$ can be neglected, the isothermal heat conductivity is independent of the magnetic field.

If instead of maintaining a zero temperature gradient in the y direction, the sample is insulated in such a manner that no heat can flow in the y direction, then

$$I_x = I_y = J_y = 0 \tag{34.37}$$

and from (34.24)

$$J_x = -\kappa_a \frac{\partial T}{\partial x} \tag{34.38}$$

where

$$\kappa_a \equiv \frac{a_5^2 + a_6^2 \mathfrak{K}_e^2}{T^2 a_5} \tag{34.39}$$

The heat current in the x direction is again proportional to the x component of the negative gradient of the temperature. The constant of proportionality κ_a is called the adiabatic heat conductivity. If terms quadratic in $\mathfrak{K}_e$ can be neglected, κ_a reduces to κ_i.

THE SEEBECK EFFECT

If

$$I_x = I_y = \frac{\partial T}{\partial y} = 0 \tag{34.40}$$

then

$$\frac{1}{e} \frac{\partial \bar{\mu}}{\partial x} = \epsilon \frac{\partial T}{\partial x} \tag{34.41}$$

where

$$\epsilon \equiv \frac{a_3}{T} \tag{34.42}$$

It follows that under the above conditions a temperature gradient will generate a gradient in the electrochemical potential proportional to the temperature gradient. The constant of proportionality ϵ is called the absolute thermoelectric power. As long as terms quadratic in $\mathfrak{K}_e$ can be neglected, the absolute thermoelectric power will be independent of the magnetic field.

THE HALL EFFECT

If

$$\frac{\partial T}{\partial x} = \frac{\partial T}{\partial y} = I_y = \frac{\partial \mu}{\partial x} = 0 \qquad (34.43)$$

then

$$\frac{\partial \phi}{\partial y} = \mathfrak{K}_e R_i I_x \qquad (34.44)$$

where

$$R_i \equiv a_2 T \qquad (34.45)$$

It follows that, under the above conditions, a current in the x direction, together with a magnetic field in the z direction will produce an electric potential gradient in the y direction. This effect is called the Hall effect. The magnitude of the potential gradient generated in the y direction will be directly proportional to the strength of the current in the x direction; and as long as terms quadratic in $\mathfrak{K}_e$ can be neglected, the magnitude of the potential gradient will also be proportional to the strength of the magnetic field in the z direction. The constant of proportionality R_i is called the isothermal Hall coefficient.

If

$$\frac{\partial T}{\partial x} = J_y = I_y = \frac{\partial \mu}{\partial y} = 0 \qquad (34.46)$$

then we obtain

$$\frac{\partial \phi}{\partial y} = \mathfrak{K}_e R_a I_x \qquad (34.47)$$

where

$$R_a \equiv T \left[\frac{a_2 a_5 + a_3 a_4}{a_5} \right] \qquad (34.48)$$

Thus, under adiabatic conditions we again obtain the Hall effect. The new constant of proportionality R_a is called the adiabatic Hall coefficient.

THE NERNST EFFECT

If

$$I_x = I_y = \frac{\partial T}{\partial y} = 0 \qquad (34.49)$$

then

$$-\frac{1}{e} \frac{\partial \bar{\mu}}{\partial y} = \eta_i \mathfrak{K}_e \frac{\partial T}{\partial x} \qquad (34.50)$$

where

$$\eta_i \equiv \frac{a_4}{T} \qquad (34.51)$$

It follows that, under the above conditions, a temperature gradient in the x direction, together with a magnetic field in the z direction, will produce a negative gradient in the y component of the electrochemical potential. This effect is called the Nernst effect. The magnitude of the gradient in the electrochemical potential will be directly proportional to the temperature gradient in the x direction; and if terms quadratic in $\mathfrak{IC}_e$ can be neglected, it will also be directly proportional to the strength of the magnetic field in the z direction. The constant of proportionality η_i is called the isothermal Nernst coefficient.

If

$$I_x = I_y = J_y = 0 \tag{34.52}$$

then

$$-\frac{1}{e}\frac{\partial \bar{\mu}}{\partial y} = \eta_a \mathfrak{IC}_e \frac{\partial T}{\partial x} \tag{34.53}$$

where

$$\eta_a = \frac{1}{T}\left[\frac{a_5 a_4 - a_3 a_6}{a_5}\right] \tag{34.54}$$

Thus, under adiabatic conditions we again obtain the Nernst effect. The constant of proportionality η_a is called the adiabatic Nernst coefficient.

THE ETTINGHAUSEN EFFECT

If

$$I_y = J_y = \frac{\partial T}{\partial x} = 0 \tag{34.55}$$

then

$$\frac{\partial T}{\partial y} = E\mathfrak{IC}_e I_x \tag{34.56}$$

where

$$E \equiv \frac{a_4 T^2}{a_5} \tag{34.57}$$

It follows that, under the above conditions, a current in the x direction, together with a magnetic field in the z direction, will produce a temperature gradient in the y direction. This effect is called the Ettinghausen effect. The magnitude of the temperature gradient will be directly proportional to the strength of the current in the x direction; as long as terms quadratic in $\mathfrak{IC}_e$ can be neglected, it will be directly proportional to the strength of the magnetic field in the z direction. The constant of proportionality E is called the Ettinghausen coefficient.

THE RIGHI–LEDUC EFFECT

If

$$I_x = I_y = J_y = 0 \tag{34.58}$$

then

$$\frac{\partial T}{\partial x} = L\mathfrak{IC}_e \frac{\partial T}{\partial y} \tag{34.59}$$

where

$$L \equiv \frac{a_6}{a_5} \tag{34.60}$$

It follows that, under the above conditions, a temperature gradient in the y direction, together with a magnetic field in the z direction, will produce a temperature gradient in the x direction. This effect is called the Righi–Leduc effect. The magnitude of the temperature gradient in the x direction will be directly proportional to the temperature gradient in the y direction; and as long as terms quadratic in $\mathfrak{IC}_e$ can be neglected, it will also be directly proportional to the strength of the magnetic field in the z direction. The constant of proportionality L is called the Righi–Leduc coefficient.

SUMMARY

Since there are only six independent coefficients a_i in Equations (34.24), these equations can alternately be expressed in terms of any six independent coefficients. In particular, if we choose the coefficients σ_i, R_i, ϵ, η_i, κ_i, and L, we can rewrite Equations (34.24)

$$
\begin{bmatrix}
-\left(\dfrac{1}{e}\right)\left(\dfrac{\partial \bar{\mu}}{\partial x}\right) \\[2mm]
-\left(\dfrac{1}{e}\right)\left(\dfrac{\partial \bar{\mu}}{\partial y}\right) \\[2mm]
J_x \\[2mm]
J_y
\end{bmatrix}
=
\begin{bmatrix}
\sigma_i^{-1} & R_i\mathfrak{IC}_e & \epsilon & \eta_i\mathfrak{IC}_e \\[2mm]
-R_i\mathfrak{IC}_e & \sigma_i^{-1} & -\eta_i\mathfrak{IC}_e & \epsilon \\[2mm]
-\epsilon T & -\eta_i\mathfrak{IC}_e T & \kappa_i & \kappa_i L\mathfrak{IC}_e \\[2mm]
\eta_i\mathfrak{IC}_e T & \epsilon T & -\kappa_i L\mathfrak{IC}_e & \kappa_i
\end{bmatrix}
\begin{bmatrix}
I_x \\[2mm]
I_y \\[2mm]
-\left(\dfrac{\partial T}{\partial x}\right) \\[2mm]
-\left(\dfrac{\partial T}{\partial y}\right)
\end{bmatrix}
\tag{34.61}
$$

In terms of the coefficients σ_i, R_i, ϵ, η_i, κ_i, and L, the remaining coefficients are given by

$$\sigma_a = \sigma_i\left(1 + \frac{\sigma_i\eta_i^2T\mathfrak{IC}_e^2}{\kappa_i}\right)^{-1} \tag{34.62}$$

$$\kappa_a = \kappa_i + \kappa_iL^2\mathfrak{IC}_e^2 \tag{34.63}$$

$$R_a = R_i + \frac{\epsilon\eta_iT}{\kappa_i} \tag{34.64}$$

$$\eta_a = \eta_i - \epsilon L \tag{34.65}$$

$$E = \frac{\eta_iT}{\kappa_i} \tag{34.66}$$

The various cross-effects that depend for their existence on the presence of a magnetic field and that were discussed in the preceding sections have many uses in the construction of diagnostic instruments and also as the basic principle in practical devices. As a sampling, the Hall effect is used to measure magnetic field strengths, the Nernst effect is used in the conversion of heat to electricity, and the Ettinghausen effect is used as a practical means of refrigeration.

PROBLEM

34.1 Determine the angle between the heat flux and the temperature gradient in the Righi–Leduc effect.

APPENDIXES

APPENDIX 1

Some Theorems
on Partial Differentiation

Let x, y, and z be three variables that satisfy the equation

$$f(x,y,z) = 0 \qquad \text{(A1.1)}$$

If values are assigned to two of the variables, the value assumed by the third is determined by Equation (A1.1); therefore, only two of the three variables are independent. We can choose any of the three pairs, (x,y), (x,z), or (y,z), as our set of independent variables.

The quantity

$$\left(\frac{\partial x}{\partial y}\right)_z \equiv \frac{\partial x(y,z)}{\partial y} \qquad \text{(A1.2)}$$

is called a partial derivative. In evaluating this partial derivative, we use Equation (A1.1) to obtain x as a function of y and z; we then take the derivative of x with respect to y, while holding z constant. It should be noted that we must express x as a function of y and z before we carry out the differentiation. We cannot, for example express x as a function of y and u, where u is some function of x, y, and z, and then take the derivative of x with respect to y while holding u constant. This is an entirely different derivative, which we designate $(\partial x/\partial y)_u$ or $\partial x(y,u)/\partial y$. Since there are many different partial derivatives of x with respect to y, it is important to indicate the quantity being held constant. Omission of the subscript, or, alternatively, failure to identify the variables of which the quantity being differentiated is to be expressed as a function, is a source of numerous and annoying errors, especially in thermodynamics.

The definition of a partial derivative can be readily extended to situations involving three or more independent variables. In the case of three independent variables, for example, the partial derivative $(\partial x/\partial y)_{z,w}$ is evaluated by expressing x as a function of y, z, and w and then taking the derivative of x with respect to y, while holding z and w constant.

A number of theorems that are very useful in the manipulation of partial derivatives will now be considered.

Theorem A. If f, g, h, x, y, and z are functions of the two independent variables u and v and satisfy the relation

$$f dx = g dy + h dz \qquad \text{(A1.3)}$$

303

then it follows that

$$f\left(\frac{\partial x}{\partial u}\right)_v = g\left(\frac{\partial y}{\partial u}\right)_v + h\left(\frac{\partial z}{\partial u}\right)_v \tag{A1.4}$$

It is easy to remember this result if one simply imagines that he starts with Equation (A1.3) and divides by du, while holding v constant.

To prove Theorem A, we note that since x, y, and z are functions of u and v, we can write

$$dx = \left(\frac{\partial x}{\partial u}\right)_v du + \left(\frac{\partial x}{\partial v}\right)_u dv \tag{A1.5}$$

$$dy = \left(\frac{\partial y}{\partial u}\right)_v du + \left(\frac{\partial y}{\partial v}\right)_u dv \tag{A1.6}$$

$$dz = \left(\frac{\partial z}{\partial u}\right)_v du + \left(\frac{\partial z}{\partial v}\right)_u dv \tag{A1.7}$$

Substituting Equations (A1.5), (A1.6), and (A1.7) in (A1.3), we obtain

$$f\left(\frac{\partial x}{\partial u}\right)_v du + f\left(\frac{\partial x}{\partial v}\right)_u dv$$

$$= \left[g\left(\frac{\partial x}{\partial u}\right)_v + h\left(\frac{\partial y}{\partial u}\right)_v\right] du + \left[g\left(\frac{\partial x}{\partial v}\right)_u + h\left(\frac{\partial y}{\partial v}\right)_u\right] dv \tag{A1.8}$$

Since u and v are independent variables, Equation (A1.8) must be true for arbitrary values of du and dv. If we set $dv = 0$, we obtain Equation (A1.4), and the theorem is proved.

Theorem B.   If x is a function of two independent variables y and z, then

$$\left(\frac{\partial x}{\partial y}\right)_z = \left[\left(\frac{\partial y}{\partial x}\right)_z\right]^{-1} \tag{A1.9}$$

To prove Theorem B, we note that since x is a function of y and z, we can write

$$dx = \left(\frac{\partial x}{\partial y}\right)_z dy + \left(\frac{\partial x}{\partial z}\right)_y dz \tag{A1.10}$$

Applying Theorem A to Equation (A1.10), we obtain

$$\left(\frac{\partial x}{\partial x}\right)_z = \left(\frac{\partial x}{\partial y}\right)_z\left(\frac{\partial y}{\partial x}\right)_z + \left(\frac{\partial x}{\partial z}\right)_y\left(\frac{\partial z}{\partial x}\right)_z \tag{A1.11}$$

Noting that $(\partial x/\partial x)_z = 1$ and $(\partial z/\partial x)_z = 0$, we obtain Equation (A1.9), and the theorem is proved.

Theorem C. If x is a function of two independent variables y and z, then

$$\left(\frac{\partial x}{\partial y}\right)_z = -\left(\frac{\partial x}{\partial z}\right)_y\left(\frac{\partial z}{\partial y}\right)_x = -\frac{\left(\frac{\partial x}{\partial z}\right)_y}{\left(\frac{\partial y}{\partial z}\right)_x} \qquad \text{(A1.12)}$$

One should note carefully the minus signs in Equation (A1.12), since there is a tendency to leave them out.

To prove Theorem C, we start with Equation (A1.10). Applying Theorem A, we obtain

$$\left(\frac{\partial x}{\partial y}\right)_x = \left(\frac{\partial x}{\partial y}\right)_z\left(\frac{\partial y}{\partial y}\right)_x + \left(\frac{\partial x}{\partial z}\right)_y\left(\frac{\partial z}{\partial y}\right)_x \qquad \text{(A1.13)}$$

Noting that $(\partial x/\partial y)_x = 0$ and $(\partial y/\partial y)_x = 1$, we obtain

$$\left(\frac{\partial x}{\partial y}\right)_z = -\left(\frac{\partial x}{\partial z}\right)_y\left(\frac{\partial z}{\partial y}\right)_x \qquad \text{(A1.14)}$$

Applying Theorem B to the last partial derivative in Equation (A1.14), we obtain Equation (A1.12), and the theorem is proved.

Theorem D. If x and y are functions of two independent variables u and v, then

$$\left(\frac{\partial x}{\partial y}\right)_v = \frac{\left(\frac{\partial x}{\partial u}\right)_v}{\left(\frac{\partial y}{\partial u}\right)_v} \qquad \text{(A1.15)}$$

To prove Theorem D, we start with Equation (A1.5). Applying Theorem A, we obtain

$$\left(\frac{\partial x}{\partial y}\right)_v = \left(\frac{\partial x}{\partial u}\right)_v\left(\frac{\partial u}{\partial y}\right)_v + \left(\frac{\partial x}{\partial v}\right)_u\left(\frac{\partial v}{\partial y}\right)_v \qquad \text{(A1.16)}$$

Noting that $(\partial v/\partial y)_v = 0$, and applying Theorem B to the partial derivative $(\partial u/\partial y)_v$, we obtain (A1.15), and the theorem is proved.

Theorem E.   If x, y, and z are functions of two independent variables u and v, then

$$\left(\frac{\partial x}{\partial y}\right)_z = \frac{\left(\frac{\partial x}{\partial u}\right)_v\left(\frac{\partial z}{\partial v}\right)_u - \left(\frac{\partial x}{\partial v}\right)_u\left(\frac{\partial z}{\partial u}\right)_v}{\left(\frac{\partial y}{\partial u}\right)_v\left(\frac{\partial z}{\partial v}\right)_u - \left(\frac{\partial y}{\partial v}\right)_u\left(\frac{\partial z}{\partial u}\right)_v} \tag{A1.17}$$

To prove Theorem E, we start with Equations (A1.5) and (A1.6). Applying Theorem A, we obtain

$$\left(\frac{\partial x}{\partial u}\right)_z = \left(\frac{\partial x}{\partial u}\right)_v + \left(\frac{\partial x}{\partial v}\right)_u\left(\frac{\partial v}{\partial u}\right)_z \tag{A1.18}$$

$$\left(\frac{\partial y}{\partial u}\right)_z = \left(\frac{\partial y}{\partial u}\right)_v + \left(\frac{\partial y}{\partial v}\right)_u\left(\frac{\partial v}{\partial u}\right)_z \tag{A1.19}$$

Multiplying Equations (A1.18) and (A1.19) by $(\partial z/\partial v)_u$, taking the ratio of the resultant equations, and noting from Theorem C that

$$\left(\frac{\partial v}{\partial u}\right)_z\left(\frac{\partial z}{\partial v}\right)_u = -\left(\frac{\partial z}{\partial u}\right)_v \tag{A1.20}$$

we obtain Equation (A1.17), and the theorem is proved.

The extension of Theorems A, B, C, D, and E to situations involving three or more independent variables is straightforward.

APPENDIX 2

Jacobians

If we are dealing with situations involving two or more independent variables, the manipulation of the various partial derivatives that arise can often be handled best by employing Jacobians.

Suppose u and v are functions of the independent variables x and y. The Jacobian $J(u,v/x,y)$ is then defined as follows

$$J\left(\frac{u,v}{x,y}\right) \equiv \begin{vmatrix} \left(\dfrac{\partial u}{\partial x}\right)_y & \left(\dfrac{\partial u}{\partial y}\right)_x \\ \left(\dfrac{\partial v}{\partial x}\right)_y & \left(\dfrac{\partial v}{\partial y}\right)_x \end{vmatrix} \tag{A2.1}$$

The extension to situations in which there are three or more variables is straightforward.

A number of theorems involving Jacobians can be derived by using the properties of determinants and the results of Appendix 1. We shall simply state them without proof.

Theorem A. If

$$f dx = g dy + h dz \tag{A2.2}$$

307

then

$$fJ\left(\frac{x,u}{v,w}\right) = gJ\left(\frac{y,u}{v,w}\right) + hJ\left(\frac{z,u}{v,w}\right) \tag{A2.3}$$

Theorem B.

$$J\left(\frac{x,y}{u,v}\right) = \left[J\left(\frac{u,v}{x,y}\right)\right]^{-1} \tag{A2.4}$$

Theorem C.

$$J\left(\frac{x,y}{u,v}\right) = -J\left(\frac{y,x}{u,v}\right) = -J\left(\frac{x,y}{v,u}\right) \tag{A2.5}$$

Theorem D.

$$J\left(\frac{x,y}{u,v}\right) = J\left(\frac{x,y}{r,s}\right)J\left(\frac{r,s}{u,v}\right) \tag{A2.6}$$

Theorem E.

$$J\left(\frac{x,v}{u,v}\right) \equiv J\left(\frac{x}{u}\right)_v = \left(\frac{\partial x}{\partial u}\right)_v \tag{A2.7}$$

Theorem F.

$$J\left(\frac{x,x}{u,v}\right) = 0 \tag{A2.8}$$

Theorem G. If c is a constant, then

$$J\left(\frac{cx,y}{u,v}\right) = cJ\left(\frac{x,y}{u,v}\right) \tag{A2.9}$$

The extension of the above theorems to situations involving three or more independent variables is straightforward.

APPENDIX 3

Maxima and Minima of Functions of Several Variables

A continuous and differentiable function $f(x,y)$ is said to have a maximum at (x,y) if, and only if,

$$f(x + u, y + v) - f(x,y) \leq 0 \qquad \text{(A3.1)}$$

for sufficiently small but arbitrary values of u and v. In this appendix we shall derive a number of conditions that will enable us to determine whether or not Equation (A3.1) is satisfied at a point (x,y).

If we expand $f(x + u, y + v)$ in a Taylor series in powers of u and v, we obtain

$$f(x + u, y + v) = f + (f_x u + f_y v)$$
$$+ \tfrac{1}{2}(f_{xx}u^2 + 2f_{xy}uv + f_{yy}v^2) + \cdots \qquad \text{(A3.2)}$$

where $f \equiv f(x,y)$; $f_x \equiv \partial f(x,y)/\partial x$; $f_{xx} \equiv \partial^2 f(x,y)/\partial x^2$; and so forth. Substituting Equation (A3.2) in Equation (A3.1), we obtain

$$(f_x u + f_y v) + \tfrac{1}{2}(f_{xx}u^2 + 2f_{xy}uv + f_{yy}v^2) + \cdots \leq 0 \qquad \text{(A3.3)}$$

Condition (A3.3) is equivalent to Equation (A3.1).

If the term that is linear in u and v does not vanish, we expect it to dominate as u and v approach zero. However, by simply reversing the sign of u and v, we can change the sign of the linear term. Therefore, Equation (A3.3) cannot be satisfied unless

$$f_x u + f_y v = 0 \tag{A3.4}$$

Equation (A3.4) must be true for arbitrary values of u and v. Letting $v = 0$ and $u \neq 0$, we obtain

$$f_x = 0 \tag{A3.5}$$

Similarly, letting $u = 0$ and $v \neq 0$, we obtain

$$f_y = 0 \tag{A3.6}$$

Substituting Equations (A3.5) and (A3.6) in Equation (A3.3), we obtain

$$\tfrac{1}{2}(f_{xx}u^2 + 2 f_{xy}uv + f_{yy}v^2) + \cdots \leq 0 \tag{A3.7}$$

If the quadratic term does not vanish, we expect it to dominate as u and v approach zero. It follows that Equation (A3.7) cannot be satisfied unless

$$f_{xx}u^2 + 2 f_{xy}uv + f_{yy}v^2 \leq 0 \tag{A3.8}$$

We now introduce a new variable

$$w = f_{xx}u + f_{xy}v \tag{A3.9}$$

Equation (A3.8) can now be written

$$\left(\frac{1}{f_{xx}}\right)w^2 - \left(\frac{f_{xy}^2 - f_{xx}f_{yy}}{f_{xx}}\right)v^2 \leq 0 \tag{A3.10}$$

Equation (A3.10) must be true for arbitrary values of w and v. If we choose $v = 0$ and $w \neq 0$, we obtain

$$f_{xx} \leq 0 \tag{A3.11}$$

If we choose $w = 0$ and $v \neq 0$ and make use of Equation (A3.11), we obtain

$$f_{xy}^2 - f_{xx}f_{yy} \leq 0 \tag{A3.12}$$

Equations (A3.11) and (A3.12) are necessary and sufficient conditions for the fulfillment of Equation (A3.10).

Gathering our results, we conclude that $f(x,y)$ will have a maximum at (x,y) only if

$$f_x = 0 \qquad\qquad f_y = 0 \qquad\qquad \text{(A3.13)}$$

$$f_{xx} \leq 0 \qquad f_{xy}^2 - f_{xx}f_{yy} \leq 0 \qquad \text{(A3.14)}$$

Similarly, we could have shown that $f(x,y)$ will have a minimum at (x,y) only if

$$f_x = 0 \qquad\qquad f_y = 0 \qquad\qquad \text{(A3.15)}$$

$$f_{xx} \geq 0 \qquad f_{xy}^2 - f_{xx}f_{yy} \leq 0 \qquad \text{(A3.16)}$$

Note that only the sign of f_{xx} changes.

In the preceding analysis, we have obtained necessary conditions only. The set of conditions (A3.13) and (A3.14) is necessary, but not sufficient for a maximum; similarly, Equations (A3.15) and (A3.16) are necessary, but not sufficient for a minimum.

Let us now consider a function of three variables. In analogy with the two-dimensional case: a function $f(x,y,z)$ will have a maximum at (x,y,z) if, and only if,

$$f(x + u, y + v, z + w) - f(x,y,z) \leq 0 \qquad \text{(A3.17)}$$

for sufficiently small but arbitrary values of u, v, and w. Equation (A3.17) is equivalent to the condition

$$(f_x u + f_y v + f_z w)$$
$$+ \tfrac{1}{2}(f_{xx}u^2 + f_{yy}v^2 + f_{zz}w^2 + 2f_{xy}uv + 2f_{xz}uw + 2f_{yz}vw) + \cdots \leq 0$$
$$\text{(A3.18)}$$

Equation (A3.18) will be true only if

$$f_x = f_y = f_z = 0 \qquad \text{(A3.19)}$$

$$f_{xx}u^2 + f_{yy}v^2 + f_{zz}w^2 + 2f_{xy}uv + 2f_{xz}uw + 2f_{yz}vw \leq 0 \qquad \text{(A3.20)}$$

Equation (A3.20) must be true for all values of u, v, and w. If we set $w = 0$, we obtain Equation (A3.8). It follows that Equations (A3.14) are also necessary conditions in the three-dimensional case.

APPENDIX 4

Constrained Maxima and Minima

Suppose we wish to find those values of x and y that maximize (or minimize) the function $f(x,y)$, subject to the constraint $g(x,y) = 0$. This objective can readily be accomplished by maximizing the function:

$$\psi(x) = f[x,y(x)] \qquad (A4.1)$$

where $y(x)$ is obtained by solving the equation $g(x,y) = 0$.

It is sometimes awkward to introduce the constraints into a function to be maximized. In such cases, we can make use of the method of Lagrange multipliers. According to this method, the values of x, y, and α, which maximize the function

$$\phi(x,y,\alpha) = f(x,y) + \alpha g(x,y) \qquad (A4.2)$$

also provide us with those values of x and y that maximize $f(x,y)$, subject to the constraint $g(x,y) = 0$. To prove this fact, we note first that the set of values of x, y, and α that maximize ϕ is obtained by setting the partial derivatives of ϕ with respect to x, y, and α equal to zero, that is,

$$\left(\frac{\partial \phi}{\partial x}\right)_{y,\alpha} = \left(\frac{\partial f}{\partial x}\right)_{y} + \alpha\left(\frac{\partial g}{\partial x}\right)_{y} = 0 \tag{A4.3}$$

$$\left(\frac{\partial \phi}{\partial y}\right)_{x,\alpha} = \left(\frac{\partial f}{\partial y}\right)_{x} + \alpha\left(\frac{\partial g}{\partial y}\right)_{x} = 0 \tag{A4.4}$$

$$\left(\frac{\partial \phi}{\partial \alpha}\right)_{x,y} = g(x,y) = 0 \tag{A4.5}$$

Let x_0, y_0, and α_0 represent the respective values of x, y, and α that satisfy Equations (A4.3), (A4.4), and (A4.5). Suppose there exists another set of values of x and y, designated x_1 and y_1, that maximizes $f(x,y)$, subject to the constraint $g(x,y) = 0$. Then $f(x_1,y_1) > f(x_0,y_0)$, and $g(x_1,y_1) = 0$. It follows that

$$f(x_1,y_1) + \alpha_0 g(x_1,y_1) > f(x_0,y_0) + \alpha_0 g(x_0,y_0) \tag{A4.6}$$

But if Equation (A4.6) is true, then x_0, y_0, and α_0 do not maximize $\phi(x,y,\alpha,)$, and our original assumption is false. Therefore, our supposition that there exists a set of values other than x_0 and y_0 that maximizes $f(x,y)$, subject to the constraint $g(x,y) = 0$, is false. It follows that x_0 and y_0 are the desired values.

We can easily extend our result to a function of a larger number of variables, subject to more than one constraint. Suppose we wish to maximize $f(x,y,z)$, subject to the constraints $g(x,y,z) = 0$, and $h(x,y,z) = 0$. We can do this in two ways, either by maximizing

$$\psi(x) = f[x,y(x),z(x)] \tag{A4.7}$$

where $y(x)$ and $z(x)$ are obtained by solving the equations, $g(x,y,z) = 0$ and $h(x,y,z) = 0$, or by the method of Lagrange multipliers, in which case we maximize the function

$$\phi(x,y,z,\alpha,\beta) = f(x,y,z) + \alpha g(x,y,z) + \beta h(x,y,z) \tag{A4.8}$$

Suppose we are given a function $f(x)$, having a derivative $g(x) \equiv df/dx$. We wish to find a function $F(g)$ that will contain exactly the same information as is contained in $f(x)$; that is, a function $F(g)$ such that if we know $F(g)$, we can calculate $f(x)$, and if we know $f(x)$, we can calculate $F(g)$.

We shall now show that the function

$$F = f - x \frac{df}{dx} \equiv f - xg \tag{A5.1}$$

when expressed as a function of g is such a function, that is,

$$F(g) = f[x(g)] - x(g)g \tag{A5.2}$$

contains the same information as $f(x)$.

To prove this, we note first that, if we are given $f(x)$, we can find $g(x)$, and if we know $g(x)$, we can solve for $x(g)$. If we substitute $x(g)$ in Equation (A5.2), we obtain $F(g)$. Therefore, if we know $f(x)$, we can find $F(g)$. To complete the proof, we must show that if we know $F(g)$, we can find $f(x)$.

Let us designate dF/dg by the letter h. Taking the derivative of Equation (A5.2) with respect to g, we obtain

$$h = \left(\frac{df}{dx}\right)\left(\frac{dx}{dg}\right) - \left(\frac{dx}{dg}\right)g - x = g\left(\frac{dx}{dg}\right) - \left(\frac{dx}{dg}\right)g - x \quad \text{(A5.3)}$$

or simply

$$h = -x \quad \text{(A5.4)}$$

Substituting Equation (A5.4) in Equation (A5.1), we obtain

$$F = f + hg \quad \text{(A5.5)}$$

But if we know $F(g)$, we can find $h(g)$. If we know $h(g)$, we can solve for $g(h)$. But $h = -x$. Therefore, knowing $F(g)$, we can find $F(x)$, $h(x)$, and $g(x)$; and then, using Equation (A5.5), we can find $f(x)$. Thus, if we know $F(g)$, we can find $f(x)$.

We have shown the desired equivalence between the function $f(x)$ and the function $F(g)$. The function $F(g)$ is known as the Legendre transformation of $f(x)$. It should be emphasized that the equivalence is between f, as a function of x, and F, as a function of g. If we know F as a function of some other variable, it is possible that we may be unable to find $f(x)$.

Let us now investigate the geometrical significance of the Legendre transformation. Suppose we are given a function $f(x)$, as shown in Figure A5.1. The equation of the tangent to the curve at the point $[x_0, f(x_0)]$ is given by

$$y = g(x_0)x + f(x_0) - g(x_0)x_0 \quad \text{(A5.6)}$$

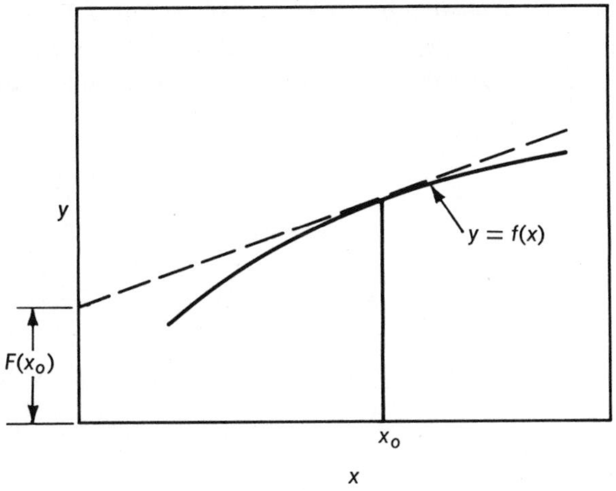

FIGURE A5.1

The line represented by (A5.6) passes through the point $(x_0, y_0) = [x_0, f(x_0)]$, and has the appropriate slope $g(x_0)$. This line intercepts the y axis when y has a value $F(x_0) \equiv f(x_0) - g(x_0)x_0$. The function $F(x_0)$ is thus the Legendre transformation of the function $f(x)$, evaluated at $x = x_0$. The Legendre transformation of $f(x)$ thus provides us with the intercept of the tangent to the curve for a given value of x. If we know the value of the intercept for a given value of the slope, that is, if we know F as a function of g, we can construct the family of tangents to the curve $f(x)$. But the family of tangents contains exactly the same information as $f(x)$, since, if we know $f(x)$, we can construct the family of tangents, and, conversely, if we know the family of tangents, we can construct $f(x)$. Thus $F(g)$ contains identically the same information as that in $f(x)$.

If we make a Legendre transformation of $F(g)$, we shall simply obtain $f(x)$ again; therefore, no advantage results from making successive Legendre transformations in the hope of obtaining additional functions that contain the same information as $f(x)$.

The extension to functions of more than one variable is straightforward. Suppose we are given a function $f(x,y)$; then

$$F_1 \equiv f - x\left(\frac{\partial f}{\partial x}\right)_y \tag{A5.7}$$

$$F_2 \equiv f - y\left(\frac{\partial f}{\partial y}\right)_x \tag{A5.8}$$

$$F_3 \equiv f - x\left(\frac{\partial f}{\partial x}\right)_y - y\left(\frac{\partial f}{\partial y}\right)_x \tag{A5.9}$$

are all Legendre transformations of $f(x,y)$. If we know F_1, as function of $(\partial f/\partial x)_y$ and y, or F_2 as a function of x and $(\partial f/\partial y)_x$, or F_3 as a function of $(\partial f/\partial x)_y$ and $(\partial f/\partial y)_x$, then we have exactly the same information as that contained in $f(x,y)$.

APPENDIX 6

Some Theorems Concerning Homogeneous Functions

A function $f(x,y,z)$ is said to be homogeneous of degree n in the variables y and z if

$$f(x,\lambda y,\lambda z) = \lambda^n f(x,y,z) \qquad (A6.1)$$

for every positive value of λ. The generalization of this definition to a function of an arbitrary number of variables r that is homogeneous in an arbitrary number s of these variables is straightforward.

In Appendix 6 we shall derive a number of theorems that will be useful in the manipulation of homogeneous functions. We shall restrict our attention to functions of three variables that are homogeneous in two of these variables. The generalization of the theorems is straightforward.

Theorem A. If $g(x,y,z)$ and $h(x,y,z)$ are homogeneous of degree n in the variables y and z, the sum of the two functions is homogeneous of degree n in the variables y and z.
The proof of this theorem is straightforward.

Theorem B. If $g(x,y,z)$ is homogeneous of degree m in the variables y and z, and $h(x,y,z)$ is homogeneous of degree n in the variables y and z,

317

then the ratio $g(x,y,z)/h(x,y,z)$ is homogeneous of degree $m - n$ in the variables y and z, and the product $g(x,y,z)h(x,y,z)$ is homogeneous of degree $m + n$ in the variables y and z.

The proof of this theorem is straightforward.

Theorem C. If $f(x,y,z)$ is homogeneous of degree n in the variables y and z, then the derivative $\partial f(x,y,z)/\partial x \equiv f_x(x,y,z)$ is homogeneous of degree n in the variables y and z, and the derivatives $\partial f(x,y,z)/\partial y \equiv f_y(x,y,z)$ and $\partial f(x,y,z)/\partial z \equiv f_z(x,y,z)$ are homogeneous of degree $n - 1$ in the variables y and z.

To prove Theorem C we take the derivatives of Equation (A6.1) with respect to x, y, and z. If we take the derivative of Equation (A6.1) with respect to x, we obtain

$$\frac{\partial f(x,\lambda y,\lambda z)}{\partial x} = \lambda^n \frac{\partial f(x,y,z)}{\partial x} \tag{A6.2}$$

and therefore

$$f_x(x,\lambda y,\lambda z) = \lambda^n f_x(x,y,z) \tag{A6.3}$$

If we take the derivative of Equation (A6.1) with respect to y, we obtain

$$\frac{\partial f(x,\lambda y,\lambda z)}{\partial(\lambda y)} \frac{\partial(\lambda y)}{\partial y} = \lambda^n \frac{\partial f(x,y,z)}{\partial y} \tag{A6.4}$$

Since $\partial(\lambda y)/\partial y = \lambda$, we obtain

$$f_y(x,\lambda y,\lambda z) = \lambda^{n-1} f_y(x,y,z) \tag{A6.5}$$

Similarly, taking the derivative of Equation (A6.1) with respect to z, we obtain

$$f_z(x,\lambda y,\lambda z) = \lambda^{n-1} f_z(x,y,z) \tag{A6.6}$$

Equations (A6.3), (A6.5), and (A6.6) constitute the proof of Theorem C.

Theorem D. If there exists an unknown function $f(x,y,z)$ about which the following information is known: (a) it is homogeneous of degree n in the variables y and z and (b) for a given value z_0 of z, the functional dependence of f on x and y is given by $g(x,y)$; then

$$f(x,y,z) = \left(\frac{z}{z_0}\right)^n g\left(x, \frac{yz_0}{z}\right) \tag{A6.7}$$

To prove Theorem D, we note first that condition (a) implies

$$f(x,\lambda y,\lambda z) = \lambda^n f(x,y,z) \tag{A6.8}$$

and condition (b) implies

$$f(x,y,z_0) = g(x,y) \tag{A6.9}$$

From Equations (A6.8) and (A6.9), it follows that

$$f(x,\lambda y,\lambda z_0) = \lambda^n f(x,y,z_0) = \lambda^n g(x,y) \tag{A6.10}$$

If we let $x \equiv u$, $\lambda y \equiv v$, and $\lambda z_0 \equiv w$ in Equation (A6.10), we obtain

$$f(u,v,w) = \left(\frac{w}{z_0}\right)^n g\left(u, \frac{vz_0}{w}\right) \tag{A6.11}$$

The quantities u, v, and w constitute an arbitrary set of variables which, for convenience, we can replace by x, y, and z, respectively. If we do so, we obtain Equation (A6.7).

As an illustration of Equation (A6.7), suppose that $f(x,y,z)$ is homogeneous of degree zero in y and z, and we know that $f(x,y,2) \equiv g(x,y) = xy^2/4$. It then follows from Equation (A6.7) that

$$f(x,y,z) = (z/2)^0 [x(2y/z)^2/4] = xy^2/z^2 \tag{A6.12}$$

Or suppose that $f(x,y,z)$ is homogeneous of degree one in y and z and that $f(x,y,2) \equiv g(x,y) = 4xy^2$. It then follows from Equation (A6.7) that

$$f(x,y,z) = (z/2)^1 [4x(2y/z)^2] = 8 xy^2/z \tag{A6.13}$$

Theorem E (Euler's Theorem). If $f(x,y,z)$ is homogeneous of degree n in the variables y and z, then

$$nf(x,y,z) = y \frac{\partial f(x,y,z)}{\partial y} + z \frac{\partial f(x,y,z)}{\partial z} \tag{A6.14}$$

To prove Euler's theorem, we first take the derivative of Equation (A6.1) with respect to λ and obtain

$$\left[\frac{\partial f(x,\lambda y,\lambda z)}{\partial(\lambda y)}\right]_{x,\lambda z}\left[\frac{\partial(\lambda y)}{\partial\lambda}\right]_y + \left[\frac{\partial f(x,\lambda y,\lambda z)}{\partial(\lambda z)}\right]_{x,\lambda y}\left[\frac{\partial(\lambda z)}{\partial\lambda}\right]_z$$
$$= n\lambda^{n-1} f(x,y,z) \tag{A6.15}$$

Noting that

$$\left[\frac{\partial(\lambda y)}{\partial \lambda}\right]_y = y \tag{A6.16}$$

$$\left[\frac{\partial(\lambda z)}{\partial \lambda}\right]_z = z \tag{A6.17}$$

and choosing $\lambda = 1$ in Equation (A6.15), we obtain Equation (A6.14).

Let (x,y) be a point in a two-dimensional space, and $g(x,y)$ and $h(x,y)$ two functions defined over the space. If we define the differential df as follows

$$df = g(x,y)dx + h(x,y)dy \qquad (A7.1)$$

then the differential is said to be an exact differential if and only if any one of the following four equivalent conditions is satisfied.

(a) There exists a function $f(x,y)$ of which df is the differential, that is,

$$df = \frac{\partial f(x,y)}{\partial x} dx + \frac{\partial f(x,y)}{\partial y} dy$$
$$= g(x,y)dx + h(x,y)dy \qquad (A7.2)$$

(b) The partial of $g(x,y)$ with respect to y is equal to the partial of $h(x,y)$ with respect to x, that is,

$$\frac{\partial g(x,y)}{\partial y} = \frac{\partial h(x,y)}{\partial x} \qquad (A7.3)$$

(c) The integral of df around any closed path C vanishes, that is,

$$\oint_C df = \oint_C [g(x,y)dx + h(x,y)dy] = 0 \qquad (A7.4)$$

(d) The integral of df between two arbitrary points (x_1,y_1) and (x_2,y_2) along a path $y = y(x)$ depends only upon the endpoints and not on the path, that is,

$$\int_{x_1,y_1}^{x_2,y_2} df \equiv \int_{x_1,y_1}^{x_2,y_2} [g(x,y)dx + h(x,y)dy] \qquad (A7.5)$$

$$= \text{fcn} (x_1,y_1,x_2,y_2)$$

To demonstrate the equivalence of (a), (b), (c), and (d), we shall show that (a) implies (b), (b) implies (c), (c) implies (d), and (d) implies (a). We note first that if (a) is true, then

$$\frac{\partial g(x,y)}{\partial y} = \frac{\partial}{\partial y}\left[\frac{\partial f(x,y)}{\partial x}\right] = \frac{\partial}{\partial x}\left[\frac{\partial f(x,y)}{\partial y}\right] = \frac{\partial h(x,y)}{\partial x} \qquad (A7.6)$$

and therefore (b) is true.

We next note that according to Green's theorem, which is proved in most texts on advanced calculus, that

$$\oint_C [g(x,y)dx + h(x,y)dy] = \iint_R \left[\frac{\partial h(x,y)}{\partial x} - \frac{\partial g(x,y)}{\partial y}\right]dxdy \qquad (A7.7)$$

where the integral on the right is a surface integral over the region R enclosed by the curve C. It follows that if (b) is true, then

$$\oint_C [g(x,y)dx + h(x,y)dy] = 0 \qquad (A7.8)$$

and therefore, condition (c) is true.

Now suppose that 132 and 142 are two arbitrary paths joining the points 1 and 2. If condition (c) is true, then the integral around the closed path 13241 vanishes, that is,

$$\oint_{13241} df = \int_{132} df + \int_{241} df = \int_{132} df - \int_{142} df = 0 \qquad (A7.9)$$

and therefore

$$\int_{132} df = \int_{142} df \qquad (A7.10)$$

Since 132 and 142 are arbitrary paths, Equation (A7.10) is merely condition (d), and therefore, condition (c) implies condition (d).

Finally, if condition (d) is satisfied, we can define a function $f(x,y)$ as follows:

$$f(x,y) = \int_{0,0}^{x,y} [g(x,y)dx + h(x,y)dy] \qquad (A7.11)$$

From (A7.11) we obtain

$$df(x,y) = g(x,y)dx + h(x,y)dy \qquad (A7.12)$$

and therefore, condition (a) is true. Thus, condition (d) implies condition (a).

From the above arguments, we conclude that conditions (a), (b), (c), and (d) are equivalent, since it is possible to show that if any one of them is true, all the rest have to be true.

For the purpose of illustration, we shall now consider particular examples of exact and inexact differentials. In order to make the situation as concrete as possible, let us suppose dx and dy represent the respective x and y components of displacement in a force field, and that $g(x,y)$ and $h(x,y)$ are, respectively, the x and y components of the force exerted on a test particle. The differential df will then represent the work done by the field as the test particle moves from (x,y) to $(x + dx, y + dy)$. If $g(x,y) = 3x^2y$ and $h(x,y) = x^3$, then the differential $df = gdx + hdy = 3x^2ydx + x^3dy$ is exact, and the work done in moving the particle between any two points will depend only upon the endpoints. Suppose, for example, we are interested in the work done in moving the particle along the path $(1,1)-(2,1)-(2,2)$ and the work done in moving it along the path $(1,1)-(1,2)-(2,2)$. In the first case, the work is

$$\int_{1,1}^{2,2} [3x^2ydx + x^3dy] = \int_{1,1}^{2,1} 3x^2ydx + \int_{2,1}^{2,2} x^3dy$$

$$= 3\int_{1}^{2} x^2dx + 8\int_{1}^{2} dy$$

$$= 7 + 8 = 15 \qquad (A7.13)$$

In the second case, the work is

$$\int_{1,1}^{2,2} [3x^2ydx + x^3dy] = \int_{1,1}^{1,2} x^3dy + \int_{1,2}^{2,2} 3x^2ydx$$

$$= \int_{1}^{2} dy + 6\int_{1}^{2} x^2dx$$

$$= 1 + 14 = 15 \qquad (A7.14)$$

The work will be the same along any path between the points $(1,1)$ and $(2,2)$. If, however, $g(x,y) = xy$ and $h(x,y) = x^2$, then the differential

$df = g dx + h dy = xy dx + x^2 dy$ is an inexact differential, and the work done in moving the particle between any two points will depend upon the path. For example, the work done in moving it along the path (1,1)–(2,1)–(2,2) is

$$\int_{1,1}^{2,2} [xy\,dx + x^2 dy] = \int_{1,1}^{2,1} xy\,dx + \int_{2,1}^{2,2} x^2 dy$$

$$= \int_{1}^{2} x\,dx + 4 \int_{1}^{2} dy$$

$$= \frac{3}{2} + 4 = \frac{11}{2} \qquad (A7.15)$$

but the work done in moving the particle between the same endpoints along the path (1,1)–(1,2)–(2,2) is

$$\int_{1,1}^{2,2} [xy\,dx + x^2 dy] = \int_{1,1}^{1,2} x^2 dy + \int_{1,2}^{2,2} xy\,dx$$

$$= \int_{1}^{2} dy + 2 \int_{1}^{2} x\,dx$$

$$= 1 + 3 = 4 \qquad (A7.16)$$

TABLES

TABLE 1   Abbreviations of Units

Unit	Abbreviation
ampere	A
atmosphere	atm
British thermal unit	Btu
calorie	cal
coulomb	C
degree Celsius	°C
degree Fahrenheit	°F
degree Kelvin	°K
degree Rankine	°R
dyne	dyn
farad	F
foot	ft
foot-pound	ft-lb
henry	H
horsepower	hp
joule	J
kilogram	kg
kilogram-force	kgf
liter	liter
meter	m
millimeter	mm
newton	N
oersted	Oe
pound	lb
pound-force	lbf
pound per square inch	psi
second (time)	sec
volt	V
watt	W
weber	Wb

TABLE 2   Symbols and Values of Selected Useful Constants

Symbol	Name	Value
A	Avogadro's number	6.02252×10^{23} molecules (mole)$^{-1}$
c	Speed of light in vacuo	2.99792×10^{8} m (sec)$^{-1}$
e	Electronic charge	1.60210×10^{-19} C
F	Faraday constant	9.64870×10^{4} C (mole)$^{-1}$
g_0	Standard acceleration of gravity	9.80665 m (sec)$^{-2}$
h	Planck's constant	6.6256×10^{-34} J sec
h	Planck's constant divided by 2π	1.05450×10^{-34} J sec
k	Boltzmann's constant	1.38054×10^{-23} J(°K)$^{-1}$(molecule)$^{-1}$
m_B	Bohr magneton	9.2732×10^{-24} A m^2
R	Gas constant	8.3143 J (°K)$^{-1}$ (mole)$^{-1}$
V_0	Molar volume of an ideal gas at 0°C and 1 atm	2.24136×10^{-2} m^3 (mole)$^{-1}$
ϵ_0	Permittivity of free space	8.85416×10^{-12} F m^{-1}
μ_0	Permeability of free space	$4\pi \times 10^{-7}$ H m^{-1}
σ	Stefan–Boltzmann constant	5.6697×10^{-8} W m^{-2} (°K)$^{-4}$

TABLE 3   Conversion Factors

1 atmosphere (atm) = 1.01325×10^5 N m^{-2}
1 bar = 10^5 N m^{-2}
1 British thermal unit (Btu) = 1.05435×10^3 J
1 calorie (cal) = 4.184 J
1 dyne (dyn) = 10^{-5} N
1 erg = 10^{-7} J
1 foot (ft) = 0.30480061 m
1 foot-pound (ft-lb) = 1.35582 J
1 horsepower (hp) = 7.45700×10^2 W
1 kilogram-force (kgf) = 9.80665 N
1 liter = 1.000028×10^{-3} m^3
1 liter atmosphere (liter atm) = 101.328 J
1 millimeter (mm) of mercury = 133.3224 N m^{-2}
1 oersted (Oe) = $(4\pi)^{-1} \times 10^3$ A m^{-1}
1 pound-force (lbf) = 4.44822 N
1 pound (lb) = 0.45359237 kg
1 pound per square inch (psi) = 6.89476×10^3 N m^{-2}
1 torr = 133.3224 N m^{-2}

$$T \text{ °C} = (T + 273.15)\text{°K}$$
$$T \text{ °F} = (T + 459.67)\text{°R}$$
$$T \text{ °R} = \left(\frac{5}{9}T\right)\text{°K}$$

TABLE 4   Specific Heats of Various Gases

$$c_p \text{ (cal/mole°K)} = A + B \times 10^{-3}\,T + C \times 10^{-6}\,T^2$$

$$300°K < T < 2000°K$$

Gas	A	B	C
H_2	6.88	0.066	$+0.279$
N_2, HBr	6.30	1.819	-0.345
O_2	6.26	2.746	-0.770
CO, HI	6.25	2.091	-0.459
NO	6.21	2.436	-0.612
HCl	6.64	0.959	-0.057
H_2S	6.48	5.558	-1.204
H_2O	6.89	3.283	-0.343
SO_2	8.12	6.825	-2.103
HCN	7.01	6.600	-1.642
CO_2	6.85	8.533	-2.475
COS	8.32	7.224	-2.146
CS_2	9.76	6.102	-1.894
NH_3	5.92	8.963	-1.764
C_2H_2	8.28	10.501	-2.644
CH_4	3.38	17.905	-4.188
Cl_2	7.5755	2.4244	-0.965

This table was copied from M. W. Zemansky, HEAT AND THERMODYNAMICS, McGraw-Hill, Inc., 4th ed., p. 124, except for the value for Cl_2, which was taken from F. T. Wall, CHEMICAL THERMODYNAMICS, W. H. Freeman and Company, 2nd ed., p. 39.

TABLE 5   Specific Heats of Selected Liquids and Solids

$$c_p \text{ (cal/mole°K)} = A$$

Pressure = 1 atm   temperature = 25°C

Substance	A
Copper	5.848
Lead	6.41
Mercury	6.65
Methyl alcohol	19.5
Silver	6.092
Sodium	6.79
Sodium chloride	11.88
Sulfuric acid	32.88
Water	17.996

These values are taken from F. T. Wall, CHEMICAL THERMODYNAMICS, W. H. Freeman and Company, 2nd ed., pp. 341–442.

TABLE 6 Coefficients of Thermal Expansion for Selected Liquids and Solids

$$\alpha(°K^{-1}) = A \times 10^{-5} + B \times 10^{-8} (T - 273.15) + C \times 10^{-8} (T - 273.15)^2$$

Material	A	B	C	Temperature range (°C) From	To
Aluminum	6.663	6.84		10	90
Copper	4.788	6.12		10	90
Iron	3.435	4.26		0	38
Lead	8.487	7.20		10	90
Silver	5.586	4.44		10	90
Acetone	132.40	761.80	−2.6395	0	54
Methyl alcohol	113.42	272.70	2.6223	0	61
Water	−6.427	1701.06	−20.370	0	33

These values are taken from H. B. Callen, THERMODYNAMICS, John Wiley & Sons, Inc., p. 532, and from M. Tribus, THERMOSTATICS AND THERMODYNAMICS, D. Van Nostrand Company, Inc., pp. 239–240.

TABLE 7 Isothermal Compressibilities of Selected Liquids and Solids

$$\beta(atm^{-1}) = A \times 10^{-6}$$

Material	A	Pressures at which valid (atm)	Temperature at which valid (°C)
Acetone	82	1–500	0
Benzene	86.8	1–18.5	12.9
Methyl alcohol	79	1–500	0
Water	47	1–500	0
Mercury	3.8	1–500	22.8
Aluminum	1.3		
Copper	0.7		
Iron	0.57		
Lead	2.30		
Silver	0.96		

These values are taken from N. A. Lange, HANDBOOK OF CHEMISTRY, McGraw-Hill, Inc., 10th ed., pp. 1670–1674, and from H. B. Callen, THERMODYNAMICS, John Wiley & Sons, Inc., p. 352.

TABLE 8 van der Waals Constants for Selected Gases

$$p = \frac{RT}{V - Nb} - \frac{aN^2}{V^2}$$

p = atm
T = °K
R = 8.207 × 10^{-2} liter atm (mole)$^{-1}$ (°K)$^{-1}$
N = moles
a = (liter)^2 atm (mole)$^{-2}$
b = liter (mole)$^{-1}$

Gas	a	b
A	1.345	0.03219
CO	1.485	0.03985
Cl_2	6.493	0.05622
He	0.03412	0.02370
H_2	0.2444	0.02661
CH_4	2.253	0.04278
NO	1.340	0.02789
N_2	1.390	0.03913
O_2	1.360	0.03803

These values are taken from N. A. Lange, HANDBOOK OF CHEMISTRY, 10th ed., McGraw-Hill, Inc., pp. 1510–1513.

TABLE 9 Debye Temperatures of Selected Solids at Atmospheric Pressure

Substance	θ	Range °K	
		From	To
Aluminum	398	19	773
Copper	315	14	773
Diamond	1860	30	1169
Iron	453	32	95
Lead	88	14	573
Rock Salt	281	25	664
Silver	215	35	873

These values are taken from F. H. Crawford, HEAT, THERMO-DYNAMICS, AND STATISTICAL PHYSICS, Harcourt, Brace & World, Inc., p. 175.

TABLE 10   Gruneisen Constants for Selected Metals

Substance	γ
Aluminum	2.1
Copper	1.9
Lead	2.3
Platinum	2.7
Silver	2.2

TABLE 11   Standard Molar Enthalpies of Formation, Standard Molar Gibbs Free Energies of Formation, and Standard Molar Entropies of Selected Substances

$p_0 = 1$ atm $T_0 = 298.15°K$

Substance	State	$h_f^°$ kcal/mole	$g_f^°$ kcal/mole	$s^°$ cal/°K/mole
C	graphite	0	0	1.3609
C	gas	171.698	160.845	37.7611
CH_4	gas	− 17.889	− 12.140	44.50
C_2H_6	gas	− 20.236	− 7.860	54.85
C_6H_6	gas	19.820	30.989	64.34
C_6H_6	liquid	11.63	29.40	
CH_3Cl	gas	− 19.6	− 14.0	55.97
CO	gas	− 26.4157	− 32.8079	47.301
CO_2	gas	− 94.0518	− 94.2598	51.061
Cl_2	gas	29.012	25.192	39.4569
H	gas	52.089	48.575	27.3927
H_2	gas	0	0	31.211
HCl	gas	− 22.063	− 22.769	44.617
H_2O	gas	− 57.7979	− 54.6357	45.106
H_2O	liquid	− 68.3174	− 56.6902	16.716
N_2	gas	0	0	45.767
NO	gas	21.600	20.719	50.339
O_2	gas	0	0	49.003
Pb	solid	0	0	15.51
PbO	solid	− 52.07	− 45.05	16.6
PbS	solid	− 22.54	− 22.15	21.8
SO_2	gas	− 70.96	− 71.79	59.40

These values are taken from F. T. Wall, CHEMICAL THERMODYNAMICS, W. H. Freeman and Company, pp. 431–442, except for the value of C_6H_6 (liquid), which is taken from N. A. Lange, HANDBOOK OF CHEMISTRY, 10th ed., McGraw-Hill, Inc., p. 1632.

TABLE 12   Inversion Curve for Nitrogen

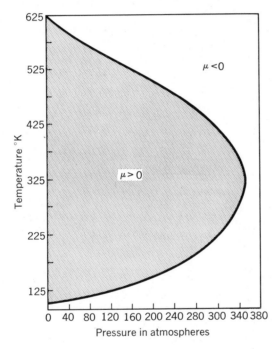

This curve was copied from A. H. Wilson, THERMODYNAMICS AND STATISTICAL MECHANICS, Cambridge University Press, p. 231.

TABLE 13 The Pressure-Volume-Temperature Surface for Water

This figure was copied from J. F. Lee and F. W. Sears, THERMODYNAMICS, 2nd ed., Addison-Wesley Publishing Co., Inc., Reading, Mass., 1963.

TABLE 14   Phase Diagram for Water

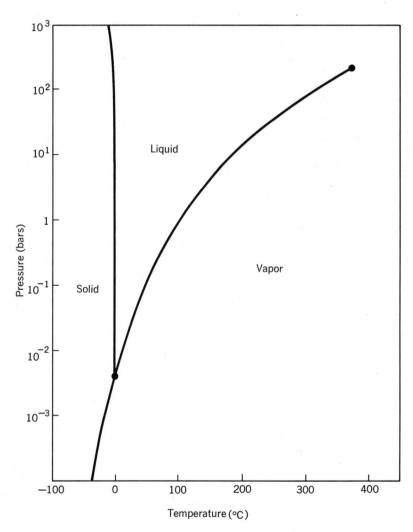

(a) *Phase Diagram for Water at Low Pressures*

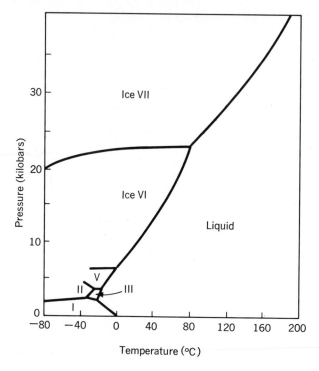

(b) *Phase Diagram for Water at High Pressures*

BIBLIOGRAPHY

BIBLIOGRAPHY

ALLEN, H. S., and R. S. MAXWELL, *A Textbook of Heat*, Macmillan & Co., Ltd., London, 1933.

ALLIS, W. P., and M. A. HERLIN, *Thermodynamics and Statistical Mechanics*, McGraw-Hill, Inc., New York, 1952.

ASTON, J. G., and J. J. FRITZ, *Thermodynamics and Statistical Thermodynamics*, John Wiley & Sons, Inc., New York, 1959.

BABITS, G. F., *Thermodynamics*, Allyn and Bacon, Inc., Boston, 1963.

BADGER, P. H., *Equilibrium Thermodynamics*, Allyn and Bacon, Inc., Boston, 1967.

BAUMAN, R. P., *An Introduction to Equilibrium Thermodynamics*, Prentice-Hall, Inc., Englewood Cliffs, N.J., 1966.

BAZAROV, I. P., *Thermodynamics*, Crowell-Collier and Macmillan, Inc., New York, 1964.

BECKER, R., *Theory of Heat*, 2nd ed., Springer-Verlag, Berlin, 1967.

BENSON, R. S., *Advanced Engineering Thermodynamics*, Pergamon Press, Inc., New York, 1967.

BENT, H. A., *The Second Law*, Oxford University Press, New York, 1965.

BOSNJAKOVIC, F., *Technical Thermodynamics*, Holt, Rinehart and Winston, Inc., New York, 1965.

BOXER, G., *Examples in Engineering Thermodynamics*, Edward Arnold & Co., London, 1966.

BRANSOM, S. H., *Applied Thermodynamics*, D. Van Nostrand Company, Inc., Princeton, N.J., 1961.

BRIDGMAN, P. W., *The Nature of Thermodynamics*, Harvard University Press, Cambridge, Mass., 1941.

BRONSTED, J. N., *Principles and Problems in Energetics*, Interscience Publishers, New York, 1955.

BRUGES, E. A., *Available Energy and Second Law Analysis*, Academic Press, Inc., New York, 1959.

BRYAN, G. H., *Thermodynamics*, Stechert-Hafner, Inc., New York, 1907.

BUCHDAHL, H. A., *The Concepts of Classical Thermodynamics*, Cambridge University Press, London, 1966.

CALDIN, E. F., *An Introduction to Chemical Thermodynamics*, Oxford University Press, New York, 1958.

CALLEN, H. B., *Thermodynamics*, John Wiley & Sons, Inc., New York, 1960.

CARNOT, S., *Reflections on the Motive Power of Fire*, Dover Publications, Inc., New York, 1960.

CLAUSIUS, R., *The Mechanical Theory of Heat*, John Van Voorst, London, 1867.

CORK, J. M., *Heat*, John Wiley & Sons, Inc., New York, 1942.

COULL, J., and E. B. STUART, *Equilibrium Thermodynamics*, John Wiley & Sons, Inc., New York, 1964.

CRAWFORD, F. H., *Heat, Thermodynamics, and Statistical Physics*, Harcourt, Brace & World, Inc., New York, 1963.

CROFT, H. O., *Thermodynamics, Fluid Flow, and Heat Transmission*, McGraw-Hill, Inc., New York, 1938.

DE GROOT, S. R., *Thermodynamics of Irreversible Processes*, North Holland Publishing Co., Amsterdam, 1951.

DE GROOT, S. R., and P. MAZUR, *Non Equilibrium Thermodynamics*, North Holland Publishing Co., Amsterdam, 1962.

DENBIGH, K. G., *Principles of Chemical Equilibrium*, Cambridge University Press, London, 1955.

DENBIGH, K. G., *The Thermodynamics of the Steady State*, John Wiley & Sons, Inc., New York, 1951.

DODGE, B. F., *Chemical Engineering Thermodynamics*, McGraw-Hill, Inc., New York, 1944.

DONNELLY, R. J., R. HERMAN, and I. PRIGOGINE, eds., *Non-Equilibrium Thermodynamics, Variational Techniques, and Stability*, The University of Chicago Press, Chicago, 1965.

DOOLITTLE, J. S., and A. H. ZERBAN, *Engineering Thermodynamics*, International Textbook Company, Scranton, Pa., 1955.

EBAUGH, N. C., *Engineering Thermodynamics*, D. Van Nostrand Company, Inc., Princeton, N.J., 1943.

EINSWILER, J. E., *Thermodynamics*, McGraw-Hill, Inc., New York, 1943.

EL-SADEN, M. R., *Engineering Thermodynamics*, D. Van Nostrand Company, Inc., Princeton, N.J., 1965.

EPSTEIN, P. S., *Textbook of Thermodynamics*, John Wiley & Sons, Inc., New York, 1954.

EVERDELL, M. H., *Introduction to Chemical Thermodynamics*, W. W. Norton & Co., Inc., New York, 1966.

EVERETT, D. H., *An Introduction to the Study of Chemical Thermodynamics*, Longmans, Green & Co., Ltd., London.

EWING, J. A., *Thermodynamics for Engineers*, Cambridge University Press, London, 1936.

FAIRES, V. M., *Thermodynamics*, Crowell-Collier and Macmillan, Inc., New York, 1962.

FAIRES, V. M., *Applied Thermodynamics*, Crowell-Collier and Macmillan, Inc., New York, 1938.

FAST, J. D., *Entropy*, McGraw-Hill, Inc., New York, 1962.

FAY, J. A., *Molecular Thermodynamics*, Addison-Wesley Publishing Company, Inc., Reading, Mass., 1965.

FERMI, E., *Notes on Thermodynamics and Statistics*, The University of Chicago Press, Chicago, 1966.

FERMI, E., *Thermodynamics*, Dover Publications, Inc., New York, 1957.

FINCK, J. L., *Thermodynamics from a Generalized Standpoint*, Flatbush Publications, Brooklyn, New York, 1951.

FITTS, D. D., *Non-Equilibrium Thermodynamics*, McGraw-Hill, Inc., New York, 1962.

FONG, P., *Foundations of Thermodynamics*, Oxford University Press, New York, 1963.

GIBBS, J. W., *The Scientific Papers of J. Willard Gibbs. Volume, I Thermodynamics*, Dover Publications, Inc., New York, 1961.

GILES, R., *Mathematical Foundations of Thermodynamics*, Crowell-Collier and Macmillian, Inc., New York, 1964.

GILMONT, R., *Thermodynamic Principles for Chemical Engineers*, Prentice-Hall, Inc., Englewood Cliffs, N.J., 1959.

GLASSTONE, S., *Thermodynamics for Chemists*, D. Van Nostrand Company, Inc., Princeton, N.J., 1947.

GOODENOUGH, G. A., *Principles of Thermodynamics*, 3rd ed., Johnson Reprint Corporation, 1965.

GRANET, I., *Elementary Applied Thermodynamics*, John Wiley & Sons, Inc., New York, 1965.

GUGGENHEIM, E. A., *Thermodynamics*, 5th ed., Interscience Publishers, New York, 1967.

TER HAAR, D., and H. N. S. WERGELAND, *Elements of Thermodynamics*, Addison-Wesley Publishing Company, Inc., Reading, Mass., 1966.

HALL, N. A., and W. E. IBELE, *Engineering Thermodynamics*, Prentice-Hall, Inc., Englewood Cliffs, N.J., 1960.

HATSOUPOULOS, G. N., and J. H. KEENAN, *Principles of General Thermodynamics*, John Wiley & Sons, Inc., New York, 1965.

HAWKINS, G. A., *Thermodynamics*, 2nd ed., John Wiley & Sons, Inc., New York, 1951.

HELSDON, R. M., *Introduction to Applied Thermodynamics*, Pergamon Press, Inc., New York, 1965.

HERCUS, E. O., *Elements of Thermodynamics and Statistical Mechanics*, The University Press, Melbourne, 1950.

HOARE, *Thermodynamics*, 2nd ed., Edward Arnold & Co., London, 1938.

HOUGEN, O. A., and K. M. WATSON, *Chemical Process Principles, Part II, Thermodynamics*, John Wiley & Sons, Inc., New York, 1947.

HOWERTON, M. T., *Engineering Thermodynamics*, D. Van Nostrand Company, Inc., Princeton, N.J., 1962.

JONES, J. B., and G. A. HAWKINS, *Engineering Thermodynamics*, John Wiley & Sons, Inc., New York, 1960.

KEENAN, J. H., *Thermodynamics*, John Wiley & Sons, Inc., New York, 1941.

KESTIN, J., *A Course in Thermodynamics*, Blaisdell Publishing Company, Waltham, Mass., 1966.

KIEFER, P. J., G. F. KINNEY, and M. C. STUART, *Principles of Engineering Thermodynamics*, John Wiley & Sons, Inc., New York, 1954.

KING, A. L., *Thermophysics*, W. H. Freeman and Company, San Francisco, 1962.

KIRKWOOD, J. G., and I. OPPENHEIM, *Chemical Thermodynamics*, McGraw-Hill, Inc., New York, 1961.

KLOTZ, I. M., *Chemical Thermodynamics*, 2nd ed., W. A. Benjamin, Inc., New York, 1964.

KRESTOVNIKOV, A. N., and V. N. VIGDOROVICH, *Chemical Thermodynamics*, Daniel Davey & Co., Inc., New York, 1964.

LACEY, W. N., and B. H. SAGE, *Thermodynamics of One Component Systems*, Academic Press, Inc., New York, 1957.

LANDSBERG, P. T., *Thermodynamics*, Interscience Publishers, New York, 1961.

LAY, J. E., *Thermodynamics*, Charles E. Merrill Books, Inc., Columbus, Ohio, 1963.

LEE, J. F., and F. W. SEARS, *Thermodynamics*, Addison-Wesley Publishing Company, Inc., Reading, Mass., 1955.

LEWIS, G. N., and M. RANDALL, *Thermodynamics*, revised by K. S. Pitzer and L. Brewer, McGraw-Hill, Inc., New York, 1961.

LICHTY, L. C., *Thermodynamics*, 2nd ed., McGraw-Hill, Inc., New York, 1948.

LUDER, W. F., *A Different Approach to Thermodynamics*, Reinhold Publishing Corporation, New York, 1967.

MACDOUGALL, F. W., *Thermodynamics and Chemistry*, John Wiley & Sons, Inc., New York, 1939.

MACKEY, C. O., W. N. BERNARD, and F. O. ELLENWOOD, *Engineering Thermodynamics*, John Wiley & Sons, Inc., New York, 1957.

MAHAN, B. H., *Elementary Chemical Thermodynamics*, W. A. Benjamin, Inc., New York, 1963.

MAXWELL, J. C., *Theory of Heat*, Longmans, Green & Co., Ltd., London, 1891.

MONTGOMERY, S. R., *Second Law of Thermodynamics*, Pergamon Press, Inc., New York, 1966.

MOONEY, D. A., *Mechanical Engineering Thermodynamics*, Prentice-Hall, Inc., Englewood Cliffs, N.J., 1953.

MORSE, P. M., *Thermal-Physics*, Rev. ed., W. A. Benjamin, Inc., New York, 1964.

NASH, K., *Elements of Chemical Thermodynamics*, Addison-Wesley Publishing Company, Inc., Reading, Mass., 1962.

NERNST, W., *The New Heat Theorem*, E. P. Dutton & Co., Inc., New York, 1926.

OBERT, E. F., and R. A. GAGGIOLI, *Thermodynamics*, 3rd ed., McGraw-Hill, Inc., New York, 1963.

OBERT, E. F., *Concepts of Thermodynamics*, McGraw-Hill, Inc., New York, 1960.

PARTINGTON, J. R., *Thermodynamics*, Constable & Co., Ltd., London, 1950.

PAUL, M. A., *Principles of Chemical Thermodynamics*, McGraw-Hill, Inc., New York, 1951.

PERKINS, H. A., *General Thermodynamics*, John Wiley & Sons, Inc., New York, 1916.

PINCHERLE, L., *Worked Problems in Heat, Thermodynamics, and Kinetic Theory*, Pergamon Press, Inc., New York, 1966.

PIPPARD, A. B., *The Elements of Classical Thermodynamics*, Cambridge University Press, London, 1957.

PLANCK, M. *Theory of Heat*, Crowell-Collier and Macmillan, Inc., New York, 1932.

PLANCK, M., *Treatise on Thermodynamics*, Dover Publications, Inc., New York, 1945.

PORTER, A. W., *Thermodynamics*, John Wiley & Sons, Inc., New York, 1951.

PRESTON, T., *The Theory of Heat*, Macmillan & Co. Ltd., London, 1923.

PRIGOGINE, I., *Introduction to Thermodynamics of Irreversible Processes*, 2nd ed., Interscience Publishers, New York. 1962.

PRIGOGINE, I., and R. DEFAY, *Chemical Thermodynamics*, Longmans, Green & Co., Ltd., London, 1954.

RANZ, W. E., *Thermodynamics and Engineering*, Pennsylvania State University Press, University Park, Pa., 1955.

REID, C. E., *Principles of Chemical Thermodynamics*, Reinhold Publishing Corporation, New York, 1960.

REIF, F., *Fundamentals of Statistical and Thermal Physics*, McGraw-Hill, Inc., New York, 1965.

REISS, H., *Methods of Thermodynamics*, Blaisdell Publishing Company. Waltham, Mass., 1965.

REYNOLDS, W. C., *Thermodynamics*, McGraw-Hill, Inc., New York. 1965.

RICE, O. K., *Statistical Mechanics, Thermodynamics, and Kinetics*, W. H. Freeman and Company, San Francisco, 1967.

ROBERTS, J. K., and A. R. MILLER, *Heat and Thermodynamics*, 5th ed., Interscience Publishers, New York, 1960.

ROCARD, Y., *Thermodynamics*, Sir Isaac Pitman & Sons, Ltd., London, 1961.

ROGERS, G. F., and Y. R. MAYHEW, *Engineering Thermodynamics*, Longmans, Green & Co., Ltd., London, 1957.

ROLLER, D., *The Early Development of the Concepts of Temperature and Heat*, Harvard University Press, Cambridge, Mass., 1950.

ROSSINI, F. D., *Chemical Thermodynamics*, John Wiley & Sons, Inc., New York, 1950.

ROSSINI, F. D., *Experimental Thermochemistry*, Interscience Publishers, New York, 1956.

ROSSINI, F. D., ed., *Thermodynamics and Physics of Matter*, Princeton University Press, Princeton, N.J., 1955.

SAAD, M. A., *Thermodynamics for Engineers*, Prentice-Hall, Inc., Englewood Cliffs, N.J., 1966.

SABERSKY, R. H., *Elements of Engineering Thermodynamics*, McGraw-Hill, Inc., New York, 1957.

SAGE, H., *Thermodynamics of Multicomponent Systems*, Reinhold Publishing Corporation, New York, 1965.

SAHA, M. N., and B. N. SRIVASTAVA, *A Treatise on Heat*, 4th ed., The Indian Press Private, Ltd., Allahabad, 1958.

SCHMIDT, E., *Thermodynamics*, Oxford University Press, New York, 1949.

SEARS, F. W., *Thermodynamics*, Addison-Wesley Publishing Company, Inc., Reading, Mass., 1953.

SEARS, F. W., *Thermodynamics, the Kinetic Theory of Gases, and Statistical Mechanics*, 2nd ed., Addison-Wesley Publishing Co., Inc., Reading, Mass., 1953.

SHORT, B. E., H. L. KENT, and B. F. TREAT, *Engineering Thermodynamics*, Harper & Brothers, New York, 1953.

SLATER, J. C., *Introduction to Chemical Physics*, McGraw-Hill, Inc., New York, 1939.

SMITH, J. M., and H. C. VAN NESS, *Introduction to Chemical Engineering Thermodynamics*, McGraw-Hill, Inc., New York, 1959.

SMITH, R. A., *The Physical Principles of Thermodynamics*, Chapman & Hall, Ltd., London, 1952.

SOMMERFELD, A., *Thermodynamics and Statistical Mechanics*, Academic Press, Inc., New York, 1956.

SOO, S. L., *Analytical Thermodynamics*, Prentice-Hall, Inc., Englewood Cliffs, N.J., 1962.

SOO, S. L., *Thermodynamics of Engineering Science*, Prentice-Hall, Inc., Englewood Cliffs, N.J., 1958.

SORENSEN, H. A., *Principles of Thermodynamics*, Holt, Rinehart and Winston, Inc., New York, 1961.

SPALDING, D. B., and E. H. COLE, *Engineering Thermodynamics*, McGraw-Hill, Inc., New York, 1959.

SPANNER, D. C., *Introduction to Thermodynamics*, Academic Press, Inc., New York, 1964.

STEINER, L. E., *Introduction to Chemical Thermodynamics*, McGraw-Hill, Inc., New York, 1948.

STOEVER, H. J., *Engineering Thermodynamics*, John Wiley & Sons, Inc., New York, 1951.

SUSHKOV, V. V., *Technical Thermodynamics*, Gordon and Breach Science Publishers, Inc., New York, 1965.

SWEIGERT, R. L., and M. J. GOGLIA, *Thermodynamics*, The Ronald Press Company, New York, 1955.

SWINBURNE, J., *Entropy*, Constable & Co., Ltd., London, 1904.

THURLOW, G., and A. B. LEE, *Engineering Thermodynamics*, English Universities Press, London, 1964.

TISZA, L., *Generalized Thermodynamics*, MIT Press, Cambridge, Mass., 1966.

TOLMAN, R. C., *Relativity, Thermodynamics, and Cosmology*, Oxford University Press, New York, 1934.

TRIBUS, M., *Thermostatics and Thermodynamics*, D. Van Nostrand Company, Inc., Princeton, N.J., 1961.

TYKODI, R. J., *Thermodynamics of Steady States*, Crowell-Collier and Macmillan, Inc., New York, 1967.

UBBELOHDE, A. R., *An Introduction to Modern Thermodynamical Principles*, Oxford University Press, New York, 1952.

VAN RYSSELBERGHE, P., *Thermodynamics of Irreversible Processes*, Blaisdell Publishing Company, Waltham, Mass., 1963.

VAN WYLEN, G. J., *Thermodynamics*, John Wiley & Sons, Inc., New York, 1959.

VAN WYLEN, G. J., and R. E. SONNTAG, *Fundamentals of Classical Thermodynamics*, John Wiley & Sons, Inc., New York, 1965.

VANDERSLICE, J. T., H. W. SCHAMP, JR., and E. A. MASON, *Thermodynamics*, Prentice-Hall, Inc., Englewood Cliffs, N.J., 1966.

VEINIK, A. I., *Thermodynamics, A Generalized Approach*. Israel Program for Scientific Translations, Jerusalem, 1964.

WALL, F. T., *Chemical Thermodynamics*, 2nd, ed., W. H. Freeman and Company, San Francisco, 1965.

WARNER, C. F., *Thermodynamic Fundamentals for Engineers*, Littlefield, Adams & Co., Paterson, N.J., 1960.

WASER, J., *Basic Chemical Thermodynamics*, W. A. Benjamin, Inc., New York, 1966.

WEBER, H. L., and H. P. MEISSNER, *Thermodynamics for Chemical Engineers*, John Wiley & Sons, Inc., New York, 1957.

WELD, L. D., *A Textbook of Heat for Upperclassmen*, Crowell-Collier and Macmillan, Inc., New York, 1948.

WILKS, J., *The Third Law of Thermodynamics*, Oxford University Press, New York, 1961.

WILSON, A. H., *Thermodynamics and Statistical Mechanics*, Cambridge University Press, London, 1957.

WORTHING, A. G., and D. HALLIDAY, *Heat*, John Wiley & Sons, Inc., New York, 1948.

YOUNG, V. W., *Basic Thermodynamics*, McGraw-Hill, Inc., New York, 1952.

YOUNG, V. W., and G. A. YOUNG, *Elementary Engineering Thermodynamics*, McGraw-Hill, Inc., New York, 1941.

YOURGRAU, W., A. VAN DER MERWE, and G. RAW, *Treatise on Irreversible and Statistical Thermophysics*, Crowell-Collier and Macmillan, Inc., New York, 1966.

ZEMANSKY, M. W., *Heat and Thermodynamics*, 4th ed., McGraw-Hill, Inc., New York, 1957.

2.4 (a) 60 J   (b) −70 J   (c) 50 J, 10 J
2.5 (a) −224 liter atm, 188 liter atm   (b) −115.5 liter atm, 79.5 liter atm
      (c) −36 liter atm, 0,   (d) −7 liter atm, −29 liter atm
2.6 $E - E_a = 3(pV - p_a V_a)/2$
2.7 560 liter atm, −372 liter atm, −46.5 liter atm, 17.5 liter atm
2.8 2.74×10^3 J
2.9 (a) 294 J   (b) 0   (c) 294 J, 0; 294 J, −294 J
2.11 $E = 2pV^2/N$
2.13 -1.38×10^{-1} J
2.14 5.88×10^4 J
2.15 (a) 270°K   (b) 6×10^4 J   (c) 3.6×10^4 J
4.6 16.77 J, 3.23 J
4.7 4 J, 2 J
4.8 2 J, 2 m³; 4 J, 4 m³
5.2 3.75×10^3 J, 6.25×10^3 J
5.7 (a) 312 cal (°K)$^{-1}$, −268 cal (°K)$^{-1}$, 44.0 cal (°K)$^{-1}$
      (b) 23.3 cal (°K)$^{-1}$
5.8 (a) 0   (b) 10 J (°K)$^{-1}$ (c) 5.49 J (°K)$^{-1}$ (d) 5.49 J (°K)$^{-1}$
5.10 33.3 J, 66.7 J
5.11 $(N/12B^2) [(2BT_2 - A^2)(A^2 + 4BT_2)^{1/2} - (2BT_1 - A^2)$
      $(A^2 + 4BT_1)^{1/2}]$

5.12   1 cal $(°K)^{-1}$

5.14   0.10 J $(°K)^{-1}$

8.1   51.7 min

8.2   300°K

10.4 $F = -(4C^3T^3VN/27)^{1/2};\ G = -C^3T^3N/27p;\ H = (4S^3p/C^3N)^{1/2}$

10.5 $F = -NRT \ln (T^{3/2}VN^{-1}) + \text{const } NT;\ G = -NRT \ln (T^{5/2}p^{-1})$
       $+ \text{const } NT;\ H = \text{const } Np^{2/5} \exp (2S/5NR)$

11.5 $NRT \ln [p_2(1 - bp_1)/p_1(1 - bp_2)]$

11.6   151 J

12.2   (a) $(Nc_p - S\alpha T)/(N\alpha^2VT - N^2\beta c_p)$ (b) $\alpha VT/Nc_p$
      (c) $S/(c_pVN - \alpha TVS + \beta pVS - \alpha pV^2)$ (d) β/α

12.15 3.8×10^{-3} J, 83 J

12.16 2.8×10^{-2} J, 7.8×10^3 J

12.17 (a) 4.4 J   (b) 1.7×10^2 J

12.18 (a) $4.3 \times 10^{-1}°K$ (b) 2.7×10^{-1} J

12.19 2.4×10^7 Nm^{-2}

12.31 $\alpha \approx a, \beta \approx b$ (b) -9.2×10^{-5} J $(°K)^{-1}$; 44 J

13.2 $V = (3aNT^4/4) - bNP + \text{const } N$

13.3 $V = (NRT/p) - (Nap/2) + \text{const } (N/p)$

13.5 $G = -(p_0^2V_0/N_0T_0) (NT/p) - Nc \ln (T/T_0)$
       $+ (N/N_0) (E_0 + 2p_0V_0 - T_0S_0)$

13.6 $F = -(b/a)T^2V + (1/2a)(V^2/N) + C_1V + C_2N$

13.7 $F = Nc[(1/T_0) - (1/T)] - (NcT/2)[(1/T_0^2) - (1/T^2)]$
       $- (p_0V_0NT/N_0T_0) \ln (VN_0/V_0N) + (NE_0/N_0) - (NTS_0/N_0)$

13.8   100.240°K

15.3 $E = (NaT^4/4) + (NbT^2/2) + E_0(V,N);\ S = (NaT^3/3) + NbT$

16.5   (a) 541 cal g^{-1} $(°K)^{-1}$ (b) 99 cal g^{-1} (c) -16 cal g^{-1}

16.7 6.16×10^4 J (mole)$^{-1}$

16.9   (a) 195.2°K   (b) 3.12×10^4 J (mole)$^{-1}$; 2.55×10^4 J (mole)$^{-1}$
      (c) 0.57×10^4 J (mole)$^{-1}$

16.12 190 cal g^{-1}

17.2 5.56×10^{-2} cal $(°K)^{-1}$

17.3 $\eta = 1 - [T_1 \ln (p_2/p_1) + (5/2)(T_2 - T_1)]/[T_2 \ln (p_2/p_1) + (5/2)$
      $(T_2 - T_1)]$

17.4 $\eta = [2(p_2 - p_1)(V_2 - V_1)]/[5p_2(V_2 - V_1) + 3V_1(p_2 - p_1)]$

17.5 $\eta = (T_2 - T_1)/2T_2$

17.6   120°K

17.7 $(T_1T_2)^{1/2};\ NC [T_1 + T_2 - 2(T_1T_2)^{1/2}]$

17.9 $\eta = 1 - \{[(V_b/V_a)^{R/c_V}]/[(c_V + R)/c_V]\}$
      $\{[(V_c/V_b)^{(c_V+R)/c_V} - 1]/[(V_c/V_b) - 1]\}$

18.1 $(a/3)(T_1^3 - T_0^3) - (aT_0/2)(T_1^2 - T_0^2)$

18.2 $E_1 - E_2 + (3N_1RT_0/2) \ln (E_2V_2^{2/3}/E_1V_1^{2/3})$

18.3 $NC[T_1 + T_2 + T_3 - 3 (T_1T_2T_3)^{1/3}]$

18.5 $\Delta S = mgh[1 - (\Delta T/2T_0)]$; $\Delta A = mgh(\Delta T/2T_0)$;
$\Delta T = mgh/(m + M)c$

19.1 $NR \ln 3$

19.2 $(NRb/2)(T_1{}^2 - T_2{}^2)$; $(3NR/2)(T_2 - T_1) + (NRb/2)(T_2{}^2 - T_1{}^2)$

19.4 0; 0; $-100R$; $100R$

19.6 $23.1°C$

19.7 $v = (\gamma/\beta\rho)^{1/2}$; 1.32×10^3 m sec^{-1}; 3.54×10^2 m sec^{-1}

20.1   (a) $a = 9Rv_cT_c/8$; $b = v_c/3$ (b) $p_c = 3RT_c/8v_c$
(c) $[p' + (3/v'^2)](3v' - 1) = 8T'$

20.2 $S = N\int[c_V(T)/T]dT + NR \ln [(V/N) - b] + \text{const } N$

20.4 $\Delta E = -aN^2/V_0$
$\Delta H = -2aN^2/V_0 + (N^2RTbV_0)/[(V_0 - Nb)(V_0 - 2Nb)]$
$\Delta S = NR \ln [(V_0 - 2Nb)/(2V_0 - 2Nb)]$

22.2 $V_f = 10^3V_i$; $p_f = 10^{-4}p_i$

22.3 $266°K$

a_i activity of species i in a multicomponent system, 206

c_p specific heat at constant pressure, 88

c_V specific heat at constant volume, 90

d exact differential of, 12

$\bar{d}$ inexact differential of, 12

E internal energy, 10

f Helmholtz free energy per mole, 197

f_i fugacity of species i in a multicomponent system, 217

F Helmholtz free energy, 78

g Gibbs free energy per mole, 197

G Gibbs free energy, 78

h enthalpy per mole, 127

H enthalpy, 78

J Jacobian of, 91

K equilibrium constant, 207

L latent heat, 127

ℓ latent heat per mole, 127

n_i mole fraction of species i in a multicomponent system, 225

N total number of moles, 9

N_i number of moles of species i in a multicomponent system, 188

p pressure, 36

*Number refers to page of first occurence.

p_i partial pressure of species i in a multicomponent system, 213

Q heat, 11

R gas constant, 154

s entropy per mole, 128

S entropy, 25

T temperature, 34

v volume per mole, 128

V volume, 9

W work, 11

W thermodynamic probability, 25

α coefficient of thermal expansion, 88

β isothermal compressibility, 88

Δ finite increment of, 114

ϵ internal energy per mole, 155

μ chemical potential in a one-component system, 78

μ_i chemical potential of species i in a multicomponent system, 189

ν stoichiometric coefficient, 196

ξ extent of reaction, 204

Index